AN IRISH HERBAL

An edited translation of *Botanalogia Universalis Hibernica*,
or A General Irish Herbal, which contains an alphabetical
listing of the plants, herbs, flowers, shrubs and trees of the
British Isles and the uses to which each may be put in the
formation of cures.

AN IRISH
HERBAL

Botanalogia Universalis Hibernica

EDITED BY MICHAEL SCOTT

Anna Livia Press
Dublin

First published in 1735
This edition first published in 1986 by The Aquarian Press

Reprinted 1991 by
Anna Livia Press Limited
5 Marine Road
Dún Laoghaire
County Dublin

ISBN: 1 871311 17 9

Cover by Bluett
Printed in Ireland by Colour Books Ltd.

Contents

Acknowledgements

I would like to express my gratitude to William Holland for his invaluable assistance, both in the editing and preparation of this work.

I would like to thank Aidan Heavey, Padraic O Tailliuir and Gus MacAmhlaigh for kindly allowing me to work from their editions of *Botanalogia Universalis Hibernica*.

A special word of thanks to Andrew Waters.

For Anna.

The Author
of
Botanalogia Universalis Hibernica
John K'Eogh
1681? – 1754

The second of twenty-one children, John K'Eogh or Keogh followed his father into the Church and became chaplin to James King, fourth Lord Kingston, before finally obtaining the living of Mitchelstown, in Co Cork. He married Elizabeth Jennings, the daughter of Dr Henry Jennings, a cousin of the Duchess of Malborough.

John K'Eogh's first work, *Botanalogia Universalis Hibernica*, was published in Cork in 1735, and immediately established itself as an important record of Irish plants and their medicinal properties.

There is not an herb, shrub, or tree in nature but that it is servicible to man either for food or medicine, or for both.

John K'Eogh
Botanalogia Universalis Hibernica, 1735

Introduction

In this age of technological-assisted impersonal medicine, it is perhaps paradoxical that man has recently returned to an earlier form of healing — that of herbalism. Part of the attraction of herbal medicine and herbal cures is that cures are effected by wholly natural means, without artificial additives or synthetic drugs, and are readily and cheaply available — sometimes in our own gardens.

Herbalism and herbal and plant cures have, of course, a very distinguished history, and at one time every town and village had its herb doctor or wise woman dispensing simples, poultices and philtres. Unfortunately, the art of herbalism became tainted by its association with witchcraft and, indeed, in many people's minds the two were almost indistinguishable, and this led to its falling into disrepute and disuse.

But the healing properties of plants and herbs have always fascinated mankind, and there are European herbals in manuscript form dating back as far as the tenth century, while Middle Eastern and Oriental herbals existed five centuries prior to that. The great renaissance of herbals began in the last few years of the sixteenth century with the publication of *The Herbal or a General History of Plants*, which is more commonly called *Gerard's Herbal*, and which was first published in 1597. Fifty years later saw the publication of possibly the most famous herbal in the English language, Culpeper's *English Physician*, but which is now more usually known as *Culpeper's Herbal*, which first appeared in 1652. Indeed, both of these herbals have remained in print almost continuously since their first publication.

John K'Eogh's *General Irish Herbal* first appeared in

1735, and differs slightly from most of the other herbals in that it is solely concerned with the plants, flowers, herbs, bushes and trees of the British Isles. It is similar to Culpeper in that it provides a description of the plant, when and where it may be found, and then goes on to detail its virtues. The herbal differs from Culpeper in that it is a much more concise work. K'Eogh's herbal remained for many years one of the standard reference works on the virtues of the flora of the British Isles. However, copies of the original work are now extremely rare, and the work was sadly forgotten. This edited version is the first reprint since the first edition of 1735, and the cures remain as effective today as they were when the book was first published over two hundred and fifty years ago.

Preface

This undertaking of *Botanalogia Universalis Hibernica*, a general Irish herbal, was never attempted by anyone before, and so, gentle reader, if I fall short of it, I hope you will be so good as to excuse me, for it is a science that is chiefly built upon daily experience which in turn leads to daily improvement.

I am convinced that if the real properties, or true qualities of all the herbs and trees growing in this Kingdom were discovered, there is not a distemper or a disease which the inhabitants presently suffer from, which might not be cured. And I am referring to a single herb, tree or shrub which, if not completely curing, might, at least remove the ill for a considerable time, without having to send for exotic herbs and drugs from foreign countries, which often destroy more than they cure.

I am also of the opinion that these drugs which are made up or compounded in druggists or apothecaries shops have much the same ill effect. Moreover, in the said shops, there are often a great many decayed slops and drugs which they sell as good and fresh, and by which means how many patients have been destroyed? Therefore the best and safest method is to make use of simple herbs, the products of our own Kingdom, whose qualities and virtues are by long experience perfectly known to us.

John K'Eogh

ABELE TREE or
White Poplar
(Populus alba)

The timber of this tree is white, and not very hard to work. The bark is smooth and whitish, the leaves are round with pointed corners — white, smooth, soft and downy on one side and green on the other. It is planted about mansion houses for shelter, and it is of quick growth.

The juice of the leaves of this tree eases pains in the ears, and heals ulcers and eruptions on the skin. The bark is useful in promoting the discharge of urine and is therefore good against the strangury (a difficulty in discharging urine).

**ADDER'S
TONGUE**
*(Ophioglossum sive
lingua serpentina)*

This is a small tender plant, about 4 or 5 in high, consisting of a single, thick oval, smooth leaf, from the bottom of which rises a stalk about 2 in high, bearing on the top a slender crenated tongue. It grows in moist meadows and is in its prime in the month of May.

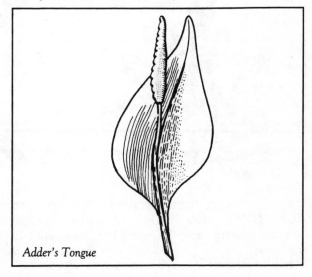

Adder's Tongue

Adder's Tongue is an excellent herb in the healing of wounds. Taken inwardly it is good against bruises, wounds and inflammation of the liver. An oil or unguent made from it can be applied to inflammations, burns, wounds, St Anthony's Fire and to all hot tumours.

AGRIMONY
(Agrimonia)

The leaves of this plant are long, hairy and serrated about the edges, almost like the leaves of hemp or strawberries. The stalk grows to about 2½ ft high, and it brings forth small yellow flowers in long spikes, which are then succeeded by rough little burrs. It grows in hedges and the borders of fields and flowers in June and July.

Agrimony opens obstructions of the liver and wonderfully strengthens it. It purifies the blood, and is good against the strangury, and pissing of blood, and its seeds taken in claret is singularly good against the bloody-flux. The leaves, powdered with hogs lard, heal old wounds when applied in a warm poultice. If the leaves are bruised and a plaster made with the yolk of an egg, flour and honey, they can be applied to a cut, or a gall after riding.

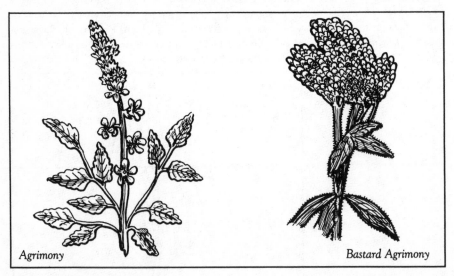

Agrimony

Bastard Agrimony

AGRIMONY, called Bastard or Water Hemp Agrimony
(Pseudohepatorium)

This has long round stalks full of white pith on which grow long blackish leaves, which are rough, hairy and serrated. On the tops of these stalks sprout many small flowers of a carnation colour. It grows in moist places near ditches and stagnated waters.

19

Agrimony is exceedingly good against opulations of the liver and spleen, and it is also useful against internal wounds and bruises, and if the leaves are bruised and mixed with the yolk of an egg they can be applied to a wound or cut.

ALDER or Aller Tree
(Alnus vulgaris)

This tree needs no description being so well known.

The bark or rind of it, because of its astringent quality is useful against the swellings of the throat. It heals and cauterizes sores and ulcers. It is often used by the common people as a black dye, and the leaves of it are made use of against ulcers and all kinds of inflammations.

ALEHOOF or
Common Ground Ivy,
or Gill Go by the
Ground
*(Hedera terrestris
chamaecissus)*

This plant has a strong earthy smell, and it grows everywhere in hedges and shady places, flowering in April. It needs no further introduction because it is so well known.

It is a great laxative, and can also cure deafness, coughs or any disorder of the lungs, it provokes urine and cleanses the ureters and, if it is steeped in brandy is of great service against the colic.

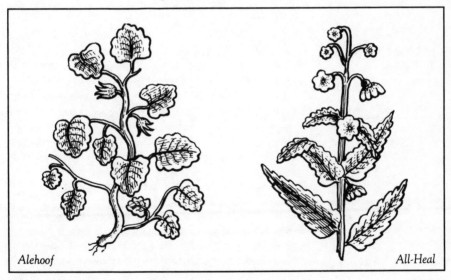

Alehoof

All-Heal

ALEXANDERS
*(Hipposelinum seu
smyrnium vulgare)*

This bears large winged leaves of a yellowish-green colour, the stalks grow to be 3 or 4 ft high and on the tops of which grow pretty large umbles of small five-leaved white flowers. It grows upon rocks by the seaside, flowering in June, and is commonly preserved in gardens.

The leaves of this plant are commonly applied to wens and hard swellings to dissolve them. The seed is also used to remove all obstructions of the liver, spleen and kidney, and it provokes sweat, urine and helps to cure the jaundice and dropsy. It is commonly boiled and eaten with salt meat. The seed is mixed with tobacco and smoked in a pipe, the fumes helping to ease a toothache.

ALL-HEAL or
Clowns All-Heal or
Clowns Woundwort
(*Panax colono gerardi,
Stachys palustris foetida*)

The stalks grow 2 or 3 ft high, are square and rough almost to pricklyness, the leaves are long, hairy, sharp pointed and indented. The flowers grow whorl-fashion towards the tops of the stalks, and are of a deep red colour. It grows in ditches and watery places, flowering in June and July.

All-Heal is an excellent herb in the treatment of wounds and is beaten into a poultice with hog's lard and applied to green wounds. It stops all sorts of haemorrhages. The decoction of the roots taken inwardly for a considerable time helps to cure tumours. The leaves, when stamped with an equal quantity of bay salt will cure the bite of a mad dog.

ALMOND TREE
(*Amygdalus*)

This tree is so like the peach tree with its leaves and blossoms that the only way to distinguish them apart is by their fruit. It is chiefly planted in gardens.

Bitter Almonds are used against all diseases of the lungs, liver and spleen and is therefore good against coughs, shortness of breath, inflammation and exulceration of the lungs. It should be taken in a sweet wine, and it is also an excellent cure against the headache when it is applied to the forehead with the oil of roses and vinegar. It is said that if a man takes five or six almonds before breaking his fast, then he will not become drunk that day.

Take 2 oz of the oil of sweet almonds, the same quantity of fresh butter, sugar candy and clarified honey, a quarter of grated nutmeg, which mixed together and taken off a liquorice stick, is an exceeding good cure for a cough.

HERB ALOE or Sea
Houseleek
(*Aloes vulgaris sive
sempervivum marinum*)

This is a purgative medicine and is frequently given to children for worms.

ANGELLICA or
Garden Angellico or
Wild Angellica
(*Angellica saliva,
Angellica sylvestris*)

Wild Angellica is like that of the garden variety, only in that its leaves are not so deeply cut and that they are narrower and blacker, the stalks are much slenderer and shorter. It grows in shady places, near riversides, and in low-lying woods. The Garden Angellico flowers and seeds in June and July, and both varieties have much the same virtues.

The root, pulverized and taken inwardly causes sweat, expels all noxious humours and prevents any malignity that proceeds from the air; it also prevents the said malignity if it be chewed in the morning before breaking the fast.

A decoction of this herb helps to cure palpitations, oppressions of the heart and it also helps to promote urine.

WOOD ANEMONE
or Wind Flower
(*Anemone flos Adonis,
Herba venita*)

There are five sorts of Anemones, but I shall only describe that species which commonly grows in this kingdom. The leaves of the Wood Anemone are very much indented, the flowers are purple or reddish and the roots are hairy.

The roots when chewed – and they are a sovereign remedy for the expelling of phlegm – boiled in wine and laid upon the eyes clear the sight, and a decoction of it mixed with a small amount of barley drank by nurses increases their milk.

ANISE or Garden
Anise
(*Anisum*)

This flowers and seeds in July, with the root dying every year after it has given seed. It grows frequently in gardens, with only the seed used in medicine.

It is an aid in expelling the wind from the body, and is exceedingly good to be given to infants in hot feeds, to prevent convulsions, the gripes and wind. The distilled oil is an excellent remedy against the pleurisy if it is applied outwardly. Anise can also be used to correct the effects of stronger purgative medicines, and the powder of it put into linen bags gives immediate help when applied to ruptures.

WILD ANISE
(*Anisum agreste*)

Wild Anise is commonly found in fertile, and sometimes in sandy soil. The leaves are somewhat rough and small, resembling the leaves of carrots and the seed is sweet scented. The virtues are the same as with the Garden Anise, but stronger and more powerful. The whole plant, but especially the seed, is a very great aid in promoting the discharge of urine.

APPLE TREE
(Malus saliva vel hortensis)

Apples comfort and cool the heat of the stomach, especially those that are somewhat sour. The leaves should be laid upon hot swellings, and they can also be applied to fresh wounds to prevent them turning bad.

ARBUTE or
Strawberry Tree
(Arbutus)

This is a small tree, not much bigger than a Quince tree, the body thereof is covered with a reddish bark, which is rough and scaly. The leaves are broad, thick and serrated, the flowers are white, small and grow in clusters, and after which follows fruit resembling strawberries, green at first, but yellowish afterwards, and at last red when ripe. It flowers in Spring and the fruit is ripe in Winter.

The fruit of this tree is of a cold nature, hurts the stomach and causes headaches.

WHITE ARCHANGEL
(Lamium album urtica mortua sive Arch-angellica flore albo non foetens folio oblongo)

This is the white-leaved, not Stinking Archangel. It grows everywhere by hedgesides, and flowers in April and May.

This herb can be recommended to be used for all swellings and it is also good against convulsions.

RED ARCHANGEL
or Red Dead Nettle or
Stinking Archangel
(Lamium rubrum)

This grows in hedges near highways, and flowers in summer, and the whole plant has a strong, earthy and unsavoury smell. Both the leaves and the flowers can be used.

This is especially good to prevent excess menstrual bleeding, and indeed, is good against all inward bleedings. When outwardly applied, it is also servicible to cure wounds and inflammations, and when compounded with salt, it cures hard wens.

ARON, Arun, Wake
Robin or Great
Cuckow Pint, spotted
and unspotted
(Arum vulgare)

The leaves are long, large and of a shining green colour, shaped like the head of a spear. Sometimes they are full of black spots and on the stem grows a cluster of red berries, each containing one round seed. It grows in hedges and dry ditches flowering in May, and the berries are ripe in July.

The whole plant is very hot and biting, inflaming the mouth and the throat for a long time. The roots are pulverized and induce vomiting, and are good to clear obstructions of the lungs, and a poultice made of them and mixed with cow dung eases the pain of the gout.

ARSMART, sharp and hot, or Water Pepper
(Persicaria nomaculata urens vel hydropiper)

The leaves are long and narrow, much like the leaves of the peach tree, but not serrated about the edges, the flowers grow on short stems and cluster together. It grows in moist places near pools, or standing waters, and flowers in July and August.

The leaves have a hot burning taste, like pepper, and are good against cold swellings, upon being applied to them. The distilled water of this plant is exceedingly good against the stone, either in the kidneys or bladder. A decoction of it in water is good for old aches and pains. It is extraordinary good for the gout, or any arthritic disorder, for it raises a blister which carries off the malignity.

The dried leaves, made into a powder may be used with meat instead of pepper.

ARSMART, dead or spotted
(Persicaria maculata mitis)

The leaves are broader in the middle and larger than the former, they are smooth and have a dark brown or black semilunar spot in the middle of each of them, the flowers are of a carnation colour and the root is yellow and hairy. It grows in back yards and rich soil flowering about the same time with the former.

It cools fresh or green wounds and prevents inflammation, when the juice of the leaves is dropped into them. It is a cure for piles when roasted in the embers of a fire and applied with a little hot honey.

ARTICHOAK
(Cinara scolymus)

The decoction of the root drank, strengthens the stomach and confirms the place of natural conception in women, which, as it is reported, makes them apt to conceive male children, but care must be taken to remove the pith first.

Artichoaks are cleansers and are also good for the jaundice, and the leaves, when stamped and applied to the skin, draw thorns and splinters. A tea made of the leaves that grow on the stalk certainly cures the ague, when drank about an hour before the fit approaches, and taken three or four times.

COMMON ASARABACCA
(Alarum vulgare)

This has smooth, round leaves of a shining green colour, like ivy, but rounder and tenderer, while the flowers are of a brown purple colour, in the form of cups. It is planted in gardens and is chiefly used in Physick as an aromatic scent; they also have a sharp biting taste.

A tea made of it helps expel urine and is good for a cough, shortness of breath, convulsions, cramps, dropsy and sciatica. When mixed with honey it brings down the menstrual flux.

ASH TREE
(Fraxinus)

The leaves, bark and tender buds of the ash tree open up the liver, provoke urine and are useful against dropsy. The inward bark is given with success against fevers, and the wood, burnt into ashes, cures scabs and ringworms.

ASPARAGUS or
Sparagus, a corruption
of Sparrow-grass
(Asparagus sativus)

Eaten with oil and vinegar it provokes urine, and is good against the strangury, and a decoction of it opens obstructions of the liver and spleen, and is therefore good for jaundice and dropsy.

MARSH
ASPARAGUS or
Sperage
(Asparagus sylvestris, Corrundus)

This herb is much like the former in its early stages, but the branches are rough and prickly when grown. It is found growing near the sea coast, and it has much the same virtues of the former.

ASP TREE or
Trembling Poplar
(Populus lybica tremula)

The leaves of this tree are almost round, they are deeply indented and are browner and harder than the leaves of the black poplar. They hang by long, but very slender stems, or root stalks, and this is the cause of their continual shaking. It grows in low, moist places.

The juice of the leaves assuages the pain of the ears, and heals ulcers of the frame, upon being dropped into them. A decoction of the bark provokes urine, relieves strangury and sciatica.

AVENS or Herb
Bennet
(Caryophillata)

The lower leaves are made up of about seven piunae which are hairy, as is the stalk, which grows to be about 2 ft high. The flowers grow on the tops of the branches on long-footed stalks consisting of five small yellow leaves, with several brown stamens in the middle, and the root is of a reddish colour which smells like cloves. It grows in woods and under hedges and flowers most part of the summer.

The roots when infused in wine render it more cordial and they ease pain arising from wind or cold in the bowels, and are also good against all kinds of haemorrhages or fluxes of the blood.

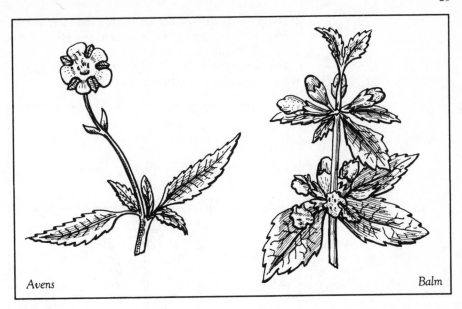

Avens   *Balm*

B

BALM or Garden
Balm
(Mellissa)

Balm cures uterine disorders. When applied to wounds, the juice heals them. It invigorates the heart, the head and the nerves; it can be used with success against fainting, palpitations and failures of the heart, and is also effective against smallpox, measles and other malignant fevers. It can be applied externally to ease the stinging of bees and wasps.

BASTARD BALM
or Bastard leafed
Archangel
(Mellissae folio)

This herb has much the same virtues as the former.

BARBERRY BUSH
or Tree
(Oxyacantha)

The bark of this tree is of an ash colour, the branches are full of sharp thorns, the leaves are oval and indented and of a sourish taste, the flowers are yellow and are succeeded by cylindrical red berries. It flowers in April and May, and the berries are ripe in September. It grows in wild places and is commonly planted in gardens.

The inner bark which is of a deep yellow colour is good for yellow jaundice, and the fruit relieves diarrhoea.

Barley

BARLEY
(Hordeum polystichum)

This has a softening, cleansing and cooling nature; a decoction is very good for urinary fevers.

BASIL
(Basilcon vulgare majus et ocimum)

The stalks of Basil are four square and somewhat hairy, the leaves are of a yellowish-green colour, almost like the leaves of Mercury. On the tops of the stalks grow whorl-like spikes of white flowers, the leaves of which, when rubbed have a fragrant smell. It grows in gardens, flowering in July and August.

Basil invigorates the head and nerves, fortifies the brain and refreshes the spirits. It helps to cure old coughs and when bruised with vinegar and held to the nose, helps recovery from fainting. It is also good for inflammations of the eye.

SMALL BASIL
(Basilicon minus)

This is like Basil, but the leaves are much smaller and the stalks are round, bearing several little collateral branches on which grow leaves with jagged edges.

Its properties are similar to Basil.

WILD BASIL
(Basilicon sylvestre)

It has square hairy stems, leaves that are smaller than those of Small Basil, and the flowers are of a purple colour. It grows in sandy ground by river sides.

It arrests the bowels, the menstrual and other discharges.

COMMON GREAT BAY TREE
(Lauris vulgaris)

The juice of the beries when externally applied helps to cure deafness and hardness of hearing. An oil made from the berries is good for bruises. When taken internally the berries expel flatulence, comfort the head, mouth and nerves, and are also good against infections. A decoction of the bark of the root removes obstructions, promotes discharges of urine, breaks up bladder stone and is good for the kidneys.

BEAN or Great Garden Bean
(Faba major hortensis)

Beans, although having but little nourishment, have the special property of inducing diarrhoea and engendering flatulence. Bean meal applied outwardly dissolves tumours, while the water, distilled from the flowers, is cosmetic.

FIELD BEAN
(Faba equina sylvestris)

These are of no great medicinal value and are used to feed horses. However, they can be used externally as with the bean.

BEARS BREECH or Brank ursin
(Acanthus branca ursina)

The leaves of this plant are large, of a shining sad green colour and deeply cut. From among the leaves lying on the ground there arises a stalk about 2 ft high which bears leaves only near the top, which consists of a head of white gaping flowers standing among small and prickly leaves. It is cultivated in gardens, flowering in July and August.

The roots promote urine and ease cramps and pulmonary consumption. This herb can be applied to burns and dislocations. It is used in suppositories and also for stone and urinary crystals.

YELLOW LADIES BEDSTRAW
(Gallium luteum)

The leaves are small and narrow, set in a circle about the stalks, which are of a dark green colour, about 1 or 2 ft in height, on top of which grow thick spikes of small yellow flowers. It grows on banks and dry barren places, flowering in June and July.

When applied to burns, the crushed flowers alleviate the inflammation and when applied to wounds, they can heal them. Such a preparation is good to stop all kinds of haemorrhages including nosebleeds.

BEET
(Beta)

There are two sorts of Beet, white and red, which have the same virtues.

Beets cleanse the stomach. The juice, with a little honey sniffed into the nose, excites sneezing and clears the nose and brain, therefore easing a chronic headache. The juice also clears the ears if it is poured into them, and opens obstructions of the liver and spleen.

WHITE BEHEN or
Spratling Poppy
*(Behen album
polemonium)*

It has tender stalks with large joints, the leaves are broad, are set opposite every joint and on the tops of the stalks grow white flowers which hang downwards. It grows frequently in cornfields and in meadows, flowering in summer.

The root is counted to be an antidote to poison, and is beneficial to the head and the heart.

White Behen

RED BEHEN or Sea
Lavender Spike
(*Limonium*)

Because its leaves resemble the leaves of the lemon-tree, it is known in Latin as Limonium. The stalks are about 1 ft high, are bare of leaves, on which grow long spikes of small purplish-red flowers. It grows in salt-marshes, flowering in July and August.

The roots and seeds of Red Behen arrest the bowels and are useful against diarrhoea, dysentery or a large menstrual discharge. It assuages any pain in urination and is good for the spleen. The root, held in the mouth and chewed, takes away a toothache.

WATER BETONY
(*Betonica aquatica
scrophularia aquatica*)

This herb is very like figworth, but the stalks are taller and the leaves larger in shape like Betony; the flowers are larger and of a redder colour, and it grows in watery places and near ditch sides.

The root is good for scrofulas tumours, piles, cancerous ulcers and itching. It also softens and disperses hard swellings.

WOOD BETONY
(*Betonica sylvestris*)

It is of a dark brown colour, bears blue flowers and is very strongly scented.

Infused in ale and drunk, it provokes periods and expels the afterbirth. It is very good against disorders of the uterus. It is also beneficial for barren women.

GARDEN BETONY
(*Betonica hortensis
vulgaris*)

The leaves are dark green, serrated about the edges, the stalks are rough and square, about 1½ ft long and the flowers grow in spikes of a red–purple colour. It flowers in May and June.

It breaks down kidney stone, provokes urine and expels clammy and viscous phlegm from the lungs. If crushed and put up the nostrils it clears migraine headaches, and cures low spirits and giddiness. It removes obstructions to the liver, spleen and menstrual discharge. A dram of crushed leaves with honey and water is a powerful cure for cramps.

BILLBERRY BUSH
(*Vaccinia*)

The Billberry bush has long crenated leaves and black fruit. The fruit is known as whortes, whortle berries or billberries. It grows on mountains and bogs.

The berries are very cooling, good against burning fevers, inflammation of the liver and scurvy. They also arrest diarrhoea and vomiting. An agreeable syrup can be made from the juice of the berries for the same remedies.

GREAT BINDWEED
(Convolvulus major albus vel volubilis major)

This herb has tender stalks and branches, winding and climbing about anything in its way; upon these grow soft leaves, almost like the leaves of ivy, but much smaller, and on the tops of the branches grow white bell-fashioned flowers. It grows in hedges, flowering in June and July.

This plant is of no great use in medicine, although the root can be employed are a purgative.

BIRCH TREE
(Betula)

The liquid that is drained off this tree in the springtime is good for dispelling urinary disorders, like stones, pains and bleeding. A decoction of the leaves, when drunk, is considered good for scurvy.

BIRD LIME or ordinary Mistletoe
(Viscus quercinus vel viscum)

This takes root in the branches of trees; the berries which grow on it are round, white and pellucid.

The leaves and berries cure swellings, abscesses and sores. The seed, pounded with white wine lees, and applied to the side, mollifies the hardness of the spleen. It is very good for the head and nerves, for apoplexy, convulsions, paralysis and giddiness. For this purpose it can be hung around the neck of the patient, or drunk in black cherry water.

LONG BIRTHWORT
(Aristolochia longa)

It has several square slender branches about 9 in long, about which grow leaves like the leaves of ivy; the flowers are pale purple with a strong scent, and these are succeeded by roundish fruit, as big as walnuts. The root is almost as thick as a man's wrist, about 1 ft long, of a yellowish colour and a bitter taste. It is planted sometimes in gardens, but commonly grows in woods.

It provokes urine and menstruation and drunk with pepper and myrrh, it expels the dead child, the afterbirth and all superfluities of the womb. There is nothing better for curing rickets in children, either used externally or internally.

ROUND BIRTHWORT
(Aristolochia rotunda)

The stalks and leaves are like the former, except that the leaves of this are somewhat rounder, the flowers are longer and narrower, and of a faint yellowish colour. The roots are round like a turnip. It is planted in gardens and grows wild in ditches and several other places.

The root is the only part used and is of value against convulsions, such as cramps and epilepsy. It clears the bowel and phlegm pretty smartly. It provokes menstrual discharge, assists birth and expels the afterbirth. It scours corrupt and dirty ulcers; it draws out splinters and broken bones. A hot, wet application made from it helps old aches, bruises and dislocations.

BISHOP'S WEED
(Ammi vulgare)

The leaves of this herb are large and indented, divided into several other long narrow leaves; the stalks are green and round, on the top of which grow large clusters of small white flowers. The seed is like parsley seed and has a hot taste. It grows in gardens, flowering in July and August.

The seed is very good against colic pains; it provokes urine and menstruation as well as flatulence. Mixed with honey, it disperses congealed blood.

BISTORT the
Greater, or Snakeweed
(Polygonum bistorta)

The leaves very much resemble the leaves of common dock, but are longer and more slender; the stalk is long, smooth and tender, and the flowers grow in spikes, like ears of corn, and are of a carnation colour. It grows in moist meadows, flowering in May.

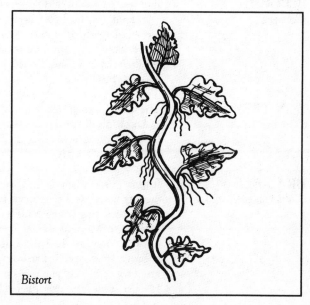

Bistort

A decoction of the root is very good against diarrhoea, dysentry and haemorrhages. If a powder of it is taken with red wine, it stops vomiting. A decoction of the leaves is very good against all sores, and inflammation of the mouth and throat. It also secures loose teeth.

BLITES or Goosefoot
or Sowbane
(Plitum album majus)

It grows about 2 ft high and has thick stalks, clothed in many leaves, like beet leaves. After the flowers come the seed remains enclosed in little flat husks. It is planted in gardens and flowers in July.

Only the leaves are used in medicine; they are cooling and softening and are sometimes put into suppositories.

**SMALL or
COMMON BLUE
BOTTLE**
(Cyanus minor vulgaris)

It has many slender whitish angular stalks, on which grow narrow sharp-pointed and indented leaves; on the top of the stalks grow small scaly buds, from which come pleasant blue flowers. It grows amongst the corn, flowering in June and July.

The distilled water of the flowers is excellent for sore, bloodshot and inflamed eyes, while an infusion of them is beneficial for jaundice. It is good for all sorts of obstructions.

BORAGE
(Borrago)

It grows in gardens and flowers in June.

It comforts the heart and makes people cheerful and merry, therefore driving away sadness and melancholy. It is an antidote to poison and good against malignant fevers, smallpox and measles. Boiled with honey and water, it is good for hoarseness.

BOX TREE
(Bauxus)

The leaves of the Box are hot, dry and astringent.

An oil distilled from the wood is used for toothache, a little lint or cotton being dipped into it and put in the hollow tooth.

BRAMBLE
*(Rubus vulgaris major
fructu nigra)*

It grows everywhere in hedges. The undertops and leaves are astringent, as is the unripe fruit.

The tops and young buds cures sores and ulcers of the mouth, throat and uvula, and held in the mouth and chewed, they secure the teeth. A decoction of them is effective in stopping diarrhoea, menstrual discharge and any flow of blood. The roots provoke urine and break up bladder stone, and the crushed leaves cure piles.

Bramble

White Briony

WHITE BRIONY
(Bryonia alba)

The leaves are something like vine leaves, but more rough and hairy. It has a great many rough, tender branches climbing on the hedges in its way. The flowers are of a whitish–green colour and are succeeded by round berries, which are in the beginning green, but afterwards red. It grows in lanes and by hedgesides, and flowers in May.

The root of White Briony powerfully purges viscous phlegm, and watery humours, both upwards and downwards. It is also excellent for all nervous disorders. An oil made from the root cures freckles and spreading sores, and if it is pounded and mixed with wine, it draws out splinters and broken bones.

BLACK BRIONY
(Bryonia nigra)

The leaves are almost like the leaves of bindweed, the stalks and branches twine and climb about hedges and trees, and the fruit clusters together like small grapes. It grows in the same places as white bryony and flowers about the same time.

The root is good for epilepsy, it provokes urination and menstruation and it cleanses the kidneys. The tender sprouts or tops of it, eaten in salads, will cleanse the stomach. It is very dangerous for women with child to make use of any part of it.

BROOKLIME
(Anagallis aquatica, Becabunga)

This herb is so well known that I need not describe it. It flowers in June, holding the leaves all winter, and grows in moist ditches and near running waters.

It is good for breaking up stone and gravel, and for easing the passage of urine. Applied as a poultice, it dissolves tumours or hard swellings of the liver and spleen.

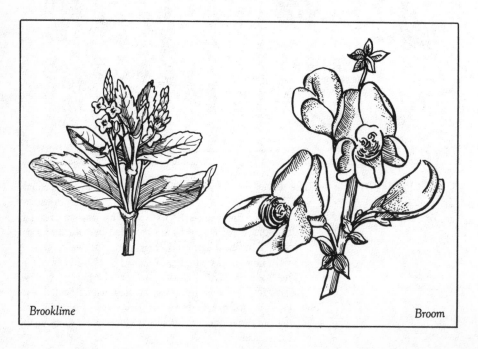

Brooklime   Broom

Butcher's Broom

BROOM
(Genista)

This flowers in April and May.

The tender branches, leaves and buds of Broom, boiled in wine or water are very good in removing any obstruction of the liver, spleen, kidneys or bladder. The seed has the same property, a dram or a dram and a half to be taken at a time. The flowers, if mixed with Hog's lard, assuage the pain of the gout. The ashes infused in white wine powerfully provokes urine, and are good for jaundice.

BROOM-RAPE
(Orobanche,
Rapum genistae)

It grows about the roots of Broom.

A decoction of it in white wine is excellent for breaking up stone and expelling gravel and provoking urination. The fresh juice or oil of broom-rape heals all corrupt and rotten ulcers.

BUTCHER'S BROOM
(Bruscus ruscus sive oximysiner)

This grows in gardens and flowers in summer.

It is mainly the root that is used in healing. A decoction of it breaks up stone, expels gravels and aids urination. It is useful against jaundice and provokes menstrual flow.

BUCKBEAN
(Trifolium paludosum)

Buckbean is so well known that it needs no description. It grows in marshy and soggy ground, flowering in May and June.

The seed is effective against a cold, coughing, diseases of the lungs and spitting of blood. Taken with honey and water, the leaves are good against scurvy, gout and rheumatism.

BUCKTHORN-TREE
(Rhamnus catharticus, Spina cervina)

This grows in woods and hedges, flowering in June, with the berries ripening about the end of September.

Made into a syrup, the berries gently purge phlegm, and are good against scurvy and gout. Ashes from the wood made into lees, cure scabs and itches.

BUCKTHORN
Plantine
(Coronopus vulgaris, Cornu cervinum)

The long and narrow leaves lie flat on the ground in a circle — from whence it is called Stella terrae, or Star of the Earth. The spikes are narrow and consist of four leaved flowers, growing on hairy stalks 3 or 4 in long. It grows in sandy ground, flowering in June.

It has a drying and binding quality when applied to wounds. It is extraordinarily good against the bites of venomous creatures, especially the bite of a mad dog.

Bugle

Burdock

BUGLE or Middle
Confound
*(Bugula,
Consolida medi)*

Bugle creeps on the ground like moonworth. It has long broad leaves on square stalks with few leaves positioned opposite to one another, which are of a dull green colour. The blue flowers grow in loose spikes, whorl-fashion. It grows in woods and hedges, and flowers in May.

It dissolves clotted or congealed blood, opens obstructions of the liver and gall, and cures ulcers and sores of the mouth. If crushed and applied to wounds, it cures them.

**GARDEN
BUGLOSS**
*(Buglossum Hortense vel
vulgare)*

When fully grown the stalks reach 2 or 3 ft in height. The stalks bear long narrow leaves, and on top grow rough thistly heads bearing purplish flowers. These flowers are succeeded by four-cornered rough seed. It flowers in June and July.

This is a great cordial herb, and it has the same properties as Borage; it is a herb which uplifts the heart and spirits.

WILD BUGLOSS
(Buglossum sylvestre)

This is a much smaller plant than the former, not growing above 1 ft high. The stalks are thick, succulent and prickly, the leaves long and narrow, and the flowers and seed are like those of the Garden Bugloss. It grows near hedges, highways and among corn, flowering in May.

It is seldom made use of in medicine, although it is considered to have the same properties as Garden Bugloss.

BULLACE-TREE
(Prunus sylvestris major)

Wild plums are astringent, of a dry cold nature, their juice stops diarrhoea and flows of blood, and may be used instead of Acacia.

**GREAT COMMON
BURDOCK** or
Clot Bur
*(Bardana major vel lappa
major)*

The plant grows in rich soil, such as backyards, flowering in June and July.

The leaves pounded with salt are very effective when applied to the bite of a mad dog, as is the juice of the leaves drunk in wine. A dram of the root pounded with kernels of pineapple is a powerful remedy for the spitting of blood. A small amount of the seed pounded and drunk with white wine, eases bowel disorders. It promotes urine and breaks up bladder stone. The leaves boiled in milk and applied as a poultice are good for gout. The roots cause perspiration and are good against poisons and fevers. The green leaves pounded with the white of eggs cure old sores and burns.

BURNET
*(Pimpinella minor
hortensis,
Sanquisorba)*

The stalks grow to about 1 ft high; they are downy and of a reddish brown colour. The leaves are feather-like; on the tops of the stalks grow round firm heads, consisting of a cluster of small reddish four-leaved flowers.

A decoction of this herb is very good against dysentry, spitting or pissing blood, menstrual disorders and all flows of blood. If the green leaves are crushed and applied to wounds they will prevent abscess and inflammation. If steeped in wine they cheer the heart and exhilarate the spirits, for, in short, it is an excellent cordial herb.

WILD BURNET
*(Pimpinella vel savifraga
major)*

It grows in meadows and in old stone walls.

It is excellent for provoking urine and for expelling stone and gravel and flatulence out of the stomach.

BURR-REED or
Burrflag or Reed Grass
(Sparganum ramosum)

It has long narrow leaves, sharp on both sides, with a sharp crest raised up so that they almost seem triangular. The stalks are 2 or 3 ft high, upon which grow round prickly heads, or burrs, as big as nuts.

It is of a cold and dry nature. A decoction of the rough burrs of this herb in wine is good against bites of venomous creatures, either if it is drunk, or if the wound is washed therewith.

BUTTERBUR
(Pelatites vulgaris)

It grows by riversides and by marshy ground, the flowers appearing in early March.

The roots of the herb powerfully provoke sweat and are therefore good against all malignant fevers. They also provoke urine and kill worms in children. Pulverized and applied to wounds, inflammations and ulcers, they act as a cure.

BUTTER-WORTH
or Mountain Sanicle
*(Pinguicula gesneri seu
sanicula montana)*

This grows in boggy moist meadows and has the same virtues as Common Sanicle.

CABBAGE and Coleworts
(Brassica sativa, Càulis)

All coleworts have much the same properties, in that they make the belly soluble.

The juice with ground fenugreek helps gout, and heals old rotten sores. Mixed with vinegar, the juice put warm into the ears is good against deafness, and for the ringing humming noise in them. The stalks, eaten raw, prevent drunkenness; the young leaves are cooling and good for laying on inflammations. The ashes of the stalks mixed with hogs lard, are good for applying to old pains and aches in the side. The leaves are great drawers and purges.

COMMON MOUNTAIN CALAMINT
(Calamentha vulgaris montana)

It is found growing on mountains near hedges and highways, flowering in June and July.

It is very good for all internal bruises, clotted and congealed blood, shortness of breath, and for obstructions of the lungs and the jaundice. It provokes urination and menstruation and expels wind from the stomach. It can also be used to expel a dead child from the womb. A decoction of it with honey and salt expels all kinds of worms out of the body.

COMMON CALAMINT of the Shops.
(Calamentha officinalis)

This Calamint is called Wild Pennyroyal. The stalks are square and downy, on which grow triangular leaves, opposite one another. The flowers grow among the leaves; they are of a pale purple colour and there are sometimes three or four on a stem. It grows near hedges and highways and has much the same virtues as mountain calamint.

WATER CALAMINT
(Calamentha aquatica)

It grows about 1 ft or more high, the stalks are square and hairy and the leaves are larger and longer than the Common Calamint. Indented about the edges, the flowers grow in very thick whorls, with the leaves on the upper part of the stalks. It grows in moist places where water has stagnated in winter and it flowers in June. It has the same qualities as mountain calamint.

CALTHROPS or the ordinary Star-Thistle (*Calcitrapa, Carduus stellatus vulgaris foliis papaveris erratici*)

The lower leaves grow flat on the ground encompassing the root in a circle; the stalk is about 2 ft high and is divided into numerous branches, and the flowers are reddish or purple. It grows near highways and on commons, flowering in June.

The root is a powerful remedy against stone, gravel cholic and convulsions. An ointment made together with foxglove, hemlock and dropworth cures abscesses and sores.

CALVES' SNOUT or Snapdragon (*Antirrhinon sylvestre*)

This herb has straight round stems full of branches and leaves that are not unlike the leaves of Pimpernel. The flowers are like the flower of Toad Flax, but are much larger and are of a faint yellow colour and are succeeded by long husks, the front part of which resembles a calves snout. It grows in gardens, flowering in July and August, and is also found growing wild. There is a lesser Calves Snout (Orontium), which grows wild in fields, near highways and under hedges.

It is thought that whoever carried about a Calve's Snout cannot be hurt by any poison or poisonous creature. The lesser Calve's Snout is hot and dry and a decoction thereof washes away the yellow colour which remains in the body after jaundice.

CAMOMILE (*Chamaemelum*)

This flowers in June and July.

It provokes urination and menstruation, expels a still-born child, aids flatulence and eases bowel disorders. A decoction of it applied to the area of the bladder and kidneys expels gravel and eases pain. An oil made of it is good for stitches, pains and old aches of the limbs, and dislocations. The flowers help to expel wind, and a powder made from them and mixed with wine is a good cure for an acute fever. Boiled with vervain in milk, and applied to an old pain or ache, camomile will help cure it. An ointment made of it with fresh butter and goosedung is an excellent remedy for a burn or a scald.

DOG'S CAMOMILE or Stinking May Weed or Wild Camomile

This has a thick green stem, full of juice, which quickly breaks underfoot; the flowers consist of broad white petals set about a yellow fistular centre. It grows frequently in

(Cotula faetida,
Chamaemelum faetidum,
Cynobotane)

waste places and among corn, flowering in May and June.

It is good for women with the falling down of the womb, if they but wash their feet with a decoction of it. A hot wet application of it will ease the swelling of haemorrhoids.

WILD CAMPION
(Lychnis sylvestris flore
rubro)

It has rough white stems, the leaves are downy, oval and sharp pointed. The flowers grow on the tops of the branches and consist of five red round sharp-pointed leaves. It grows in ditches and moist places, flowering in May. There is another sort of wild Campion which bears white flowers (Lychnis sylvestris flore albo) which in all other respects is like the former.

Both types are very good against the bites of venomous creatures. A small quantity of seed will eliminate bile. The red flowers are good against an excessive menstrual flow.

CARAWAYS
(Carum sive careum)

It is very good for helping digestion, expelling all kinds of wind and flatulences, and is therefore good for bowel disorders. It is useful for headache and weakness of sight. It is like annise seed in operations and virtues.

Camomile

CARLINE THISTLE
(Carlina,
Chamaeleon albus
humilis)

It bears long rough narrow and prickly leaves, deeply cut on both sides. The stem is not more than a hand and a half high. The flowers consist of a border of white shining, sharp-pointed petals set about a yellow fistular centre. It flowers in July and August.

The root provokes urination and menstruation and is an antidote to poison. If a powder made from it and the quantity of a dram is taken inwardly, it is an excellent protection against disease, for, as we may read, the army of the Emperor Charlemaigne was, by the help of this root, preserved from pestilence. Held in the mouth, it is good against toothache. Being externally applied with vinegar, it cures the scurf and itch.

CARROT
(Pastinaca tenuifolia sativa)

Carrot roots when eaten are indifferent nourishment, and usually provoke urination and excite sexual desire. If made into a powder and drunk with mead, they open obstructions of the liver, spleen and kidneys, and are therefore good against jaundice, and gravel.

WILD CARROT or Bird's Nest
(Daucus vulgaris, Pastinaca silvestris tenuifolia)

The wild carrot is not unlike the garden carrot, except that the leaves are more finely divided, rougher and more hairy. The stalks grow 2 or 3 ft high, upon the tops of which grow small white flowers and when these fall off they close themselves into a hollow round form like a bird's nest. It grows frequently in pasture grounds and fallow fields, and it flowers in June.

Wild Carrot

The seed provokes urination, menstruation and the breaking up of stone. It is believed that it makes women fruitful if taken often. A handful of finely chopped leaves boiled in 2 or 3 pints of milk whey will expel the worst attack of gravel and ease urination. If the flowers are not available, you may use the root.

CATMINT or Nep
*(Nepeta,
Mentha selina)*

This has square hairy soft stalks, full of joints; the leaves are like those of Dead Nettle, and the flowers, which are white, grow on the tops of the stalks in long whorled spikes. It grows in gardens and sometimes wild, in lanes and hedges, flowering for most of the summer. It is called Catmint because cats are very fond of it, especially when it is withered, for then they roll themselves in it, and chew it with great pleasure.

It provokes urination and menstruation; it expels the still-born child; it opens obstructions of the lungs and the womb, and it is good for internal bruises and shortness of breath. Drunk with salt and honey, it expels worms from the body.

**GREAT
CELANDINE**
*(Chelidonium majus,
Hirundinaria)*

It grows in gardens and sometimes wild among rubbish, on walls and old buildings, and it flowers in May.

It is an excellent medicine to preserve the eyesight; it removes inflammations, specks and films from the eyes, and

Catmint   Great Celandine

it can also strengthen them. The root removes obstructions of the liver and spleen, and cures jaundice. When it is chewed, it eases toothache. A strong decoction is very good against skin eruptions, ringworms and scorbutic sores.

It is called Chelidonium — in Greek, Swallow Herb — because, as Pliny wrote, it was first discovered by swallows when it restored sight to their young ones.

SMALL CELANDINE or
Pileworth
(Chelidonium minus)

This is a low herb with small brownish stems; the leaves are small and somewhat round; the flowers are yellow and the root has several little whitish tubers. It grows in meadows and moist pastures, and flowers in April.

It provokes vomiting and a discharge of phlegm from the chest. If a decoction of it is gargled, or if the juice of the root mixed with honey is sniffed into the nostrils, the brain is purged and a stoppage of the nose unblocked. The root, pounded in a little wine or urine and applied to piles, dissolves and heals them.

Small Celandine

LESSOR CENTORY
or Red Ordinary Small
Centory
*(Centaurium minus
vulgare flore purpureo)*

A decoction of it purges bilious and phlegmatic conditions.
It removes obstructions of the liver and spleen and it eases
cramps and convulsions. The juice dropped into the eyes
with honey clears them. It is also good for the stomach.

It may also be used as part of an infallible cure for the
cholic. Take this:

> Two handfuls of centory, agrimony and camomile
> flowers. One ounce each of gentian roots and carduus
> seed. Two drams each of cubebs, galingal roots,
> Cardamum, nutmegs, cinnamon, cloves, mace. Half an
> ounce of caraways seed, civil orange peel, lemon peel.
> One handful of elder berries, and a few grains of whole
> pepper, all infused in a gallon of aqua vitae.

**YELLOW
CENTORY**
*(Centaurium luteum
perfoliatum)*

The root conglutinates and heals all fresh wounds, and it
stops all kinds of flows and haemorrhages.

It takes its name from the Centaur Chiron who, by using
it, cured himself of a wound he received from one of the
arrows of Hercules.

CHARLOCK or Wild
Mustard
(Rapistrum)

It flowers from April to Midsummer.

This herb, but especially the seed, is hot and dry. It is
boiled and eaten by the common people in Spring, instead
of Coleworts. Made into a poultice, it is good against cramps
and convulsions.

**RED CHERRY-
TREE**
(Cerafus vulgaris rubra)

This tree bears red cherries (Cerafa rubra), which are of a
cooling moist nature. They purge and comfort the stomach,
assuage thirst, and ease the conditions of stone, gravel and
epilepsy.

**BLACK CHERRY-
TREE**
(Cerafus nigra)

These cherries are good for all uneasiness of the head and
nerves, such as epilepsy, convulsions and paralyses. They
also provoke urination and break up stone, and in general,
the distilled waters of these cherries is of great use in
medicine.

**COMMON
GARDEN
CHERVIL**
*(Chaerefolium vulgare
sativum)*

It is a small low plant, with winged leaves, smaller and finer
than Parsley, and on the tops of the stalks grow small
clusters of five-leaved white flowers. Its virtues are much the
same as those of Parsley.

A handful of chervil squeezed into ale or whey and drunk

is very good for pleurisy. It provokes urination and breaks up stone. It cures rickets, and helps rheumatic pains, used externally and internally. It is also useful for stoppping vomiting and diarrhoea.

CHESTNUT TREE
(Castanea)

It is thick-set with long, narrow and sharp-pointed leaves, deeply serrated around the edges, while the catkins are long, thin and slender. It is frequently planted in gardens and parks. Chestnuts, although quite nourishing, are hard to digest.

They are good for chest problems, and for arresting the bowels. A paste made from them is good against coughing and spitting of blood.

EARTH CHESTNUT or
Earth-Nut or Pignut
(Bulbocastanum)

This plant has a root as big as a large nutmeg; the leaves are finer and smaller than those of meadow Saxifrage and on the tops of the branches grow thin clusters of small white flowers. It grows in sandy places, flowering in May.

The root, which is the only part used, when roasted has a pleasant taste and is nourishing. It promotes sexual desire and also eases dysentery and menstrual flow.

CHICKWEED
(Alsine vulgaris)

Boiled in water and salt, it is a powerful remedy against the heat of scurvy, and the itching of hands. It is cooling and moistening, good against inflammations, boils, hot

Earth Chestnut   Chickweed

Cinquefoil

swellings and pains in any part of the body. For these remedies, the juice, or a poultice with hog's lard is applied.

CINQUEFOIL
(Pentaphyllum vel quinquefolium)

The stalks lie on the ground, emitting small fibrous roots from the joints, by which it easily propogates itself. At every joint grow five leaves, set together on a 1 ft stalk. The flowers are yellow and consist of five leaves. It grows in hedges and by waysides, flowering all summer.

The roots of Cinquefoil boiled in water until a third part of the water has been boiled away, ease the raging pain of toothache, if held in the mouth. They help to cure dysentery and all other diarrhoeas. Fevers can be cured by giving a small amount of root-powder two or three times a day. The juice of the leaves mixed with honey and water, or in vinegar whey has the same effect.

GARDEN CLARIE
(Horminium hortense)

It flowers in June and July.

It is of a hot and dry nature. The seed, pounded and tempered with water, draws out thorns and splinters, and dissolves all kinds of swellings. The leaves infused in wine, comfort a cold windy stomach. Fried with eggs they strengthen the kidneys and the back.

48

WILD CLARIE
(Horminium sylvestre ceu oculus Christi)

Wild Clarie bears wrinkled and serrated leaves; the stalks are square and somewhat hairy while the flowers are of a deep blue colour, like the flowers of Lavender. It grows in gravelly ground, flowering in June and July.

The seed mixed with honey cures inflammations of the eyes and cleanses and strengthens them. If drank in wine, the seed excites bodily lust.

CLIVERS or Goose Grass Clivers
(Aparine)

It grows in hedges.

It provokes urine, breaks up stone and gravel, and sweetens the blood. Being externally applied, it stops the bleeding of fresh wounds, and it is also good against scrofula, and lumps on the skin. It eases stitches, and disperses cold blockages in the joints. It cures the pain of the ears if the juice is dropped into them.

It is known as Goose Grass Clivers, because it is exceeding good to fatten geese.

CLOVE JULY Flower *(Caryophyllum rubrum)*, also Double Clove July Flower *(Caryophyllum multiplex)*, and The Great Garden July Flower *(Caryophyllum altile majus)*

These flowers have a pleasant aromatic smell and are cultivated in gardens, flowering in July.

Made into a syrup, they are useful for all diseases of the head and nerves. They are also a good antidote to poison, as well as being beneficial for the heart. Toothache will be cured with a medicine which is made up from $\frac{1}{2}$ oz of refined oil of Clove July, a little camphire and $\frac{1}{2}$ oz of four times-distilled spirits of Turpentine. This liquor will infallibly cure the toothache, if you dip a little cotton into it and apply it to the aching tooth.

CLOVER-GRASS or the Great Trefoil
(Trifolium majus purpureum sativum)

It is of a hot and dry nature. The leaves and flowers, or the seed infused or boiled in water and taken internally, are good against pains of the side, and uterine disorders, as well as provoking urination and menstruation. It is a good antidote against acute fevers and poisons as well as hysteric fits.

CLUBMOSS or Wolf's-Claw
(Museus clavatus, Lycopodium)

It spreads on the ground, sending out several distinct branches, which are thickly set and covered with a kind of hair which is of a changeable colour, between green or yellow. These branches send out other branches, the ends of which resemble the claws of a wolf. It grows in unmanured fields and woods.

If inserted into the nose, it stops bleeding, and is a useful ingredient of astringent ointment. A decoction of it in claret helps stop diarrhoea.

COCKLE or Bastard Nigella
(Lychnis segetum, Melanthium sylvestre)

It has a striped stalk of about two spans long; the leaves are ashen-coloured resembling the leaves of dill. The flowers are like the flowers of garden Nigella, only bluer, and it grows in fields, flowering in June and July.

The seed helps to provoke menstruation, dissolve flatulence, expels worms from the body and cure shortness of breath. A decoction of it in water and vinegar held in the mouth, eases toothache.

WILD COLEWORT
(Brassica sylvestris)

It is of a hotter and drier nature than the large Coleworts, stronger and more purgative and cleansing, and is therefore not to be eaten. When pounded, the leaves heal wounds, dissolve tumours and draw out rottenness from running sores and from bilious conditions. If made into a syrup with sugar and liquorice, it cures an abscess of the lungs.

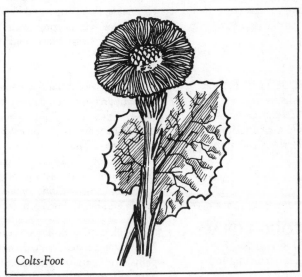

Colts-Foot

COLTS-FOOT or Folefoot
(Tussilago farfara)

It grows in moist places, and flowers at the end of February.

It is good for all diseases of the lungs, for coughs and consumption. The leaves, pounded with honey, cure all skin inflammations.

GARDEN COLUMBINE
(Aquilegia)

It is good for obstructions of the liver and spleen, for jaundice, sore mouths, and inflammations of the jaws and throat.

WILD COLUMBINE
(Aquilegia sylvestris)

It grows like Garden Columbine, but the flowers are of a paler blue and the leaves are longer. It grows in woods and flowers in May and June.

It cures ulcers, and itchy and scabby skin, but especially the mange on cattle or dogs.

COMFREY
(Symphitum, Consolida major)

It grows in gardens, but sometimes in ditches and watery places, and it flowers in June and July.

The roots are exceeding good for all them that spit blood, for they heal all inward wounds and ruptures, and also to clear up and purge phlegm. They also glutinate and heal external wounds, and are good for hot tumours and inflammations. The roots, beaten into a poultice, ease gout.

CORN-SALLET or
Lamb's Lettuce
(Lactuca agnina)

It grows on the borders of fields, by waysides and in cornfields, flowering in July and August.

It provokes urine, promotes sleep and alleviates pain. The juice, mixed with breast-milk, cures burns and clears the sight.

COSTMARY or
Alecoath
(Balsamita mas, Costus hortorum, Herba divae mariae)

It has hard round slender stalks, about 1 ft high; the leaves are light green, serrated about the edges and the flowers are like the flowers of Tansy, but smaller. It has a pleasant strong smell and is of a bitter taste. It is planted in gardens, and flowers in July.

It heals colic pains, stops vomiting and the looseness, and the spitting and pissing of blood. It strengthens the stomach, expels wind, opens obstructions of the liver, spleen and brain, and stops superfluous catarrhs.

COUCH-GRASS or
Dog's Grass
(Gramen cranium)

It provokes urine and opens obstructions, especially of the kidneys and bladder. A decoction of it is useful for colic pains and painful urination. The leaves and roots, if pounded, heal wounds and prevent bleeding.

COWSLIP or Paigle
(Paralysis, Primula veris major)

Cowslips grow in gardens and moist meadows, flowering in April.

They purge the stomach, promote sleep and are good

against epilepsy, paralysis, apoplexy and headaches. Tea is commonly made from the flowers to promote sleep and a salve made from the leaves strengthens the nerves.

CRAB-TREE or
Wilding
(*Malus sylvestris*)

Crab-tree grows frequently in hedges, and flowers in April and May, with the fruit ripening in September.

The juice of crabs is a useful ingredient in astringent gargles for ulcers of the mouth, throat and also for dropped uvulas. It is also used for burns, scalds and inflammations.

CRANES-BILL or
Doves-Foot
(*Geranium colum binum
pes columbinus*)

It has tender reddish hairy and slender stalks, the leaves are small and round, while the flowers are small, and of a pleasant pale red turning to purple, which are succeeded by long heads, each resembling the head and bill of a crane. It grows among weeds, in rocky places and by hedgesides, flowering in May and June.

It provokes urine and dissolves gravel and stone. It is also very good in stopping all kinds of flow.

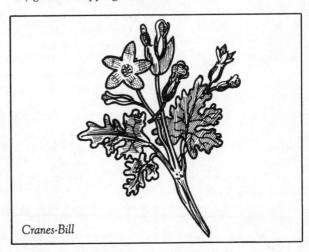

Cranes-Bill

GARDEN-CRESS or
Tongue Grass
(*Nasturtium hortense*)

It grows in gardens, and flowers in May.

The leaves are good for the nerves. and for curing diseases of the mouth. The seed purges the stomach, expels worms, opens obstructions of the spleen, provokes menstruation and expels a dead child and the afterbirth. Made into a poultice with honey, it cures hardness of the spleen, swellings and scabby skin.

52

WATER CRESS or Watergrass
(Nasturtium aquaticum)

It grows in moist ditches, standing waters and springs, and flowers in June.

It provokes urine, breaks up stone and gravel, and is useful against jaundice.

SWINES CRESS
(Coronopus ruellii)

It grows near highways and on banks, flowering in May and June.

Its nature is hot and dry, being astringent. The root, roasted in embers and eaten is good against a flux proceeding from the coldness of the stomach, and it is also useful in dispersing scrophulous tumours.

WILD CRESS or Churles Cress
(Nasturtium sylvestre vel rusticum)

It bears long large leaves, cut about the edges; the stalks are round, about 1 ft long and divided into several branches, on which grow small husks like those of Shepherds Purse, and which contains sharp biting seeds. It flowers at the end of Spring and is in seed all Summer.

It is of a violent hot and dry nature, especially the seed. It purges violently, both upwards and downwards, and also provokes menstruation and breaks up internal abscesses. If applied externally, like mustard seed, it is good for sciatica.

Cuckow Flowers

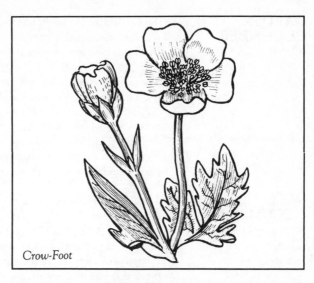

Crow-Foot

CROSS WORT
(Cruciata)

It has many square stalks, full of joints, the leaves are small, broad and round-pointed, with four leaves growing at every joint, opposite one another in the form of a cross; the flowers are yellowish, and consist of four leaves. It grows near trenches, water courses and in hedges, and it flowers in July.

It heals and conglutinates wounds. It is also good for ruptures, but the herb must be boiled before it is applied to the grieved part.

CROW-FOOT or
Common Creeping
Crow Foot or
Buttercup
(Ranunculus pratensis repens)

There is also round or knobbed rotted Crow Foot, Water Crow Foot and Round-leaved Water Crows Foot. All these species of Crow foot have much the same properties, being caustic. If pounded and laid on any part of the body, they raise blisters. If the roots are pounded and sniffed into the nose, they provoke sneezing. The pounded leaves can be applied beneficially to eruptions, scabs and warts.

**CUCKOW
FLOWERS**
(Cardamine, Nasturtium pratense majus)

Its leaves are pinnated, the stalks smooth and round, and the flowers consist of four roundish white leaves. It grows in meadows and flowers in April.

It provokes urination, breaks up stone and is good for the kidneys and nerves. It is also beneficial against scurvy, cancerous ulcers, freckles, epilepsy and the pissing of blood.

GARDEN CUCUMBER
(*Cucumis sativus*)

This is cold and moist in nature, and it is therefore good for inflammations of the stomach and bowels. It yields bad and small nourishment, and it is not good to eat too much of them, for they fill the veins with fevers and other diseases. The green leaves crushed with wine heal dog-bites. The seed is cooling, it provokes urine and breaks up stone.

An infallible cure for pleurisy consists of taking unpeeled cucumbers, slicing them into a frying pan, covering them with salad oil, and cooked on the fire until they are well-fried. Do this thrice, but retain the cooked oil. This oil can also be rubbed onto stitches in the side.

WILD CUCUMBER or
Squirting Cucumber
(*Cucumis agrestis*,
Afininus)

The leaves are rougher and smaller than the leaves of Garden Cucumber; the stalks are round and rough, creeping on the ground, while the flowers are pale yellow with each flower consisting of one single leaf. The fruit is as big as a large olive, which if gently pressed, will squirt out with great violence. It grows in gardens and wild places, and it flowers in July.

The dried juice is a great purgative, and if mixed with oil and outwardly applied, will heal inflammation of the throat. The juice of the leaves can ease the pain of the ears and the root steeped in vinegar alleviates the pain of gout.

CUDWEED or Herb
Impious
(*Gnaphalium vulgare*,
Filago,
Herba impia)

The leaves are small and covered with a fine woolly substance; it has one woolly stalk about 1 ft high, and it bears naked yellow flowers growing together in clusters. It grows in dry barren places near the sea coast, and in fallow fields.

It has a dry astringent nature. A decoction in red wine is good against dysentery, haemorrhages and all kinds of flow.

CUMMIN
(*Cuminum vel cyminum*)

It bears fine slender leaves like Fennel, only much smaller; the flowers are reddish white and grow in small clusters, and it is about 1 ft high, while the seed is long and brown and it is sown yearly in gardens.

Cummin seed is useful for expelling wind from the stomach and bowels, and for clearing obstructions of the lungs, it having a hot and dry nature.

CYPRESS TREE
(*Cupressus*)

It is planted in gardens for its pleasant verdure, being a perennial or evergreen.

It stops bleeding and heals wounds. A decoction of the cones, taken internally, is very good against dysentery, diarrhoea, haemorrhages and the spitting of blood, and also vomiting and involuntary urination.

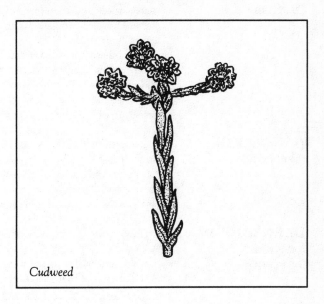

Cudweed

D

GREAT DAISY
(Bellis major)

It bears long leaves, serrated about the edges. The stalks are about 1 ft high and the flowers are composed of several broad white petals set about a broad yellow centre. It grows in meadows and moist pastures, and it flowers in June.

It is of a cold moist nature, and is good against burning ulcers, abscesses, inflammations and wounds. It is excellent in curing diseases of the lungs, and also for coughs, shortness of breath and consumption.

SMALL DAISY
(Bellis minor)

It is good against fevers, inflammations of the liver, inflamed eyes, scrofula and coagulated blood.

DAFFODIL
(Narcissus)

There are several sorts of Daffodils, but they all have the same virtues and therefore I shall not treat particularly of them. They grow in gardens and sometimes wild, flowering generally in April.

They have a hot and dry nature. The roots, pounded with honey are good against burns, bruised sinews, dislocations and old aches. They take away freckles and heal abscesses and sores, and they draw out thorns and splinters. A decoction of the roots is a great emetic.

DANDELION
(Dens leonis)

It grows in fields and meadows, flowering for most of the summer.

It has a cold and dry nature. It strengthens the stomach, causes good digestion, reduces inflammation of the liver and cleanses the kidneys and bladder.

DARNEL GRASS or Ray-Grass
(Loliumrubrum)

It grows along the borders of fields, and ripens in July and August.

A decoction of it in red wine stops dysentery, diarrhoea and disorders of menstruation and urination.

Daffodil

Devil's Bit   Dill

DEVIL'S BIT
(Morsus diaboli, Succisa)

It grows in meadows and pastures, flowering towards the latter part of the summer.

It is an antidote to poison, prevents fevers, dissolves the congealed blood which causes bruises and removes obstructions of the liver and spleen. Added to a bath it is good for old aches, strains and rheumatic pains.

DILL
(Anethum)

It very much resembles common Fennel, but it seldom grows so tall or so much branched. It grows in gardens, flowering in July, and the whole plant has a strong scent.

Dill has a hot dry nature. It expels flatulence, alleviates colic pains, stops vomiting and diarrhoea, and provokes urine. Applied externally it eases pain and heals tumours. The seed is a remedy to stop hiccups and also vomiting.

DITTANDER or
Pepperwort
(Lepidium, Piperitis)

It has long broad serrated leaves; the stalks and branches are round and smooth, growing about 2 ft high, and the flowers are small, white and four-leaved. It grows in moist places and near rivers, flowering in June and July. It has a hot sharp taste.

The roots and leaves are very good against sciatica when mixed with goose-grease and applied to the afflicted area.

When chewed, they draw catarrh from the glands of the throat in great amounts.

SHARP POINTED DOCK
(Lapathum acutum vel oxylapathum)

The broad, round leaved Wild Dock is much of the same nature with this, so I shall not particularly mention it.

The roots, made into an ointment with tobacco, are a great cure for itchy and scabby skin. A decoction of the roots in ale or whey, taken internally is an excellent cure for any scurvy. The seed is useful for stopping all haemorrhages and flows of blood.

GREAT WATER DOCK
(Lapathum maximum aquaticum)

The root is thick and large; the leaves are 2 ft long and not more than four fingers broad, the stalks are large and thick, about 4 or 5 ft high, while the flowers are yellow and set in thick whorls about the branches. It grows in large ponds.

It is very good against scurvy, ulcers of the mouth and gums and against all kinds of flow.

GARDEN DOCK or
Patience or Monk's Rhubarb
(Lapathum hortense folio oblongo, Lapathum sativum, Patientia)

This dock frequently grows 5 or 6 ft high; it has long pointed leaves, the stalk is red and the flowers are staminous.

It is somewhat purgative, it removes obstructions and is beneficial for the liver and spleen.

DODDER
(Cuscuta major)

This is a strange herb, having neither leaves nor root. It consists of a number of slender red filaments twisting itself around neighbouring plants and sucking nourishment from them. It bears several white flowers.

It has a hot dry nature, but this nature is changed by the influences of surrounding herbs. It removes obstructions of the liver, spleen and bladder, and is good against old fevers, jaundice and itchy conditions. The Dodder that grows upon Flax, if taken internally, helps to break up gravel.

DODDER OF THYME or Small
Dodder
(Epythymum sive cuscuta minor)

This grows on thyme (as opposed to the Greater Dodder which grows on nettles, flax and so on).

It is beneficial for conditions of the spleen and for all eruptions of the skin. It is also a good cleanser.

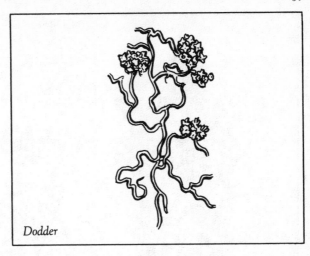

Dodder

DOGBERRY-TREE
or Gatter-Tree
(*Cornus*)

It is a low tree, or rather a shrub which, being dry, is difficult to cut. It is knotty with many joints, and full of pith. The flowers are white, growing in tufts, being succeeded by small round berries, which are black when ripe. It grows in hedges and under woods, and flowers in April and May while the berries ripen in September.

The fruit is cold, dry and astringent. It is therefore good against diarrhoea and dysentery. It also strengthens weak stomachs. The leaves and tender buds will heal fresh wounds and stop bleeding.

DOG BRYAR or
Wild Rose or Hip-Tree
(*Rosa canina,
Cynosbatos*)

It grows in hedges, flowering in June, while the fruit ripens in October.

The flowers are very good against excessive menstrual flow. The pulp of the hip or berries is good for disorders of the mouth and chest. The hips, when reduced to powder, and a spoonful taken in white wine, twice or three times, seldom fails to cure the gravel.

GREAT DRAGONS
(*Dracontium majus*)

The roots are good for asthma, bad coughs, catarrhs, malignant ulcers and eruptions of the skin. The juice of the root, dropped into the eyes, removes cataracts and morbid growths. The green leaves are beneficial when applied to wounds and are excellent to drive away any malignity from the heart.

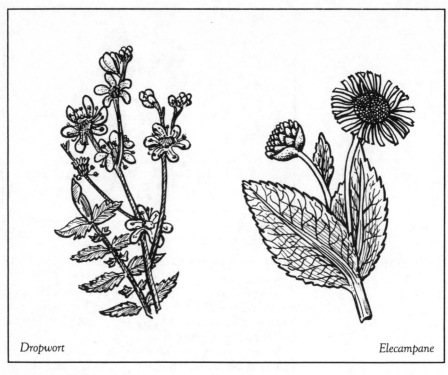

Dropwort   *Elecampane*

DROPWORT
(Filipendula)

It grows in gardens and also wild, flowering in June and July. It provokes urine, cleanses the kidneys and bladder, and expels flatulence. It is also benficial for diseases of the mouth.

WATER DROPWORT or
Hemloc-Dropwort
(Denanthe cicutae facie)

It grows in and near running water. It has a poisonous nature and anyone who eats any quantity of it dies within twenty-four hours.

The roots crushed and mixed with honey is effective in curing abscesses. The leaves pounded and mixed with bay salt cure several disorders of the skin.

DUCKS MEAT
(Lens palustris)

It frequently grows in ponds and ditches, covering the whole surface of the water.

It has a cooling nature and, mixed with wheaten flour or barley meal, it is very beneficial for boils, acute fever, gout and all kinds of inflammations.

DYERS WEED or
Common Would
(*Luteola falicis folio*)

The leaves are long and narrow; the stalks are hollow and channelled, and are about 3 or 4 ft high. The flowers grow in long spokes of a pale yellow colour. It grows commonly in uncultivated places, and flowers in May.

It has a hot dry nature, and is useful for curing both wounds and scrofula.

E

ELDER TREE
(*Sambucus*)

This flowers in May with the berries ripening in September.

The leaves, tender tops and the inner green bark, purge bilious conditions. A small amount of the seed pounded and taken in wine will disperse an accumulation of watery fluid. The green leaves are good against all sorts of inflammations, while the flowers expel wind from the stomach. The berries can be used in gargles for sore mouths and throats.

DWARF-ELDER or
Dane Wort or Wall
Wort
(*Ebulus chamaeacte vel sambucus humilis*)

It grows in moist fruitful ground, and has much the same nature and virtues of Common Elder.

It is very beneficial in causing watery evacuations.

ELECAMPANE
(*Enula campana, Helenium*)

It grows wild in meadows, and is often planted in gardens.

It is the root that is principally used in medicine. It provokes urination and menstruation, cures consumptive coughs and shortness of breath, aids digestion, alleviates pains in the joints and, made into an ointment, cures itchy conditions. It is also very good for chest problems, and cures most disorders of the lungs, such as difficulty or suspension of breathing, hurried respiration and asthma.

ELM TREE
(*Ulmus*)

The leaves and inner bard heal and consolidate wounds, bruises and fractured bones. The liquid that is found in the leaves removes freckles, pimples and spreading eruptions. The bark is abstersive and is frequently used in gargles for sore mouths and throats. The inner bark being scraped off and steeped in water for twenty-four hours, is exceeding good to be applied to burns and scalds.

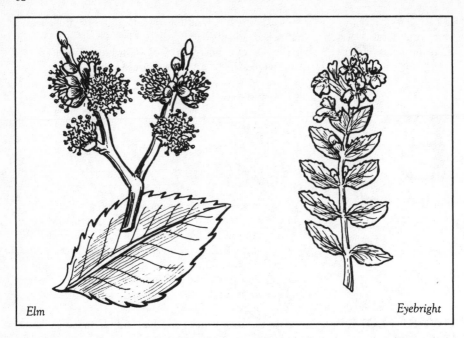

Elm

Eyebright

GARDEN ENDIVE
(Endiva,
Scariola)

It grows wild and flowers in June.

It comforts and refreshes a weak stomach, stops burning diarrhoea, opens obstructions of the liver and is good against jaundice and burning fevers. Externally applied, it is beneficial for inflammations and abscesses. The leaves mixed with oil of roses and laid against the forehead, alleviates a headache.

ERINGO or Sea Holly
(Eryngium marinum)

It grows near the seaside, flowering in June and July.

It is the root that is principally used. It provokes urination and menstruation, it encourages flatulance and removes obstructions of the liver, kidneys and bladder. It cures colic pains, is good for the nerves and as a general restorative. It is also useful against cramps and convulsions, and is good for consumptive persons.

EYEBRIGHT
(Euphrasia)

It grows in meadows and common pastures, flowering in July and August.

It is good for all disorders of the eyes, the juice being mixed with white wine or distilled water and dropped into the eyes.

Eringo

In short, it generally strengthens the eyesight wonderfully. The pounded leaves cure whitlows.

EYEWORT

It is a small plant like the violet. It bears blue flowers and grows on rocks.

A decoction taken internally is very good against epilepsy, lethargy, apoplexy and migraine, and is also a powerful cleanser.

F

FEATHERFEW
(*Matricaria, Parthenium*)

It is commonly planted in gardens, and it flowers in June and July.

Externally applied, it is good for burning fevers, boils and all bilious inflammations. It is useful for most disorders of the womb. It is also good for all kinds of acute fever, especially if 2 oz of the juice is taken before a fit begins. A poultice made with featherfew, rue, oaten meal, milk and rusty bacon is extraordinarily good against boils, in order to break them and afterwards to draw the corruption out of them.

FELIX WEED
(Sophia chirurgorum)

The leaves are jagged and somewhat hairy; the stalks are round and hard, about 2 ft high, while the flowers are small, yellow and four-leaved. It grows frequently in sandy ground and among rubbish, and it flowers in June.

The seed is excellent for dysentery and for all flows of blood; if pounded and applied to all ulcers and sores, it heals and conglutinates them. It provokes urine, and is good for stone and gravel.

COMMON FENNEL
(Foeniculum vulgare)

It is planted in gardens and flowers in June.

The leaves and seed increase milk in nurses. The roots are very good against stone and gravel, and the whole plant is extraordinarily good in opening obstructions of the liver, spleen and lungs. The seed strengthens the stomach and prevents vomiting. It is a powerful optic medicine, excellent for most disorders which the eyes are subject to, for it strengthens them wonderfully. The leaves pounded with vinegar are very good against boils and other inflammations.

HOGS FENNEL or Sulpher Wort or Sow Fennel
(Peucedanum)

This herb has a weak slender stalk, the leaves being larger than the leaves of Fennel. It bears five-leaved small yellow flowers. It grows near the seashore, and flowers in July.

It provokes urination and menstruation and removes obstructions of the kidneys. It is good against coughs and shortness of breath. The juice, mixed with egg and applied with oil of roses and vinegar, eases an old headache and is useful in an epilepsy. Taken into the nostrils, it is good against apoplexy and lethargy.

FENUGREEK
(Foenum graecum)

It is planted in gardens, and the seed is the only part used.

It causes abscesses, boils and all kinds of tumours to suppurate. It is also excellent in curing bites of mad dogs.

FEMALE FERN or Brake
(Filix foemina vulgaris)

It grows in woods and mountains.

The root crushed and $\frac{1}{2}$ oz of it taken with honey and water will expel worms from the body. A decoction of it in wine will remove obstructions of the liver and spleen. Around midsummer, the country people burn the stalks and leaves of it in order to make ashes with which to whiten their linen clothes.

MALE FERN
(Filix mas vulgaris)

It grows in hedges and shady places, and has the same virtues which are attributed to the female fern.

The roots, which are the only part used in medicine, open obstructions of the liver and spleen and are good in curing rickets in children.

WATER FERN or
Flowering Fern or
Osmund Royal
*(Fixil florida,
Osmunda regalis)*

This is the largest of all the ferns, and not much unlike the female Fern, only that is is not indented about the edges. It grows in woods and marshy boggy places.

The roots are good against bruises, dislocations and ruptures. It is sometimes put into healing plasters.

FIG TREE
(Ficus)

The milk or juice of the figs is good against freckles, spreading sores, itching and roughness of the skin. A little cotton dipped in it will ease a toothache. The ashes of the tree mixed with oil of roses will cure burns. Figs break up stone of the bladder and help heal lung disorders. When applied as a poultice, they cure scrofulous tumours and extract broken bones.

FIGWORT
(Scrophularia major)

It has square brown fistulous stalks, about 3 ft high; the leaves are indented at the edges like Nettle leaves and they smell like elder. The dark purplish flowers grow in small clusters. It grows along the borders of fields, under hedges and about lakes and ditches, and flowers in June.

It dissolves all kinds of hard swellings and heals ulcers and cankers if it is pounded and applied with salt. Washing with its juice takes away redness of face and it is good against scrofulous tumours and boils.

WATER FIGWORT
(Scrophularia aquatica)

It is larger and taller than figwort, and the root has no knots or tubercles. It grows in moist places and by ditch sides, flowering in June.

The virtues of figwort may be attributed to this. It is useful in healing wounds and itchy conditions.

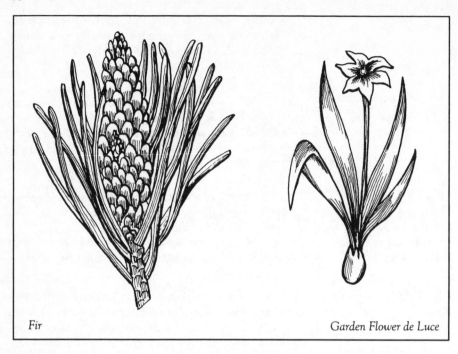

Fir   *Garden Flower de Luce*

FIR TREE or Male Fir
Tree
(Abies mas)

The leaves and top of this tree can be used against scurvy.
The turpentine or liquid resin that can be extracted from
the tree is somewhat purgative, and also provokes urine and
is beneficial to the bladder, kidneys and arthritic
conditions. It is good for wounds, being healing and
cleansing.

**YELLOW WATER
FLAG** or Bastard
Acorus or Water
Flower de Luce
*(Acorus adulterinus,
Pseudoacorus,
Gladeolus luteus,
Iris palustris lutea)*

The roots have a cold dry nature, and have great binding
qualities. A decoction made from them stops dystentery,
diarrhoea, haemorrhages and excessive menstrual flow.

MANURED FLAX
(Linum sativum)

Linseed softens and breaks abscesses and tumours. It takes
away spots and freckles from the face. A decoction

strengthens and clears the eyes. Taken in suppositories it eases colic pains, and taken as a paste, it is good for all disorders of the lungs. Linseed is very good when applied to burns or scalds.

PURGING FLAX or Dwarf Wild Flax or Millmountain
(Linum cartharticum herba minuta)

This is but a small plant, seldom growing above a span high. It has round slender stalks, having two oblong small leaves at each joint; it has many branches, bearing several five-leaved white flowers, which are succeeded by seed vessels, which are in the shape of the Common Flax, but much smaller. It grows on dry ditches and hilly places, flowering in June and July.

When boiled in ale and drunk, it is a powerful purgative and the common people frequently make use of it.

WILD NARROW LEAVED FLAX
(Linum sylvestre)

The leaves are thinly set and the flowers are blue.

It provokes urine, breaks up stone and opens obstructions of the liver and spleen. It is particularly good for curing jaundice.

FLEA BANE
(Conyza vel pulicaria minor flore globoso)

The stalks are hard and of a reddish-brown colour. The leaves are small and woolly, and about 1 in long. The flowers are yellow like the flowers of Tansy. It grows in moist places, flowering in August and September.

It provokes urination and menstruation, and expels a still born child. It is good against jaundice, colic pains, epilepsy, wounds and swellings. It is known as Pulicaria because it destroys fleas.

GARDEN FLOWER DE LUCE
(Iris nostras hortensis)

This flowers in May and June.

The roots encourage sneezing and vomiting; they provoke menstruation and they eliminate bile and cleanse the lungs, clearing them of all obstructions.

FLOWER GENTLE
(Amaranthus ceu flos amoris)

The stalks are large and channelled, about 3 or 4 ft high, the leaves are long and broad, and of a light green colour, and on the tops of the stalks grow long spikes or deep red staminous flowers. It is planted in gardens, flowering in July and August.

The flowers stop haemorrhages and flows of all kinds.

FLUELLIN or Male
Speedwell
(*Veronicamas supina
vulgatissima*)

The stalks generally lie on the ground, shooting out fibres at the lower joints. The leaves are oval, hairy, notched about the edges and of a pale green colour, while the flowers grow in short spikes, each with one small bluish purple leaf, cut into four parts. It grows in woods and shady places, flowering in June.

It is good against all obstructions of the kidneys; it heals wounds, cleanses the blood, and is good against all sorts of flows and haemorrhages.

FLUELLIN or Female
Speedwell
(*Elatine,
Veronica faemina*)

It is a long low plant creeping on the ground. It has slender hairy stems, bearing large, soft and hairy leaves. The flowers have the same shape as the flowers of Toad-Flax or Larkspur. It grows in cornfields and moist places.

It has the same virtues of the former, only this herb is weaker in operation.

FOOL STONES or
Dog Stones or Male
Satyrion or
Standergrass
(*Satyrium mas,
Orchis*)

It bears five or six smooth long shiny leaves which are almost like lily leaves, only that these are black spotted. The flowers grow in spikes and have a purple colour. It has two oval roots, which are nearly as big as small olives, and which are of a whitish colour. It grows in moist meadows, and flowers in May.

Fluellin   Fool Stones

A decoction of the roots drunk in goat's milk excites sexual desire, aids conception and strengthens the genitals. The roots restore the strength of someone suffering from consumptive fever. They also stop diarrhoea, and if externally applied, they purify rotten ulcers. It is said that if men eat the largest roots, they will beget sons, and if women eat the smallest roots they shall bring forth daughters.

FEMALE FOOL STONES or Female Satyrion
(Satyrium faemina, Orchis faemina, Morio faemina)

This is smaller than the former herb, having no spots on the leaves. The flowers are also smaller and some of these are deep violet, some white and some of a carnation colour. It grows in the same places with the former, but flowering somewhat later.

It has the same properties as the former.

Foxglove

FOXGLOVE
(Digitalis)

It grows in mountains, ditches and highways, flowering in June and July.

A decoction drunk dissolves viscous, clammy and slimy phlegm. It opens obstructions of the liver and spleen. It is a great purgative and it encourages vomiting. It is good for any obstructions of the lungs and also for epilepsy. Made into a poultice with hogs lard, it cures scrofula.

Fumitory

FUMITORY
(Fumaria)

It has square stalks with many branches; the leaves are weak, tender and finely divided. The flowers grow in spikes and are purple above and white underneath. The whole plant has a bitter taste. It grows along the borders of fields and tilled grounds, among wheat and barley, flowering in May.

The juice dropped into the eyes sharpens the sight. Taken internally, it cleanses the blood; externally applied, it is good against all eruptions of the skin.

FURZ
(Genista spinosa)

The leaves have a hot dry nature, and are therefore astringent. A decoction prevents excessive menstrual flow and also diarrhoea. The seed is good for jaundice and for killing worms.

GARLICK, manured
(*Allium sativum*)

It is a great antidote to poison, and good for diseases of the mouth and lungs. It has a hot, dry nature and Galen, the Prince of Physicians, called it the Poor Man's Treacle. It is good for coughs, asthma and bowel conditions and for expelling flatulence. Pounded with vinegar, it eases toothache, headache and dissolves hard swellings.

To cure any cough, asthma or shortness of breath, boil a handful in 2 quarts of spring water. Allow 1 quart to boil away and strain it, then add 1 quart of honey to make a syrup, then take a spoonful of this at a time.

CROW-GARLICK
or Wild Garlick
(*Allium sylvestre tenuifolium*)

Instead of leaves it has long round small and hollow blades, from which grows up a round hard stem, about 2 or 3 ft long; upon this grows the flower and seed. It grows in pasture fields, hedges and meadows, flowering in June.

The roots are good against scalds, itches, leprosy and swellings. They provoke menstruation and eliminate the afterbirth. If they are infused in white wine overnight and drunk in the morning before breaking the fast, they give relief from the pain of stone and gravel.

Take the roots and blades of this garlic, let them be well pounded, then strain 1 quart of juice out of them, then add a $\frac{1}{4}$ oz of pounded aromatic cloves. This will infallibly cure rheumatism or rheumatic pains if the patient is well rubbed with it twice daily for three days, in the morning before he arises and at night when he retires. However, he must ensure that he keeps himself warm for an hour after the operation is performed, likewise, he must not stir out of his chamber during the said three days lest (his pores being open), he should take a cold.

BOG GAUL or Sweet
Willow or Dutch
Myrtle or Wild Sumac
(*Myrtus brabantica,
Eleagnus cordi,
Rhus sylvestris*)

It has a strong smell and a bitter taste. It grows in bogs, low land, meadows and near rivers, and flowers in May and June.

It has a hot dry nature. It is useful in destroying vermin and the common people sometimes put it on their drink instead of hops.

BASTARD GENTIAN or Dwarf Felwort
(Gentianella)

A decoction of it drank encourages vomiting and clears the lungs. It is generally good against infection and, when applied externally, it heals wounds and ulcers.

GERMANDER
(Chamaedrys, Trissago)

This grows in gardens, flowering in June and July.

It opens obstructions of any part of the body, especially the liver and spleen. It is good for coughs and the loosening of phlegm. It provokes urination and menstruation.

WATER GERMANDER
(Scordium)

It has square downy stalks about 1 ft high; the leaves are round, wrinkled, soft and whitish, and serrated about the edges. The flowers grow in thin whorls, and are of a reddish colour. It has a strong aromatic smell. It grows in moist meadows and fens, and flowers in June.

It is very good in provoking urine. It removes obstructions of the liver, spleen, kidneys, bladder and womb.

WILD GERMANDER
(Chamaedrys sylvestris)

It usually grows in rich soil, and is very like Garden Germander both in shape and qualities, but is more effective.

It is good against arthritis, rheumatism and gout. It

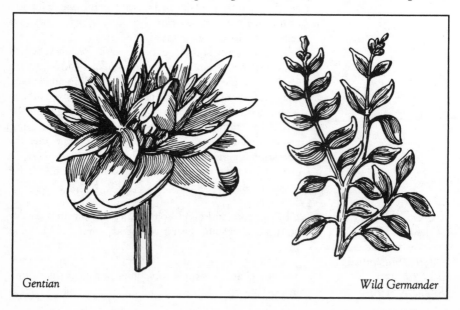

Gentian   *Wild Germander*

Gladwyn

removes pains in the joints, and opens obstructions in any part of the body. It is very good for convulsions in children, either taken internally or worn around the wrist or neck.

SEA-GIRDLE
(Fucus phasganoides)

It has long narrow leaves; the root is rough and thick and full of fibres, and it grows on rocks in the sea.

It is good against boils, inflammatory tumours and gout.

STINKING GLADWYN
(Spatula foetida, Xyris)

It bears long narrow sharp-pointed leaves of a dark green colour. The stalks are smooth and round, on which grow flowers, which are like the flower De Luce, but which are smaller and of an ash colour. It grows in stony places, hedges and borders of woods, flowering in June.

The seed, taken internally, provokes urine and cures obstructions and hardness of the spleen. It is a remedy for scrofula and scrofulous swellings. It also kills the stinking insects, called bugs, and which were of late years brought to this Kingdom, if the place where they frequent be rubbed with the juice.

GLASSWORT or
Saltwort
(*Kali spinosum*)

It has thick brittle stalks about 1 ft high; among the leaves, which are long, sharp-pointed with prickly tops, grow small yellow flowers. It grows near the sea shore and has a dry nature.

From it is made Sal alkali, which is an ingredient of the finest glass. A kind of fine salt can be extracted from its ashes. It is purgative and removes all kinds of obstructions.

YELLOW GOATS BEARD or Go to Bed at Noon
(*Tragopon luteum*)

This plant grows near running water and in pasture ground.

The roots are restorative for consumption. They break up stone and are good for asthma and painful urination.

GOATS-RUE
(*Gaelega,
Ruta capraria*)

It grows to a height of 3 ft, and has blue flowers growing in long spikes which hang downwards. It is planted in gardens and grows wild in rocky places, and flowers in June and July.

It is very good against poisons and malignities, for it expels the poison through the skin by inducing perspiration. It will kill and eliminate worms from children, either by drinking the juice or if the juice is boiled in linseed oil and applied to the child's navel. A spoonful of the juice of this herb is good

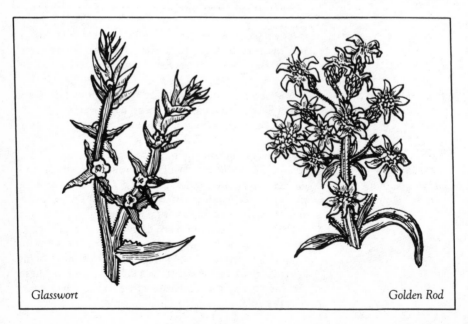

Glasswort

Golden Rod

to be given to children every morning to drink, against convulsions.

GOLDEN ROD
(Virga aurea)

It has long broad leaves spreading on the ground near the root and indented about the edges. The stalks are round, hairy and full of fungous pith, growing to about 3 ft high, with the flowers growing in small yellow spikes. It is usually planted in gardens, but it is also found growing wild. It flowers in July.

It helps to break up stone in the kidneys and expel it in the urine; it clears obstructions of the liver and spleen. It heals all curable wounds, and is used in gargles for ulcers of the mouth and throat.

GOOSEBERRY BUSH
(Grossularia)

The unripe berries stop diarrhoea and flows of blood, and are very good in applications to boils and inflammations. Eaten with meat, they provoke the appetite, and cool the heat of the stomach and liver. The leaves provoke urine and break up stone in the kidneys.

GOOSE TONGUE
(Lingua anserina)

It grows generally in gardens and is good against fainting.

WILD GOOSE TONGUE
(Lingua anserina sylvestris)

The stalks are small, about 1 ft high; the leaves are small, rough and somewhat indented and the flowers are yellow.

It is a remedy for epilepsy and hysterical fits and is useful for all kinds of convulsions.

GOURD
(Concurbita major sessilis)

This plant is grown yearly from seed in gardens, flowering in July. The fruit, which ripens in September, is very large and in the shape of a bottle which will hold several quarts. The leaves are large, rough and woolly, and the flowers are white.

The juice is good against boils, inflammations and burning fever.

SEA GRAPE or
Jointed Glass-Wort
(Salicornia, Kali genticulatum)

This plant has stalks without leaves, divided into several branches with knots, each as big as grains of wheat and easily pulled off. It has a salt taste and is full of juice. It grows near the sea.

It has a very dry nature, and is pickled like Samphire to create an appetite.

Gromwell

GRASS OF PARNASSUS
(Gramen parnassi vel flos hepaticus)

It has round leaves like the leaves of ivy, only smaller, among which spring up two or three small stalks about 1 ft high, bearing fair white flowers. It grows in moist places, flowering in July.

It strengthens a weak stomach, stops diarrhoea, provokes urine and expels gravel. It also stops the bleeding of wounds and heals them.

GROMWELL or Gromill
(Lithospermum seu milium solis)

It has long slender hairy stalks; the leaves are brown, rough, oblong and sharp-pointed, and the flowers, which are cut into five segments, are succeeded by white, shining hard seeds, like pearls. It grows in fields, hedges and rough stony places, and flowers in May.

Gromwell has a hot dry nature. The seed, if pounded and drunk in white wine, breaks up the stone in the bladder, expels gravel from the kidneys and provokes urine. Two drams of it taken internally, is an excellent remedy to facilitate labour. It is used in baths for strains, sciatica, and rheumatic pains.

GROUND PINE
(Chamaepitys,
Ivy arthritica)

This is a small tender plant creeping on the ground. It has many crooked stalks, the leaves are small, narrow and hairy and the yellow flowers are labiated. It grows in fallow fields and stony ground, flowering in June and July, and has a strong scent.

A decoction in white wine, drunk for seven mornings, cures jaundice, and every day for a month, cures sciatica. It clears obstructions of the liver and spleen, provokes urine and cures wounds, ulcers and lumps of the breast. Made into a poultice with white bread, sweet milk, nerve oil and saffron, it alleviates rheumatic pains. It opens obstructions of the womb, and promotes menstrual flow.

GROUNDSEL
(Erigeron vel senicio)

It grows on banks, walls and among rubbish, flowering in June and July.

It has a cooling digestive nature. The leaves and flowers crushed with wine are beneficial in applications for

Ground Pine

inflammations. The down of the flowers crushed with a little salt, heals scrofula, while the juice taken in ale encourages vomiting. It helps cure jaundice and kills worms.

H

HARE-BELLS or English Hyacinth
(Hyacinthus anglicus)

If the roots are boiled in wine and taken internally, they stop diarrhoea and dysentery and provoke urine. These disorders are more effectually cured by the seed. The roots drank in wine are very good against epilepsy.

HARES FOOT
Trefoil
(Lagopus ceu pes leporinus)

It has small narrow hairy leaves like clover, and rough round stalks, on the tops of which grow small purple flowers. It is found among corn and in fallow fields, flowering in June and July.

It has a dry nature. A decoction of it drunk in wine stops diarrhoea, dysentery and excessive menstrual flow.

HART'S TONGUE
(Lingua cervina vel phyllitis)

It bears long narrow leaves about a span or two long and 2 in wide and their upper parts are smooth and plain. The seeds grows on the underside of the leaves. It grows in shady places, around fountains and stony moist places.

It is dry and astringent. If a decoction is drunk, it will stop diarrhoea and dysentery. It is also good for coughs, consumption and in opening obstructions. It is very good for hysteric and convulsive fits.

GREAT HAWK-WEED
(Hieracium magnum)

The stalks are reddish and rough, the leaves are long and jagged having sharp prickles almost like the leaves of milk thistle. It bears double yellow flowers like those of dandelion, except smaller. It grows in untilled places, in ditches and along the borders of corn fields, and spends most of the summer in flower.

This herb is, in virtue and operation, much like Sowthistle, and is used in the same manner. It is cold and dry and the juice is good for strengthening the eyes.

HAW-THORN or
White-Thorn
*(Spina alba,
Oxyacanthus)*

This tree grows almost everywhere in hedges, flowering in May, with the haws ripening in September. The fruit is dry and astringent.

It stops flows and excessive menstruation. The flowers are very good for breaking up stone in the kidneys and bladder.

HAZEL-NUT Tree
*(Avellana vel corylus
sylvestris)*

Hazelnuts provide little nourishment, are hard to digest, cause shortness of breath, and if a lot are eaten, encourage flatulence. A decoction in mead cures an old cough. If roasted and taken with a little pepper, they are beneficial for catarrh and runny nose or eyes. If burnt and applied with hogs lard, they cure a scald.

HEARTS-EASE or
Three Faces under a
Hood
*(Pansies,
Viola tricolor)*

This grows in gardens, flowering for most of the summer.

The flowers cure convulsions in children, cleanse the lungs and breast and are very good for fevers, internal inflammations and wounds.

COMMON HEATH
or Ling
(Erica vulgaris)

It grows on barren mountains and flowers about midsummer.

It has a dry nature. The juice of the leaves dropped into the eyes strengthens and cures them if inflamed. About a half pint of a decoction in spring water drunk warm, is very good against stone in the bladder if taken for thirty days. After which, the patient must take a bath made of a decoction of it, and this process must be often repeated. The bark is beneficial for diseases of the spleen.

**HEDGE-BERRY
TREE** or the Wild
Cluster Cherry or
Bird's Cherry
*(Cerasus avium nigra,
Racemosa)*

It has a binding quality, it strengthens the stomach, and stops diarrhoea.

HEDGE-MUSTARD
*(Erysimum vulgare sive
irio)*

It grows everywhere along waysides, and in untilled stony places, flowering in June and July.

A syrup made from the seed and some honey loosens viscous and clammy phlegm. It is also good against an old cough, shortness of breath, sciatica, jaundice and colic pains. A decoction in wine is very good for cholic.

HELLEBORE or
Great Bastard Black
Hellebore or Bears-Foot
or Sellerwort
(Helleboraster maximus,
Contiligo,
Helleborus nigra foetidus)

It grows on mountains, flowering in early spring.

The roots are cleansing. Thrust into the ears of cattle, it helps them against the diseases of the lungs, for it draws the malignity from them into the ears, which is soon after evacuated. Taken inwardly, it cures jaundice; applied externally, it cures abscesses and sores, leprosy, itches and eruptions of the skin.

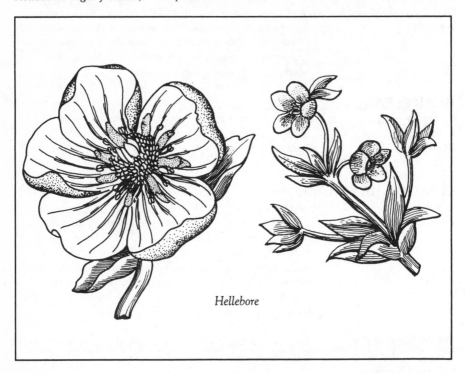

Hellebore

HELM or English
Seamatweed or
Marram
(Spartum anglicanum ceu
gramen sparteum)

The stalks are woody, on which grow few sharp-pointed leaves, and the flowers, which appear yellow and not much unlike the flowers of common Broom, appear in June.

It has a hot dry nature. The flowers and seed provoke vomiting, but not to a dangerous extent. The juice, taken while fasting is beneficial for sciatica and inflammation of the throat.

HELMET FLOWER
(Napellus)

It is a small tender plant, having spotted round leaves. The stalk rises about 1 ft high, on which grows a double flower, divided into two parts, one yellow and the other blue.

It helps children with rickets, and is also good for a prolapsed womb.

HEMLOCK or the Ordinary Great Hemlock
(Cicuta major)

It has a very cold nature, and is therefore good against boils, inflammations, burning fever, the hardness of the liver and the spleen. It also has a poisonous nature – the best cure, if eaten accidentally, is to drink plenty of good old wine.

LESSER HEMLOCK or Fools Parsley
(Cicutaria tenuifolia)

It has spotted stalks and grows in moist rich soil and in kitchen gardens.

The root has a hot and dry nature. It provokes menstruation and assists births and expels the afterbirth. It is also beneficial for chest problems and is generally strenthening.

WATER HEMLOCK
(Cicutaria palustris, Phellandryum)

It has a thick jointed stalk, shorter than that of ordinary hemlock. It has large-winged leaves, finer and more tender than common hemlock, and the flowers are white, but with a red cast. It grows in running waters, ditches and ponds, flowering in June.

It is thought to be similar in virtues to Common Hemlock, but more poisonous.

HEMP or Manured Male Hemp
(Cannabis mas sativa)

It has a hot dry nature. The seed encourages flatulence, and, pounded and taken in white wine, cures jaundice. It is good for removing obstructions of the liver and easing old coughs. The juice of the green leaves, dropped into the ears, alleviates their pain and expels all kinds of vermin out of them. A decoction of the roots helps to cure contractions of the sinews, and eases gout.

HENBANE or Common Black Henbane
(Hyoseyamus nigra)

The stalks are large, round and soft, growing 2 or 3 ft high. The leaves are broad, downy and greyish, and the flowers are bell-shaped, have but a single petal, and are of a pale yellow colour, full of purple veins. It grows near highways and paths, and in sandy ground.

It is good against all kinds of inflammations, if the leaves or juice are applied. The seed is beneficial for coughs, catarrh, spitting of blood and excessive flows of blood. It alleviates the pain of gout and the swelling of women's breasts after delivery of a child.

HENBIT or Great
Henbit
(*Altine haederula major*)

It has several upright round knotty stalks; the leaves are not unlike Pellitory of the Wall, but are longer and less hairy, and it bears small white flowers, deeply cut. It grows in moist shady places, under hedges and bushes. It flowers about midsummer.

It is good for inflammations and ulcerations of the eyes. If the juice is dropped into them, it is beneficial for pains in the ears.

SMALL HENBIT or
Ivy Chick-Weed
(*Alsine haederacea minor*)

It is similar to the Greater Henbit, except that it is smaller and spreads on the ground rather than growing upwards.

A decoction is a powerful remedy against the heat of scurvy, and the itch of the hands, if they are bathed in it.

HERB ROBERT
(*Geranium robertianum vel gratia dei*)

It has round, tender, hairy reddish stalks, full of joints. The leaves resemble chervil leaves, and the flowers, which grow at the joints, are of a clear purple colour, inclining to red and are succeeded by heads which resemble the head and beak of a crane; it is a kind of Cranes-Bill. It grows in stony places, old walls and under hedges.

It stops the bleeding of wounds if crushed into an application. A decoction is good against rotten ulcers and sore mouths, and it is particularly good for scrofula.

HOLLY-TREE
(*Agrifolium*)

The berries have a hot nature, and it is believed that five of them when eaten relieve cholic and act as a purgative. The bark is sometimes made into birdlime.

HOLLYHOCKS
(*Malva arborea seu hortensis*)

It grows in gardens, flowering in July and August.

The leaves eaten with a little salt, help to ease the pains and ulcerations of the kidneys. It breaks up the stone of the bladder and kidneys. It is also used in gargles for swelling of the tonsils and to relax the uvula.

HONEY-TREE
(*Melianthus*)

It can be grown in gardens with very little cultivation and industry. It bears a yellow flower, which is succeeded by a lump of congealed honey.

HONEY-SUCKLE
or Woodbind
(*Caprifolium, Matrisylve, Percilymenum*)

It grows in hedges, flowering in June and July.

This has a hot dry nature, and the fruit cures obstructions and hardness of the spleen, if it is drunk in wine for forty days. It is also beneficial for coughs, shortness of breath, and assists women in hard labour. The leaves are used in gargles for sore throats and the flowers for cramps and convulsions. The leaves and fruit however, are dangerous for pregnant women. A powder made from the leaves is exceeding good for the ague, taking as much of it as can be put on a shilling in a glass of white wine, before the fit comes on.

HOPS Manured
(Lupulus sativus)

The flowers are of a hot, dry nature. They open obstructions of the liver, spleen and kidneys, and purge the blood through the urine. They are also good for those who are troubled with the itch, or such like infirmities. The juice dropped into the ears, cleanses them.

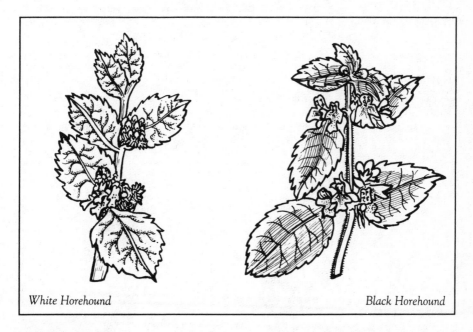

White Horehound

Black Horehound

HOREHOUND or
White Horehound
(Marubium album ceu prassium)

It grows in gardens, flowering in June.

It removes all obstructions of the liver and spleen. A syrup made from it is very effective in curing old coughs, tuberculosis, and ulcerations of the lungs. A decoction in wine opens obstructions of the womb, encourages menstruation, expels the afterbirth and stillborn child and assists women in hard labour. Pain of the ears is relieved by the juice being dropped into them. A decoction of the leaves cure jaundice.

HOREHOUND or Black or Stinking Horehound
(Marubium nigrum vel ballote)

It is taller and more branched than the White Horehound. The stalks are square, and hairy but of a blackish colour, the leaves are larger, longer and darker, resembling dead Nettle leaves. The flowers grow whorl-fashion round about the stalks, and it grows in untilled places, near highways, in hedges and borders of fields, flowering in July.

Pounded with salt it can be applied to those bitten by a mad dog, while the leaves, roasted in a cale leaf, repel piles. It can be applied with honey to rotten ulcers. Taken inwardly, it is good against fits, and is useful against poison.

WATER HOREHOUND
(Marubium aquaticum)

The leaves are of a dark green colour, hairy and somewhat wrinkled, while the flowers are white and smaller than the flowers of other Horehounds. It grows near moist ditches and water courses, and flowers in July.

It has properties similar to the other Horehounds.

HORN BEAM TREE
(Betulus sive carpinus)

The roots infused with wine are good, when taken internally against pains of the side. The fruit mixed with grease, heals burns and scalds. A decoction of the bark in vinegar, is useful in preventing toothache, and the leaves can be used against swellings and inflammations.

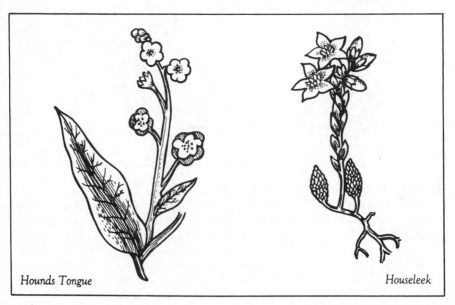

Hounds Tongue   Houseleek

HORSETAIL or the Great Marsh Horsetail *(Cauda equina vel equisetum)*

It grows in ditches and marshy grounds.

A decoction of it taken internally stops excessive menstruation, dysentery and all flows of blood. If it is pounded or crushed and applied to wounds, it stops the bleeding and any further inflammation. A decoction of the whole plant is good against a cough and difficulty of breathing. The juice, if sniffed into the nose, will stop a nosebleed.

NAKED HORSETAIL or Shavegrass *(Equisetum folis nudum non ramosum ceu juncum)*

It grows in fenny and marshy ground, and its virtues are as the Stinking Water Horsetail.

STINKING WATER HORSETAIL *(Equisetum foetidum)*

This species grows in muddy pools, dirty ditches and drains. Both this kind and the former have much the same qualities as the Great Horsetail.

HOUNDS TONGUE *(Cynoglossum vulgare)*

It has a hard rough brown stalk, about 2 or 3 ft high; the leaves are long, much like the leaves of Garden Bugloss, but narrower, smaller and not so rough, being covered with a fine down like velvet. It grows in sandy ground, under hedges and near paths and highways, and it flowers in June and July.

The root is very good for wounds, ulcers, inflammations, discharges of the lungs, haemorrhages and gonorrhoea.

HOUSELEEK or the Great Houseleek *(Sedum majus vulgare vel sempervivum majus)*

It grows on old walls and thatched houses, flowering in July and August.

It has a cold dry nature. A decoction of its juice taken internally is good for dysentery and diarrhoea. Mixed with barley meal and oil of roses, it is effective in easing a headache, while the juice dropped into the eyes is good for inflammations. It is also useful for burns, scalds, inflammations, burning fever and the gout.

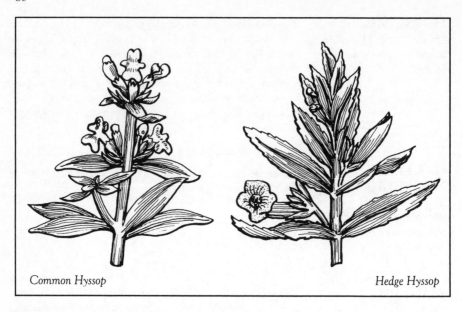

Common Hyssop

Hedge Hyssop

HYSSOP or Common Garden Hyssop
(Hyssopus)

It is planted in gardens, flowering in June and July.

It is very beneficial for moist asthma, and will open phlegmatic obstructions of the lungs. A decoction in vinegar, if held in the mouth, eases toothache. It dissolves congealed blood, black and blue marks and cures itchiness, scurf and mange, if the skin is washed therein. It is also good for diseases of the head and nerves. It is specifically good for disorders of the lungs.

HEDGE HYSSOP
(Gratiola)

It has square stalks scarcely 1 ft high, the leaves are narrow and sharp-pointed and the flowers, similar to those of the Foxglove in shape, have a pale yellow colour. It grows in sandy hills, and flowers in July.

It is a powerful purgative and it helps to eliminate clammy phlegm that accumulates in the lungs.

I & J

IRON-WORT or Narrow Leaved Allheal *(Sideritis arvensis rubra)*

The stalks are hard and square, the leaves long and the flowers red.

It is very useful in treating all wounds and ulcers. It effectively prevents the spitting and pissing of blood.

IVY-TREE *(Haedera arborea corymbifera)*

It flowers in June, with the fruit ripening in winter.

The juice of the leaves cures wounds, ulcers, burns and scalds and, when applied with oil of roses, it cures a headache. Sniffed into the nose it purges and cleanses the head. A decoction of the flowers in wine drunk twice a day, stops dysentery and the gum removes spots and freckles.

JACK BY THE HEDGE or Sauce Alone *(Alliaria)*

This herb, when it first springs up has roundish leaves, almost like the leaves of March Violets, but much larger. The stalks are about 2 ft high, on the tops of which grow many white flowers. It grows about the borders of meadows, in moist pastures and in hedges, flowering in May.

It has a hot dry nature. It provokes urine, encourages sweating, is good for the lungs and is an effective antidote to poison. It is also outwardly applied with good success against gangrene.

JASMINE or Jessamy *(Jasminum)*

It is planted in gardens, and flowers in June and July.

It has a hot dry nature. It cures red spots and pimples, and dissolves swellings and lumps on the skin. It also clears catarrh, and facilitates the process of birth.

JERUSALEM ARTICHOKE *(Flos solis pyramidalis)*

It grows in gardens, and is effective in opening vessels, provoking urine and increasing male fertility. It has much the same properties as potatoes or common artichokes.

JEWS-EAR
(Fungus sambucinus,
Auricula judae)

This is a fungus which frequently grows on the trunk of the elder-tree, being wrinkled and turned up like an ear, whitish on the outside and black inside, having several little veins.

Made into a powder, it cures chilblains, dissolves swellings, cures inflammations of the tonsils and throat.

ST JOHNS-WORT
(Hypericum)

It has a brown red stalk about 2 ft high; the leaves are long and narrow, which if held against the light, appear full of small holes (therefore it is known as Perforata) and the flowers are yellow. It grows near highways, along the borders of fields, in hedges and among bushes. It flowers in June and July.

It has a hot dry nature. It provokes urine and breaks up stone in the bladder. It stops diarrhoea and cures fevers. The seed, boiled and drunk for forty days, heals sciatica, and if pounded, it makes an effective application to burns, wounds and ulcers.

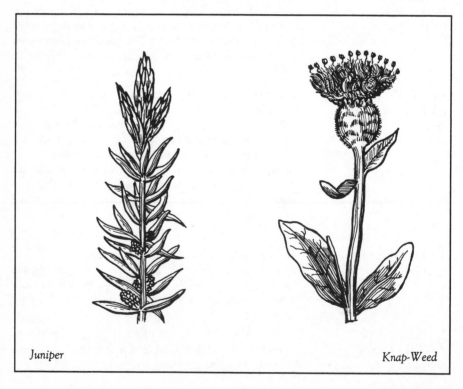

Juniper

Knap-Weed

WHITE STOCK
JULY FLOWER
(Lucoium album)

It grows in gardens, and flowers most of the summer.

It provokes urination and menstruation and expels the afterbirth, if a decoction of the flowers is drunk. If the flowers are made into a plaster with oil and wax, they can be effectively applied to ulcers and inflammations. The juice, dropped into the eyes, strengthens and clears them.

JUNIPER-TREE
(Juniperus vulgaris)

It grows on rocky mountains and in shady places.

The berries provoke urine, and cure old coughs, flatulence and colic pains. The gum of the tree expels worms from the body and stops excessive menstrual flow.

K

KINGS-SPEAR
(Asphodelus verus luteus vel hasta regia)

This herb bears narrow sharp-pointed leaves like a swordblade; the stalks are round, and the flowers grow in yellow spikes. It is planted in gardens but it is sometimes found growing wild near rivers. It flowers in May and June.

The root provokes urination and menstruation. A decoction boiled in the lees of wine and taken internally is effective when applied to sores, ulcers and abscesses. An oil made from it cures burns and chilblains.

KNAP-WEED
(Jacaea nigra vulgaris)

This herb grows to be about 2 ft high; the leaves are long, narrow and bluntly cut about the edges. On the tops of the round stalks grow small round buttons, like those of the blue bottle, from which emerge purple hairy flowers. It grows in meadows and pastures, flowering in June and July.

It has a hot dry nature. It cures abscesses of the mouth and throat if gargled.

KNAWELL or
Parsley Piert or Parsley
Break Stone
(Percepier anglorum vel alchimilla minima montana)

It bears many small narrow hairy leaves, and the flowers are small, growing in clusters at the joints. It grows in sandy places and in fallow fields.

It provokes urine and breaks up kidney stone.

KNOT-GRASS
(Polygonum mas centinodia, Gramen nodosum)

It has a lot of slender stalks full of joints and creeping on the ground. The leaves are oval and sharp-pointed, and between the leaves and joints grow small staminous flowers, sometimes white, sometimes of a carnation colour. It grows in streets and by waysides, flowering in summer.

It is very good against all haemorrhages, spitting and pissing of blood, diarrhoea, dysentery and excessive menstrual flow. Nosebleeds can be stopped by some juice being placed into the nose. Applied externally the leaves are good for boils and inflammations.

L

LADIES MANTLE
or Lyons-Foot
(Alchimilla)

This has large roundish leaves with eight corners, which are finely serrated at the edges, and when they first spring up, they are plaited or folded together. The stalks are small and weak, bearing clusters of yellowish green flowers. It grows in gardens and sometimes in meadows and woods, and flowers in May. This has the same virtues as Sanicle, being a species of it.

It removes the pain and heat of all inflamed wounds, ulcers and boils. It can be applied to women's breasts to make them small and firm. It stops internal bleeding and menstrual flow. It can cure burns and scalds, and it is also good for encouraging conception in women.

LARKSPUR
(Delphnium vel consolida regalis)

The dark green leaves are round and tender and divided into many deep sections. It has a straight round stem about 3 ft high; the flowers grow on the tops of the branches in long spikes, sometimes blue, sometimes white and sometimes of a carnation colour. It grows in gardens and also wild, flowering for most of the summer.

If the juice is sniffed into the nose it is good for headaches and migraine. It also helps to heal wounds.

COMMON LAVENDER or
Narrow Leaved Lavender or Lavender Spike
(Lavendula augustifolia)

It has a hot dry nature. It provokes urination and menstruation and expels the afterbirth, and also a still-born child. The flowers cure palpitations of the heart, and jaundice and are particularly good for apoplexy, vertigo and palsy.

LAVENDER COTTON
(Abrotonum foemina, Chamaecyparissus)

It is planted in gardens, flowering in July and August. This has much the same virtues as Sothernwood.

It provokes urination and menstruation and breaks up stone. It is also beneficial for the liver, chest and womb. It clears obstructions and dissolves swellings. Taken inwardly, it is a specific medicine against worms.

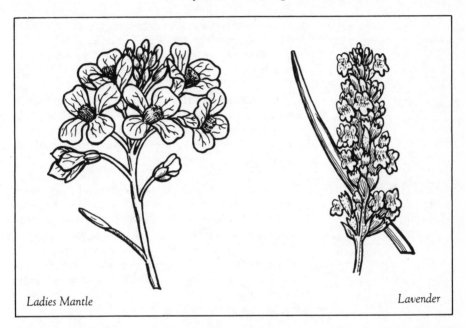

Ladies Mantle

Lavender

LEADWORT or Toothwort
(Dentario cue dentillaria)

The leaves are long, narrow and of a whitish-green colour; the stalks are slender, and the flowers are purple and grow in short thick spikes.

It has a hot biting nature. If masticated, it is good for a toothache. (In fact, it is such a good remedy that, it is said, it will cause a cure even if it is merely held in the hand.) A decoction made with Plantain, wild Tansy, Slow Tree bark, allum and honey of Roses, will fasten loose teeth. A decoction of it alone will provoke urine and break up stone.

GARDEN LEEK
(Porrum)

It is effective in cleansing the chest and a bath made of it with sea water opens obstructions of the womb and provokes menstruation. It will stop bleeding, especially of the nose and mixed in a powder with Frankincense and applied as a poultice, will dissolve swellings. It is exceeding good to make women fruitful.

LEMON TREE
(Limonia malus)

Lemon-trees are preserved from the inclemency of the air in this country by several curious gentlemen, who keep them in greenhouses.

The leaves of this tree have a very fragrant smell and the fruit quenches a thirst, revives the appetite and is useful in fevers of all kinds, being cooling. The juice, mixed with the salt of Wormwood, stops vomiting and strengthens the stomach.

However, I do not take lemon to be good for tender constitutions, for its bitter little particles grate too much on the fibres of the stomach, and induce belchings, flatulence and headaches. Moreover, there is another reason why it cannot be wholesome, for the fruit, when it is sent to us, is not fully ripe.

LENTILS or
Common Lentils
(Lens vulgaris)

The leaves are small, grow on short stalks, and have clasping tendrils by which they stick fast to anything that touches them, and the flowers are small and white. It grows in fields, flowering in May, with the seed ripening in July.

The first decoction aids digestion, and the second decoction is effective in stopping diarrhoea and excessive menstrual flow. A meal of lentils mixed with honey, cleanses ulcers and rotten sores; boiled in vinegar, it dissolves lumps and swellings.

LETTUCE
(Lactuca)

It creates a good appetite, quenches the thirst, aids digestion, promotes sound sleep, provokes urine and increases milk in nurses. The green leaves when bruised, can be applied to burns, scalds, boils and inflammations.

LICORICE
(Glycyrisa liquiritia)

It is planted by us in gardens, and it is brought to great perfection in my Lord Kingstons Gardens at Mitchelstown, where the root may be seen as thick as a man's finger. It is extraordinary pleasant to the taste, far exceeding what is commonly brought to us from foreign countries, so you see, how by a little industry, the most exotic plants may be brought to perfection in this country, which demonstrates what a fertile, prolific land we live in.

The virtues of this plant are so well known, almost to

everyone that I need not enlarge much upon it. The roots are beneficial for coughs and obstructions of the lungs; they also provoke urine, break up stone and are good for the liver and disorders of the mouth.

WHITE LILY
(Lilium album)

It grows in gardens, flowering in June.

The roots are useful in softening and easing pain in swellings and cysts. They are often taken inwardly as an emetic.

LILY OF THE VALLEY
(Lilium convallium)

By distilling the flowers in strong wine, and drinking a spoonful, speech will be restored after an apoplexy; this remedy is also effective for gout and paralysis. A small amount of the root, crushed and taken in wine and vinegar is a great antidote to poison, as it causes the patient to perspire, and is also useful in an apoplexy.

Take 2 drams of the flowers with a dram of the root of White Hellebore and let them be mixed and pulverized, and then sniff the powder up the nostrils. This will be found to be a singular remedy for apoplexy.

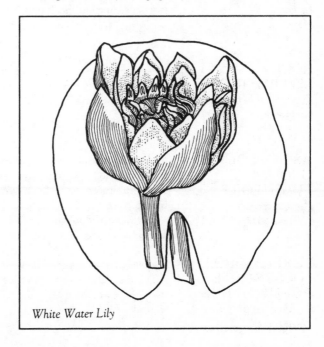

White Water Lily

WHITE WATER LILY
(Nymphaea alba major aquatica)

It grows in pools, rivers and large lakes, flowering in June.

It has a cold dry nature, lacking in sharpness. A decoction of the roots or seed is very effective against sexual desire or fleshly lust. A preparation of the flowers is useful against fevers and headaches, for it causes sweat and quiet sleep, and it also helps to cure diarrhoea, dysentery, gonorrhoea and flows of any kind. The roots applied to wounds, prevent bleeding and the leaves heal boils and inflammations.

YELLOW WATER LILY
(Nymphaea lutea)

This kind of water lily bears yellow flowers; the leaves are large and round and lie on the surface of the water and they are found in pools, rivers and large lakes.

It has the same virtues of the former, but in a weaker degree. It is cooling and binding, and is effective against boils and inflammations.

COMMON LIVERWORT or
Ground Liverwort
(Hepatica vulgaris, Lichen, Hepatica terrestris)

It grows in moist shady places.

It has a cold dry nature, and is very good against inflammations and obstructions of the liver and blood, fever, gonorrhoea and jaundice. If applied externally, it stops bleeding and heals itchy and spreading scabby skin.

ROCK LIVERWORT
(Lichen seu hepatica paetraea)

It grows on rocks and in stony places near rivers, where they are shaded from the sun. It has the same qualities and virtues as the former.

ASH-COLOURED GROUND LIVERWORT
(Lichen terrestris cinereus terrestris)

It consists only of thick crumpled leaves, ash-coloured on the upper side and somewhat whiter underneath, and it bears no flowers or seeds. It grows all year round in dry barren places.

If crushed and taken internally, it is effective against the bites of mad dogs and other venomous animals.

PURPLE SPIKED LOOSE STRIFE or
Spiked Willow Herb
(Lysimachia purpurea spicata)

It grows in moist ditches, flowering most of the summer.

The distilled water is good for sore eyes. A salve made from the leaves is useful in preventing inflammations in wounds.

YELLOW LOOSE STRIFE or Yellow Willow Herb (*Lysimachia lutea*)

It grows in moist places, and by riversides.

It is very good in stopping all flows of blood, such as nosebleed and excessive menstrual flow and also in sealing wounds.

Loose Strife

Lovage

LOVAGE (*Levisticum*)

It grows in gardens, flowering in June and July, and has a hot dry nature.

It expels flatulence from the stomach and aids digestion, provokes urination and menstruation, clears the sight, and removes spots, freckles and redness from the face.

TREE LUNGWORT (*Muscus pulmonarius lichen arborum*)

It is a kind of moss which grows on trees and somewhat resembles liverwort only that it is larger, having great scales placed one upon another. It is green on the outside and ashen coloured underneath. It has a bitter taste and a binding nature.

It is very good for inflammations and ulcers of the lungs, if it is crushed and drunk in water. Drinking a decoction of it in wine stops spitting and pissing of blood, diarrhoea and excessive menstrual flow. It is very good against yellow jaundice.

LUPIN or White
Garden Lupin
(Lupinus sativus alba)

It has round hard stalks on which grow many leaves, and the flowers grow in white spikes on the tops of the branches, shaped somewhat like Peas Blossoms. It flowers in June. There are also Wild Lupins, which bear yellow and blue flowers. These have the same virtues of the Garden Lupin, but are more powerful in operation.

The seed opens obstructions of the liver and spleen, encourages menstruation, kills worms and expels the stillborn child. If used externally, it removes freckles and spots, and beautifies the face. It can be used against lumps, abscesses and ulcers. A decoction of the flowers in vinegar alleviates the pain of sciatica and cures scrofula.

M

MADDER or Red
Garden Madder
*(Rubia tinctorum,
Sativa hortensis)*

It is planted in gardens, and flowers in May and June.

The roots open obstructions of the liver and spleen, kidneys and womb. They are good against jaundice and internal bruises and, if pounded finely and applied with vinegar to the skin, it cures itching and mange. They also provoke urine, but care must be taken, for they may make the patient piss blood.

**WILD HEDGE
MADDER &
LITTLE FIELD
MADDER**
*(Rubia sylvestris,
Rubeola arvensis)*

These are like the garden madder, but smaller and less rough; the roots are very small, tender and sometimes reddish, and the flowers are not so white.

They are not made much use of in medicine, but they are useful in opening obstructions of the liver and spleen, and they also cure jaundice.

**TRUE
MAIDENHAIR**
*(Adjanthum vulgare seu
capillus veneris)*

The leaves are small, round and serrated, and the stalks are black, shiny and slender, nearly 1 ft high. It grows on stone walls and rocks.

It helps cure asthma, coughs and shortness of breath. It is good against jaundice, diarrhoea, spitting of blood and the bites of mad dogs. It also provokes urination and

Madder

menstruation, and breaks up stone in the bladder, spleen and kidneys.

BLACK MAIDENHAIR
(Trichomanes mas sive polytrichum)

It grows about 3 in high. The stalks are smooth, slender and black, the leaves are deeply indented, sharp pointed and shining green. The back of the leaves have the edges covered with a brown dusty seed. It grows in shady places and at the roots of trees.

Its virtues and qualities are similar to those of the former.

WHITE MAIDENHAIR or
Wall Rue or Tent Wort
(Adjanthum album seu ruta muraria)

The leaves are set on short stems, resembling the leaves of Garden Rue, but they are smaller and somewhat indented. The stalks are slender and whitish and it seldoms grows higher than 3 in. It grows on old walls and ruinous buildings.

It has the same qualities as the other Maidenhairs. Taken internally it provokes urine, and breaks up stone in the bladder and the kidneys. The juice is effective in removing films and cataracts from the eyes.

GREAT GOLDEN MAIDENHAIR or Goldilocks
(*Adjanthum aureum vel polytrichum aureum majus*)

This is a large kind of moss, about 4 or 5 in high, bearing hard, short leaves, with the seed vessel covered with a woolly reddish yellow cap. It grows on healthy and boggy ground.

This has much the same virtues with the former Maidenhairs. Washing the head with a decoction increases hair growth, and prevents hair loss.

SMALL GOLDEN MAIDENHAIR or Little Goldilocks
(*Adjanthum aureum minus ceu polytrichum aureum medium*)

It grows in boggy places, and while similar in properties to the other Maidenhairs, it is also beneficial for scrofulous conditions.

MALLOWS or Common or Ordinary Mallows
(*Malva vulgaris*)

It grows in gardens and is very often found growing wild by waysides, and it flowers in May and June.

It provokes urine, breaks up stone and urinary crystals in the bladder and kidneys, aids digestion and cures colic pains. If applied externally, it softens and dissolves all kinds of abscesses and swellings, draws out splinters and eases wasp and bee stings.

MARSH MALLOWS
(*Althea, Bismalva, Ibisius*)

It is usually planted in gardens, but it sometimes grows in salt marshes, and flowers in July.

If a decoction of the root is drunk in wine, it is very good against urinary crystals, dysentery, coughing and hoarseness. When applied externally, it heals wounds, and dissolves, softens and suppurates cysts, abscesses and swellings. The leaves applied with oil heal burns and scalds and also bites of mad dogs, and wasp and bee stings. An ointment made from it is good for stitches and pains.

VERVAIN MALLOWS
(*Alcea vulgaris major, Maloa sylvestris*)

The stalks are round, straight and hairy and the flowers have a clear red or carnation colour. The cheese-like seed vessel is larger and blacker than that of the Common Mallows. It grows in hedges and along the borders of fields, and flowers in June.

If a decoction of the root is drunk in water or wine, it stops dysentery and heals internal wounds and ruptures.

MAPLE TREE
(Acer majus)

The timber of this tree is hard, the leaves are broad and five cornered, very much like the leaves of Sanicle, and the fruit is long and flat.

The roots, pounded in wine and drunk are beneficial for pains in the side.

MARIGOLD
(Calendula ceu caltha vulgaris)

(Marygolds are called calendulae because they flower at the beginning of the month.)

They provoke menstruation, cure the inflammation of the eyes and trembling of the heart. Because they promote perspiration, they are frequently used to eliminate smallpox and measles. They are also good against jaundice.

CORN MARIGOLD
(Chrysanthemum segetum vel cellis lutea major)

It grows in cornfields, flowering in Summer.

It has a hot dry nature. A decoction drunk in wine, cures jaundice, and the seed has the same virtues.

MARSH MARIGOLD
(Caltha palustris ceu populago)

It grows in marshy grounds, and has qualities similar to the former.

SWEET MARJORAM
(Majorana, Sampiucus, Amaracus)

It is planted in gardens, and flowers in July and August.

It has a hot dry nature. It provokes urination and menstruation, opens obstructions of the liver and spleen, is good for colic pains and for disorders of the head and nerves, such as apoplexy, epilepsy and migraine. A plaster made of it with oil and wax, softens growths and is good to be applied to dislocations.

WILD MARJORAM
(Origanum vulgare)

The stalks are brown, hairy and brittle, and about 1 ft high; the leaves are broad, round-pointed and brownish-green, and the flowers are small and purple. It grows in hedges and thickets and flowers in July.

Wild Marjoram has a hot dry nature. It is good against pains of the stomach and heart and also useful for coughs, pleurisy and obstructions of the lungs and womb, and it also comforts the head and nerves. Externally applied, it is beneficial for swellings of the ears, ulcers of the mouth, dislocations, bruises and eruptions of the skin. The distilled oil eases toothache.

MASTERWORT or False Pellitory of Spain
(Imperatoria seu astrantia)

It bears large rounded leaves, serrrated about the edges, among which grow tender knotty stalks, about 1 ft high, and on the tops of which are clusters of small white five-leaved flowers. It is cultivated in gardens, and flowers in July.

It has a very hot and dry nature. The root is a good antidote to poison and infection, cures old fevers, induces perspiration, helps digestion, quickly heals internal bruising, bites of mad dogs, bowel disorders, and all nervous conditions of the head. Made into a poultice, it cures abscesses and sores.

HERB MASTICK
(Marum vulgare)

It is planted in gardens, flowering in June and July.

Taken internally, a decoction in wine is useful against cramps and ruptures, and for easy urination. It encourages menstruation and expels a stillborn child, and the after-birth. It is also good for disorders of the head and nerves. This has much the same virtues as sweet Marjoram.

MEADOW-SWEET or Queen of the Meadow
(Ulmaria, Regina prati)

It grows in moist meadows and by riversides, flowering in June.

A decoction or powder made from the roots stops diarrhoea, dysentery and all kinds of flow, while the flowers infused in white wine are beneficial for fevers.

MEDLAR TREE
(Mespilus sative)

It grows only in gardens and it flowers in May, with the fruit ripening in November.

Medlars have a cold, dry astringent nature. When hard and green, they are useful in stopping diarrhoea. If the crushed stones of the Medlar are drunk in a solution, they break up stone in the bladder.

COMMON MELILOT or Garden Melilot
(Melilotus vulgaris)

It is planted in gardens, flowering in June.

It is good against boils and all kinds of swellings. The juice dropped into the ears eases their pain, and applied to the forehead with oil of roses and vinegar, cures a headache, and dropped into the eyes, clears the sight, and dissolves

Mastick

films and cataracts. If the herb is mixed in a plaster, it will draw out infection from wounds. A decoction in wine provokes urine and expels urinary crystals.

WILD MELILOT
(Melilotus sylvestris)

It frequently grows in cornfields, upon high banks and in hedges, and it flowers in June.

This Melilot is stronger and more effectual in its operation than the former. It dissolves abscesses, sores and swellings, cures jaundice and disperses hard obstructions. A decoction is good against palpitations of the heart.

The effectiveness of this herb was made known to me by a Gentlewoman of my acquaintance who had a swelling for a year or more on her right side, which was cured by three or four times rubbing the grieved part with an oil made of this herb, when as before all other medicines proved ineffectual.

COMMON MELON
or Musk Melon
(Melo vulgaris)

Sown yearly in the Spring, they ripen in July and August.

These have a cold moist nature. The seed is good against fevers, and help provoke urine and break up stone. Melons must be eaten moderately.

ENGLISH MERCURY or Good Henry or All Good
(Bonus henricus,
Tota bona,
Maercurialis,
Lapathum unctuosum)

The leaves grow on long stalks and are of triangular shape (like Spinage) and are yellow–green in colour; on the tops of the stalks are spokes of small herbaceous flowers. It grows in waste places and among rubbish, and flowers in Spring.

Drinking a decoction aids digestion and purges cold phlegm. The young shoots are good for scurvy and provoke urine. Pounded with butter, it can be used as an enema.

MILKWORT
(Polygala vulgaris)

This is a small herb with slender pliant stalks creeping on the ground. The leaves are small and narrow, like the leaves of small Hyssop, and the flowers, which are of a blue colour and which are very much like the flowers of Fumitory, are succeeded by small pods, like those of Shepherd's Purse. It grows on dry healthy ground, and flowers in May.

It has a hot moist nature, and it encourages the production of milk in nursing mothers.

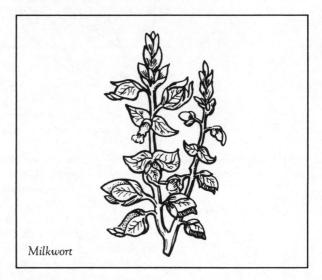

Milkwort

GARDEN MINT or
Spearmint
(Mentha sativa)

It is planted in gardens, flowering in July.

It is good for diseases of the mouth and stomach, stops vomiting, gonorrhoea and excessive menstrual flow. it also expels worms from the body.

WATER MINT
(Mentha aquatica seu sisymbrium)

It grows near rivers and in low lying meadows, flowering in June and July.

It is aromatic, and good for most disorders of the stomach, expelling wind from it. It also opens obstructions of the womb and provokes menstrual flow.

WILD MINT or
Horse Mint
(Menthastrum seu menthastrum)

Being of a hot nature, it is very good in dissolving swellings and is useful when applied to dislocations. It helps cure flatulence and colic pains.

MONEYWORT or
Herb Two Pence
*(Nummularia major
vulgaris lutea)*

The stalks are small and slender and creeping on the ground, shaped somewhat like a silver penny, and the flowers are yellow like gold cups. It grows in moist meadows near ditches and watercourses, flowering for most of the summer.

It has a dry nature. Drinking a decoction in wine and honey heals wounds and ulcers of the lungs. It is also very good against coughs, especially the chin cough (whooping cough) which children are subject to.

MOON-WORT
(Lunaria)

This plant bears only one leaf, which is cut into several sections standing around the middle of the stalk; on the top it bears several bunches of small globular heads, in which the seed is contained; it seldom grows more than 3 in high. It grows on dry grassy hills or mountains, appearing only in May and June, but disappears afterwards.

It is good for healing all kinds of wounds that are curable and also to stop bleeding. If an ointment made from it is applied to the kidneys, it can cure dysentery.

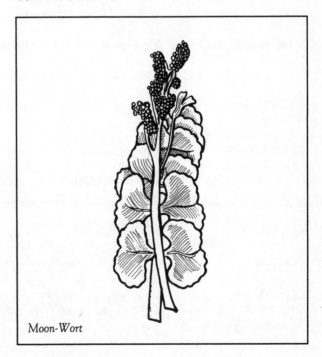

Moon-Wort

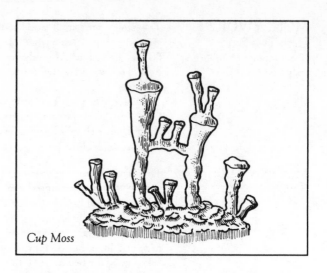

Cup Moss

The common people say that this herb has a singular virtue of opening locks, and also, that if a horse were only to trod upon it, his fetters would presently drop off.

MOOR BERRIES or Moss Berries, Bog Berries, or Red Whortes
(Vaccinia rubra palustria)

These berries are usually preserved and made into tarts. They quench the thirst, and are good against hot and acute fevers and all inflammations of the blood.

TREE MOSS
(Muscus arboreus)

This moss has a dry astringent quality. A decoction externally applied is good against excessive menstrual flow. It stops nosebleeds if put into the nose and also other flows of blood.

SEA MOSS or Coralline
(Corallina)

This has many small hard stalks of a stony substance.
It is useful when applied to boils and gout. Crushed into a solution, it is a powerful remedy for worms.

COMMON GROUND MOSS
(Muscus terrestris vulgaris)

This moss like the rest, has a binding quality, and is therefore good against flows and haemorrhages of all sorts.

MOSS (Growing on Dead Men's Skulls)
(Muscus innatus cranio humano seu usnea)

This has a binding quality, is good for stopping nosebleeds and other haemorrhages.

CUP MOSS
(Muscus pixidatus)

This moss has many hoary or whitish green leaves, spread on the surface of the ground, among which grow whitish dusty cups, a $\frac{1}{4}$ in high. It grows on banks and dry barren ground.

If a decoction sweetened with sugar is drunk, whooping cough will be cured.

MOTHER OF THYME or Wild Thyme
(Serpyllum vulgare)

The stalks are slender and woody; the leaves are like the leaves of Garden Thyme, only larger. The reddish purple flowers grow on the tops of the stalks, whorl fashion. It grows in untilled stony places, flowering in June and July.

It is good for diarrhoea, spitting or vomiting of blood, cramps, catarrh and old coughs, it aids digestion and lack of appetite. It provokes menstruation and is useful for all disorders of the head and nerves, if a decoction is taken internally. The juice externally applied with oil of roses and vinegar eases headache, and the distilled oil eases a toothache.

Mother of Thyme

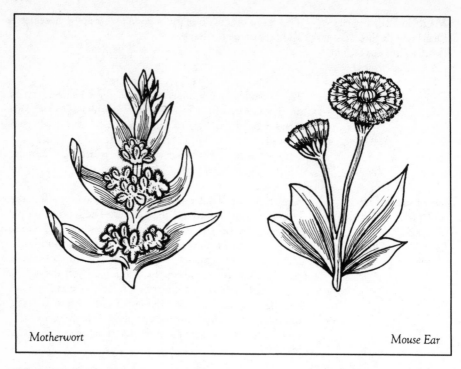

Motherwort   Mouse Ear

MOTHERWORT
(Cardiaca)

It has square brown woody stalks; the leaves are large, broad, deeply indented and have three sharp points, like Nettle or Horehound leaves, and the flowers have a reddish purple colour. It grows in untilled places, around old walls and lanes, flowering in June and July.

If bruised and applied to wounds it prevents inflammation and abscess, and stops them bleeding and heals them. It is good against disorders of the heart, such as palpitations and it is also used against disorders of the spleen and womb. Birth can be facilitated by drinking a dram of crushed Motherwort in wine.

MOUSE EAR
(Auricula muris vel pilosell)

It grows under hedges and along the borders of fields, flowering in June and July.

It has a dry nature, and is good against the spitting of blood, all kinds of flow, coughs, ulcers of the lungs, mouth and eyes, and shingles.

MUGWORT or the Great Common Mugwort
(*Artemisia major vulgaris*)

It grows along the borders of fields, in highways and waste places, flowering in June.

If pounded and applied with the oil of sweet almonds, it cures the pain of the stomach. If the juice is mixed with the oil of roses and applied, it will ease pains or aches in the joints and cramps. It also provokes menstruation. If it is added to barrels of ale, it will prevent them from souring.

MULBERRY TREE or Common Black Mulberry-tree
(*Morus*)

This tree grows in gardens, and the fruit ripens in August and September.

The unripe mulberries are cold, dry and astringent. They stop diarrhoea, dysentery and vomiting. If applied with oil, the leaves heal burns and scalds. The bark of the root of the tree is cleansing and abstersive. It opens obstructions of the liver and spleen, aids the digestion, expels worms from the body, and if held in the mouth, eases a toothache. The root, if cut about the latter end of harvest, will yield a gum which is also very good for toothache. The ripe fruit is cooling and good for alleviating the heat of burning fevers and creating an appetite.

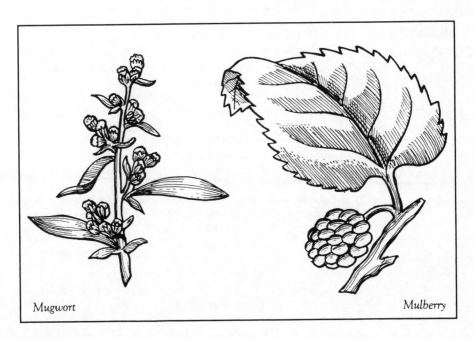

Mugwort

Mulberry

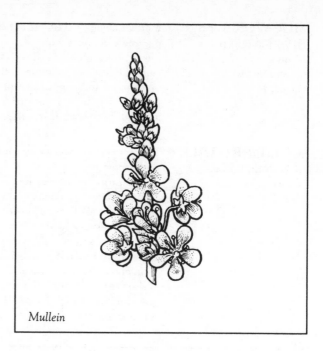

Mullein

MULLEIN or
Hightaper
(Verbascum vel tapsus barbatus)

It has broad woolly leaves about 1 ft long; the stalk is round, single and hoary, about 5 or 6 ft high, and the flowers are yellow. It grows in gardens and in wild places, flowering in July.

A decoction of the leaves with the flowers is good against the diseases of the lungs, such as coughs and spitting of blood. It is also good for colic pains. Applied externally, the leaves are useful against swellings, ulcers, inflammations of the eyes, burns and scalds. A fomentation made from them is a remedy for piles.

Country people say that carrying it about one preserves the wearer from enchantments and witchcraft, not without some justification, because Mercury gave it to Ulysses to defend him from the enchantments of Circe – but I look upon this as fabulous.

MUSHROOM or
eatable Mushroom
(Fungus campestris esculentus)

Mushrooms are of a cold moist and crude nature and hurtful to the stomach, and it is therefore dangerous to eat any great quantities of them.

GARDEN MUSTARD
(Sinapi)

It grows in waste places, amongst rubbish, and is frequently sown in gardens, flowering in June.

Mustard seed has a very hot and dry nature. It aids the digestion, warms the stomach, creates an appetite, loosens phlegm, provokes urination and menstruation, and is good against scurvy, apoplexy, lethargy and paralysis, especially of the tongue. A gargle made of it with honey and vinegar is useful against tumours of the uvula and the glands of the throat. This would also be useful against fevers. It is exceeding good for any one that is troubled with gout for, if the seed is pounded and applied in a plaster, it will raise a blister which will carry off the malignity. I have been acquainted with some gentlemen who, by this means, got rid of it for several years.

TREACLE MUSTARD or Penny Cress
(Thlapsi)

It has a very hot and dry nature. The seed encourages menstruation, breaks up internal abscesses, and purges bilious matter. It also provokes urine, and is useful against gout and sciatica.

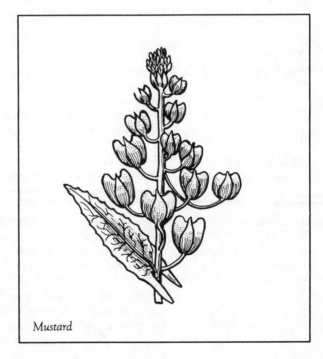

Mustard

MYRTLE-TREE
(Myrthus)

The leaves and berries have binding properties and are good against haemorrhages. They are also generally effective against disorders of the lungs and against running eyes and noses.

NAVELWORT or
Wallpennywort
(Cotyledon vel umbilicus veneris)

The leaves are round, thick and succulent; the stalks are about a span long, on the tops of which grow the flowers in long spikes of a whitish or carnation colour. It grows on old stone walls, and flowers in May.

It has a cold moist nature. The juice is a good remedy against all inflammations, chilblains, burning fevers and piles. Taken internally it provokes urine, and cures disorders of the liver.

SWEET NAVEW
(Napus dulcis)

The leaves are large, like the leaves of Turnip, but are smoother, while the stalk grows two or three feet high and on which grow many yellow flowers. It grows in gardens, and flowers in April.

The seed is good against poison as well as small-pox and measles. It also provokes urination and menstruation.

WILD NAVEW
(Napus sylvestris)

This is smaller than the Sweet Navew and its leaves are more jagged, but otherwise it is similar both in appearance and properties. However the seed is hotter and stronger.

**STINGING
NETTLE**
(Urtica major vulgaris urens)

It has a hot dry nature. The seed mixed with honey and taken internally, cleanses the lungs of phlegm, it is also good for shortness of breath and whooping cough. A gargle of the juice of the leaves is useful for a fallen womb and about half a pint of this juice taken internally stops vomiting and spitting of blood, and all haemorrhages and flows. If crushed leaves are applied to wounds, they stop the bleeding or if pounded with salt, they are useful for the bites of mad dogs. The root provokes urine and is a remedy for jaundice.

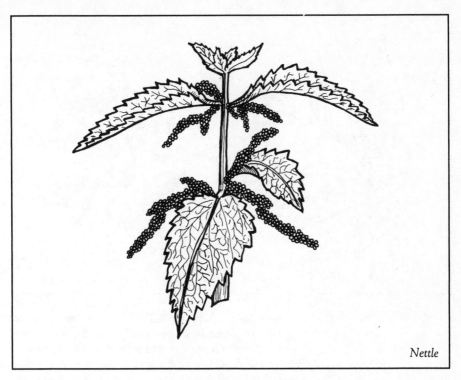

Nettle

COMMON GARDEN NIGHTSHADE
(Solanum hortense vulgare)

It has round, brittle, succulent stalks, the leaves are large, blackish, soft and full of juice, the white flowers grow in clusters and it bears berries of a black shiny colour when ripe. It grows about old walls, under hedges and near highways, and flowers in August, with the berries ripening in September.

It has a very cooling astringent nature. It is a good cure for burning fevers, boils, ulcers, inflammations, burns and scalds.

DEADLY NIGHTSHADE or Dwale
(Solanum lethale)

It has tall blackish angular stalks about 5 or 6 ft high, on which grow broad dull green leaves; the brown bell-fashioned flowers are succeeded by black shining berries as large as cherries. It is found in woods and hedges, with the berries ripening in August.

The leaves and fruit have a very cold nature. The green

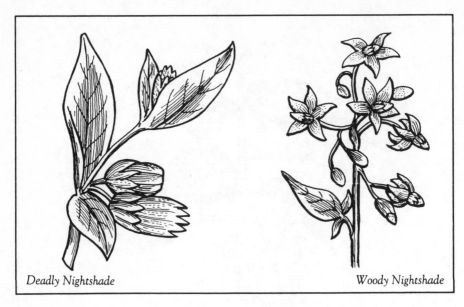

Deadly Nightshade   *Woody Nightshade*

and fresh leaves can be applied externally as with those of Common Nightshade, to burning fevers, swellings of the breast and similar inflammations, but caution must be used. The fruit is deadly, and if eaten, it causes a deep sleep, followed by an outrageous passion of anger which continues until death.

WOODY NIGHTSHADE or Bitter Sweet *(Solanum lignosum seu amara dulcis)*

It has small tender branches of a woody substance, the leaves are smooth, green and sharp-pointed, like the leaves of Ivy, and the purple flowers consist of one leaf, which is laid open like a star. The berries, when ripe, are of a pure shining red. It grows in moist places, about ditches and ponds, and flowers in May.

It has a hot dry nature. A decoction in wine taken internally opens obstructions of the liver and spleen, and is therefore good for jaundice. It also heals all internal wounds, bruises and ruptures, for it dissolves congealed blood, causing it to be passed by the urine.

NIPPLEWORT or Tetter-Wort *(Lampsana)*

This herb is good for sore nipples, and helps ease painful eruptions on the skin.

O

COMMON OAK TREE
(Quercus vulgaris)

All parts of the oak have a binding nature, and are therefore useful against diarrhoea, dysentery, haemorrhages and flows of all kinds. The bark can be used in gargles for dropped uvula.

There is also a fungus which grows on this tree (Incrementum fungosum querceum); this too can be used in medicine.

OATS
(Avena)

Oatmeal has a hot, dry and astringent nature, not easily digested. Therefore it is fit only for labourers who can expel its heat by perspiring freely, otherwise it is apt to cause itchiness. Hot oats put into a bag and applied to the grieved spot are good for pleurisy and bowel disorders.

Oak

ONION
(Cepa)

Onions have a hot nature, creating wind in the stomach. They provoke urine, aid digestion and are good for coughs and diseases of the breast. Being externally applied with oil and vinegar, they cure piles. The juice dropped in the eyes, cleanses them, and if dropped into the ears, it is good against deafness and a humming or ringing in the ears. Sniffed into the nose it causes sneezing, and it therefore clears the brain. Mixed with salad oil, it is exceeding good to be applied to burns and scalds before they rise to blisters. If mixed with rue and salt, it can effectively be applied to dog bites. It will also restore hair to parts that are bald.

BOG ONION
(Cepa palustris)

This grows in bogs. The root is bulbous and is divided into cloves like Garlic.

A clove of this placed in a glass of water and left for half an hour, will make the water very thick and ropy, and it can then be beneficially applied upon a cloth to dislocations.

COMMON WILD ORAGE or Lambs Quarter
(Atriplex sylvestris vulgatior)

It is cooling and moistening, aiding digestion. The leaves are frequently boiled and eaten with salt meat, like Colewort. The seed opens obstructions of the liver and is therefore good against jaundice, and when crushed, it is effective against boils, inflammations, burning fevers and gout.

STINKING ORAGE or Arrach
(Atriplex olida)

It grows in rich soil, on dunghills and near highways.

It provokes menstrual flow, facilitates labour and expels the afterbirth, if a decoction is taken internally.

ORANGE TREE
(Aurantia malus)

Orange trees grow plentifully in foreign countries, but of late years they have been transplanted here, and now, by the industry and cultivation of curious gentlemen are, in some gardens brought to perfection. I have seen about seventy or eighty oranges taken off one tree in the Right Honourable, the Lord Kingstons Garden at Mitchelstown, and these were as good as any I have seen brought hither from Spain, or the West Indies, so you see what a prolific and fertile soil we live in, where the most exotic plants might, by a little care and industry, flourish.

Oranges are good against scurvy and diseases of the mouth, and prevent nausea and vomiting. They are an effective antidote to infection and the seed kills and expels worms.

Orpine   Ox Eye

ORPINE or Live Long
(*Crassula vel fabaria*)

It has round brittle stalks, on which grow thick, fat, oval leaves indented about the edges, and the flowers grow in small purple clusters. It is found in gardens, but grows wild in moist shady places, and flowers in June.

It is binding and cooling, good against dysentery. It can be used externally against boils, inflammations, scalds and burns.

OSIER
(*Salix aquatica folio longissimo*)

It grows in moist places and by riversides.

It has a cold dry astringent nature. A decoction of the leaves and bark in claret taken internally, is good against spitting or vomiting of blood, excessive menstrual flows and all other flows. The ashes of the bark, mixed with vinegar and applied to warts causes them to fall off. It also takes away callous or hard skin on hands and feet and the sap is good for inflammations of the eyes and for blood-shot eyes.

OX-EYE
(*Buphthalmus*)

It is about half a cubit high, with three or four stalks bearing tender winged leaves, like Yarrow, and the flowers have a bright yellow colour, almost like the flowers of Marygolds. It is planted in gardens and also grows wild, and it flowers in June and July.

It has a hot dry nature. The flowers crushed and mixed with oil and wax are beneficial when applied to swellings. A decoction in wine is good for jaundice.

P

PALMI CHRISTI or the Greater Spurge
(Cataputia major vel ricinus)

It has a smooth, round stalk taller than a man, and the leaves are large and roundish, cut into five, seven or nine sections and serrated about the edges. The flowers grow in clusters like grapes, and are succeeded by triangular husks, which contain white seeds, which are somewhat smaller than kidney beans.

The seed crushed and taken in whey purges phlegm and bile. It is also good against jaundice. The oil extracted from the seed is beneficial against itching and kills lice in children's heads.

GARDEN PARSLEY
(Petroselinum vulgare seu apium hortense)

This aids both appetite and digestion. A decoction of the root and seeds taken internally open obstructions of the liver, kidneys and all internal organs. It provokes urine, and breaks up and expels bladder stone. It is also good for jaundice.

MACEDONIAN PARSLEY
(Petroselinum macedonicum)

It grows in gardens and is of a hot and dry nature.

The seed provokes urination and menstruation, breaks up stone in the bladder and kidneys, and expels flatulence from the stomach.

WILD PARSLEY
(Apium sylvestre)

It bears large jagged leaves like those of Wild Carrot, but larger. The stalks are round and hollow, 4 or 5 ft long, of a brown red colour, on the tops of which grow round tufts of white flowers. It is found in moist places about ponds and ditches, flowering in June.

It has a hot dry nature, and if the root is held in the mouth and chewed, it eases a toothache.

PARSNIP
(Pastinaca sativa)

Parsnips have a hot dry nature, and they provide better nourishment than Carrots. They provoke urine, and are beneficial for the chest and kidneys.

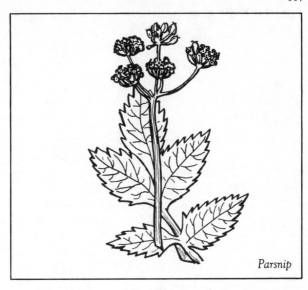

Parsnip

WATER PARSNIP
(Sium latifolium)

It grows in rivers and moist ditches, and flowers in May and June.

The leaves provoke urine, expel urinary crystals, and remove obstructions of the liver, spleen and kidneys. Externally applied, they are good against cancerous tumours in the breast.

COW PARSNIP
(Sphondilium)

The stalks are long, round and full of joints, the leaves are rough and dark green, and on the tops of the stalks are clusters of white flowers. It grows along the borders of fields and meadows, and flowers in July.

It has a hot nature, and when bruised and applied to swellings, it disperses and dissolves them.

WILD PARSNIP
(Pastinaca sylvestris)

The leaves, flower and seed are much like those of Garden Parsnip, although the leaves are smaller, the stalks more slender, and the root harder, smaller and not good for eating. It grows under hedges and near highways and paths, flowering in June.

The seed is very good against all poison, and the bites of venomous creatures. The roots and seed provoke urination and menstruation, encourage flatulence and are beneficial for the liver and spleen.

GARDEN PEA
(Pisum)

Peas encourage flatulence in the body, but not as much as beans. When green they are a pleasant nourishing food, which sweetens the blood.

PEACH TREE
(Persica malus)

It is planted in gardens, flowering in March and the beginning of April, with the fruit ripening in August and September.

The leaves open obstructions of the liver and spleen and aid digestion. If applied to the navels of young children, they expel worms, and if crushed and applied to wounds, they cure and heal them. The kernels are beneficial for the liver and chest and if they are finely crushed and boiled in vinegar until they dissolve and become like pap, they wonderfully restore the hair. The flowers are purgative and open obstructions.

PEAR TREE
(Pyrus)

Pears nourish more than apples, especially those that are sweet-sour. They are however, very unwholesome if eaten raw, unless wine is drunk after them.

Pears stop the diarrhoea, and can also be applied to fresh green wounds, which they heal.

PELLITORY OF THE WALL
(Parietaria vel helxine)

It grows on old stone walls, and flowers in May.

It has a cold moist nature, and is very useful against bilious inflammations, burning fevers, boils, ulcers, spreading sores and scabs, if crushed and applied with a poultice. It is good for the chest, and breaks up stone in the bladder and kidneys. A decoction taken internally, provokes urine, or a hot poultice may be applied to the region of the bladder.

PELLITORY OF SPAIN
(Pyrethrum)

It is planted in gardens, and flowers in July.

The roots have a very hot nature and are good against apoplexy, epilepsy and toothache. If chewed or held in the mouth, they clear the head. An oil made from them is very good when applied to bruised parts or limbs that have become numbed by the cold or afflicted with palsy.

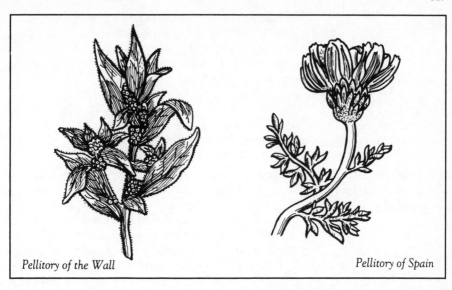

Pellitory of the Wall   Pellitory of Spain

PENNY ROYAL
(Pulegium vulgare)

It is cultivated in gardens, and has a hot dry nature.

It provokes urination and menstruation, and it eliminates the stillborn child and the afterbirth, as well as the un-natural birth. It is good for the chest and is useful for opening obstructions of the lungs, and also against coughs and asthmas. If it is boiled in water and vinegar it stops vomiting. A decoction of the leaves sweetened with sugar is a good remedy for whooping cough and also eases the pain of gout.

MARSH PENNY WORT or White Rot
(Cotyledon aquatica)

It has smooth round hollow leaves, somewhat like Wall Pennywort, but the white flowers are smaller, smoother and more deeply indented, and are to be found growing under leaves. It grows in low meadows and moist valleys, flowering in July.

It has no particular value in medicine, but this herb is hurtful to sheep.

MALE PEONY
(Paeonia mas)

It is planted in gardens, flowering in May.

Drunk in honey and water, the powder of the root provokes menstruation and cures the gripes which women are subject to who have just given birth. It opens obstructions of the liver and kidneys. Wearing the root and seed around the neck is useful against convulsions, especially in children.

Sixteen of the black seeds drunk in wine is a specific remedy for nightmares.

FEMALE PEONY
(Paeonia faemina)

This has larger and greener leaves than the Male Peony; its flowers are smaller and paler. It has similar properties to the Male Peony.

PERIWINKLE
(Vinca pervinca clematis daphnoides)

It has many slender, long branches, on which grow oval leaves, much like bay-leaves, only smaller. The flowers are blue, and grow among the leaves in short spikes. It grows in hedges and shady places, flowering in Summer.

It has a dry and astringent nature. A decoction of it taken in wine stops diarrhoea, dysentery, excessive menstrual flow and spitting of blood. If it is bruised and placed in the nose, it stops a nosebleed, if chewed, it eases a toothache. Likewise, it is extraordinarily good for healing bruises.

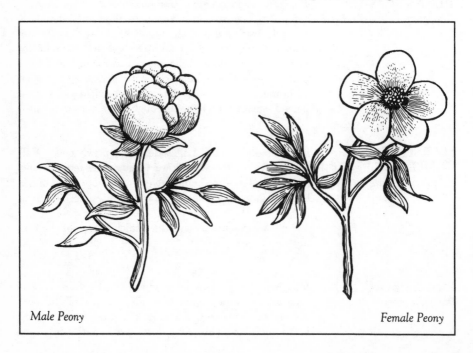

Male Peony

Female Peony

ST PETER'S WORT
or Square St John's Wort
(*Ascyron vulgare*)

The leaves are like the leaves of St John's Wort, only larger and greener, covered with a fine soft down, and having no small holes, while the flowers are paler than those of St John's Wort, but are otherwise similar. It grows in uncultivated places, in hedges and copses, flowering in July and August.

If the seed is drunk in honey and water for a long time, it cures sciatica. Crushed seed is good when applied to inflammations. A decoction of the leaves in wine may be used to wash out and heal wounds.

MALE OR RED FLOWERED PIMPERNEL
(*Anagallia terrestris mas*)

It has small square tender stalks about six inches high. The leaves are small, like the leaves of small Chickweed and full of black specks, and the flowers are a beautiful scarlet colour. It grows in gardens and among potherbs and in cultivated fields, flowering in May and June.

Its properties are similar to those of the Female Pimpernel.

FEMALE PIMPERNEL
(*Anagallis foemina*)

This is like the Male Pimpernel in every respect, except in the colour of its flowers, which are blue.

It has a hot dry nature without any sharpness. Taken

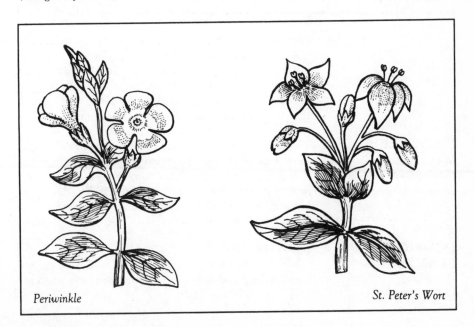

Periwinkle   *St. Peter's Wort*

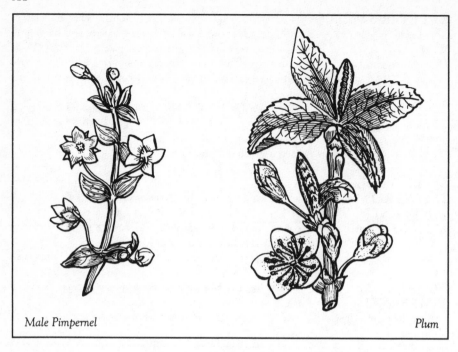

Male Pimpernel

Plum

internally, a decoction is good for opening obstructions of the liver and kidneys, and for drawing phlegm from the head, if the juice is sniffed into the nostrils. It heals and cleanses corrupt ulcers and decaying sores, as well as drawing out thorns and splinters. If bruised and applied, they are good against inflammations and hot tumours.

PINE TREE or
Manured pine
(Pinus sativa)

The bark leaves and cones are of a dry astringent nature. They stop diarrhoea and dysentery and provoke urine. Boiled in vinegar, the leaves alleviate toothache. The kernels of the pine apples are beneficial for the lungs, kidneys, liver and spleen. They loosen phlegm and are good for consumptive coughs.

COMMON PLANTAIN or
Waybread
(Plantago latifolia vel septinervia)

It grows by waysides, flowering in May.
   It has a hot astringent nature. It is very good against haemorrhages and flows of all kinds; it also heals wounds.

GREAT WATER PLANTAIN
(Plantago aquatica major)

It has broad green leaves and it bears small white flowers, each divided into three parts, which are succeeded by triangular husks. It grows in rivers and brooks, flowering in July.

It has the same properties as Common Plantain.

PLUM TREE
(Prunus hortensis)

Plums are cooling, they alleviate thirst and are somewhat purgative.

POLYPODY or Wall Fern & **POLYPODY OF THE OAK**
(Polypodium vulgare)
(Polypodium quercinum)

It is very good against bowel disorders, and purges bilious substances. If crushed and drunk in honey and water with a little aniseed, it is good for opening obstructions of the spleen, and easing fevers. Made into a powder and sniffed into the nostrils, it is useful against polyps.

POMPKIN
(Pepo)

It has a cold moist nature. If crushed finely, the powder heals inflammations of the eyes when applied to them. If the seed is pounded with Barley Meal and its own juice added, it removes freckles and spots from the face. A dram of the crushed dried root taken in honey and water, excites vomiting.

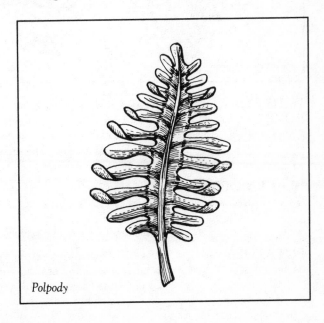

Polpody

WILD RED POPPY
(Papaver rubrum erraticum)

It grows among corn, flowering in June and July.

It has a cooling and refreshing nature. By drinking a decoction of five or six heads in wine, pain is alleviated and sleep is induced. The same result can be achieved by taking the seed with honey. The bruised leaves of the green heads can be applied to boils, hot ulcers and burning fevers. The flowers are useful against inflammatory fevers.

Wild Red Poppy

Primrose

WHITE GARDEN POPPY
(Papaver album sativum)

It grows in gardens, flowering in June, and the heads should be gathered at the end of July.

It eases pain and promotes sleep, and is very good against catarrhs and coughs. The green heads can be applied to boils and inflammations.

BLACK POPPY
(Papaver nigra sativum)

It grows in gardens, flowering in June.

If the seed is drunk in wine it stops diarrhoea, and excessive menstrual flow. The leaves can be applied to inflammations and hot swellings.

POTATOES
(Poma terrestria)

They are a healthy nourishing food (which is evident by the robust constitutions of a vast number of the natives who are almost entirely supported by them). They provoke urine and are generally strengthening.

COMMON PRIMROSE
(Primula veris minor vulgaris)

It grows in thickets and under hedges, flowering in March and April.

It has a dry nature, and is good for disorders of the head and nerves. The juice of the root encourages sneezing, therefore clearing the head of viscous phlegm.

PRIVET or Prim Print or Bindweed
(Lingustrum vulgare)

It has a small shrub, bearing small oblong leaves. The branches are tough and pliant, on the tops of which are thick spikes of white flowers. It grows in hedges, flowering in May and June.

It has a binding and cooling nature, good for ulcers and inflammations of the mouth and throat.

PURSLAIN
(Portulaca)

It grows in gardens and is of a cold moist nature.

It comforts a weak inflamed stomach, and is good against burning fevers, worms, haemorrhages, boils and flows of all kinds. The seed kills and expels worms.

Q

QUICKEN-TREE or Roan tree or Wild Service Tree
(Sorbus torminalis vel mespilus sylvestris non spinosa)

The leaves are cut into seven sharp-pointed segments, pale green above and whitish underneath. It grows very tall and has a whitish bark. The flowers appear in yellowish white clusters, while the fruit is set on long stalks, and is twice as big as the Common Haw. It grows frequently in woods and thickets.

The unripe fruit is cold, dry and astringent. A decoction stops diarrhoea, dysentery and all kinds of flow of blood. When ripe, the fruit is beneficial to the stomach, aiding digestion.

QUINCE TREE
(Malus cydonia vel cotonea)

It flowers in May, with the fruit ripening in September.

Quince stops diarrhoea, dysentery and haemorrhages of all kinds. They also strengthen the stomach, aid digestion and stop vomiting.

R

GARDEN RADISH
(Raphanus hortensis)

It grows in gardens, and flowers in May.

It has a hot dry nature. The finely pounded roots applied with vinegar cure the hardness of the spleen. The seed provokes urination, menstruation and vomiting. Drunk with vinegar and honey, it kills and expels worms from the body.

HORSE RADISH
(Rapahanus sylvestris seu rusticanus)

It has a hot dry nature; and only the root is used. It promotes a good appetite and digestion and is useful against jaundice and scurvy. If made into an ointment, it cures itchy and scabby skin.

WATER RADISH
(Raphanus aquaticus)

It has leaves like the Common Radish, only smaller and more jagged; the stalks are about $1\frac{1}{2}$ ft long, on which grow several yellow flowers, and the root is as thick as a finger. It grows by ditch sides, and near pools and rivers, and flowers in June.

It has a stronger and more biting nature than garden radish and its properties are similar, only more powerful. It is very good in provoking urine.

RAGWORT or St James Wort
(Jacobaea vulgaris)

It grows usually in fields and on banks, and flowers in June and July.

It has a hot dry nature. It is especially good in healing wounds and ulcers; gargling the juice cures inflammations, tumours and abscesses of the throat. A plaster made from it is useful for sciatica. Made into a plaster with oatmeal and butter, it is good against inflammations and all hot tumours.

BROAD LEAVED MARSH or WATER RAGWORT
(Jacobaea latifolia palustris)

A poultice of the leaves is accounted good for sciatica, and an ointment made of them clears filthy ulcers.

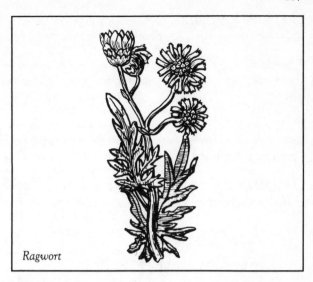

Ragwort

RAMSONS
(Allium ursinum)

It usually has two broad blades, or leaves, almost like the leaves of May Lillies from which grows a stem bearing many small white flowers. It grows in moist shady places, and flowers in April and May.

It has a hot dry nature. Taken internally it kills worms; if bruised and applied to the temples it eases a headache, and applied to the teeth with vinegar, it eases a toothache. It is also good in provoking urination and menstruation, in removing obstructions from the kidneys and chest, and in expelling flatulence.

RASPBERRY or
Hindberry Bush
(Rubus idaeus)

This flowers in May, with the fruit ripening in June and July.

An application of the flowers bruised with honey is beneficial for inflammations of the eyes, burning fever and boils. A decoction is useful for weak stomachs. The fruit is good for the heart and diseases of the mouth.

RED RATTLE or
Lowsewort
(Pedicularis pratensis rubra)

It bears very small leaves deeply indented at the edges, spreading on the ground. The stalks are weak and small, on which appear reddish purple flowers like those of Red Nettle. It grows in moist meadows, and flowers in May.

It has a cold dry astringent nature. Drinking a decoction of it in wine is useful against menstrual flow and all other flows of blood.

128

YELLOW RATTLE
or Lowsewort or
Coxcomb
*(Pedicularis,
Crista galli,
Lutea)*

It has a straight stem, on which grow long, narrow leaves deeply indented about the edges, while the flowers are like those of Red Rattle, only of a pale yellow colour. It grows in dry meadows, and flowers in June and July.

It has properties similar to the former.

BUR REED or Burr
Flag
(Sparganum ramosum)

It grows in moist meadows, rivers and ditches.

A decoction of burrs is good against the bites of venomous creatures, if it is drunk or the wound washed with it.

COMMON REED
(Arundo vallatoria)

It has a hot dry nature. The finely crushed root draws out thorns and splinters; mixed with vinegar it alleviates the pain of dislocated limbs. The leaves are good against inflammations and boils.

Rest Harrow

REST HARROW or
Cammock or Purple
Rest Harrow
*(Anonis ononis,
Resta bovis)*

It grows along the borders of fields and near roadsides, and flowers in June and July.

It has a hot dry nature. It provokes urine, breaks up stone and urinary crystals, and opens obstructions of the liver and spleen. Externally applied, it cures abscesses and dissolves tumours.

TRUE RHUBARB
(Rhabarbarum verum)

It has a dry astringent nature. It is good against colic pains, disorders of the stomach, and obstructions of the liver, spleen, kidneys and bladder. It is also beneficial for sciatica, spitting of blood and dysentery, helps jaundice and kills worms in children.

RIBWORT or Ribwort Plantain
(Plantago angustifolia, Quinquenervia)

It grows in fields and meadows, and flowers in May and June.

It has a binding nature and has similar qualities as Common Plantain. It is particularly good for worms in children. The juice of it is given before the fit of an ague, to prevent its approaching.

RIE (Rye)
(Secale vulgatius)

It is of a hot and dry nature. Externally applied, ryemeal alleviates a headache, draws out thorns and splinters, and suppurates tumours and cysts. It can also be put into poultices for abscesses and gout.

ROCKET or Garden White Rocket
(Eruca sativa alba)

It grows in gardens, and flowers in June.

It has a hot dry nature, and can be eaten with Lettuce, Purslain and other cold herbs in a salad. It excites sexual desire, especially the seed, which is also beneficial to the mouth.

WILD ROCKET
(Eruca sylvestris)

This is like the Garden Rocket, only the leaves are much smaller. It grows in stony places near highways and paths, and flowers most of the summer.

It has the same properties as Rocket.

WHITE ROSE
(Rosa alba)

It has a binding cooling nature. It is good against inflammations of the eyes, swellings of the breast and burning fevers. A water may be distilled from them which is very good for all eye troubles.

Take one handful of white roses, vervein, celandine, rue, fennel, eye-bright, daisy roots and houseleek, and boil them well in 2 quarts of Spring Water, until only 1 quart remains, then strain it, and add a noggin of pure virgin honey, boil it again, and then remove the scum that will form on the surface. Allow the remaining liquid to cool, and then bottle it. For some eye problems, such as webs or films, it may be necessary to add a little white Copperas to the liquid.

This remedy never fails to cure any external disorders of the eyes, even though all other cures may prove to be ineffectual.

DAMASK ROSE
(Rosa damascena et apllida)

The flowers aid digestion, purge bilious substances, opens obstructions of the liver and are good against jaundice. The distilled water is useful in fevers.

RED ROSE
(Rosa rubra)

The flowers stop diarrhoea, menstrual and other flows of blood, strengthen the stomach, prevent vomiting and tickling coughs, and are useful in consumption. A rose cake steeped in hot vinegar cures headaches, and pains from any inflammation. A conserve is beneficial for consumptive fevers.

ROSEMARY or Narrow-Leaved Garden Rosemary
(Rosmarinus hortensis)

It is planted in gardens, and flowers in April and May.
It has a hot dry nature, and it is good against all disorders of the head and nerves. It secures loose teeth, and if rubbed with it, cleans them. It is useful for coughs, asthma, running nose and eyes, and obstructions of the lungs. Used in baths,

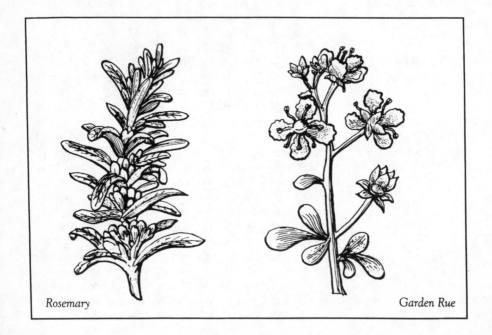

Rosemary   Garden Rue it disperses clammy and viscous juice lodged in the joints and strengthens them. A fine powder made from one dram of the following cures migraine and apoplexy, Rosemary, Sage, Lily of the Valley, the tops of Sweet Marjoram, Nutmegs and Asarabacca roots, if sniffed into the nose.

GARDEN RUE
(Ruta hortensis)

It is good against infections and epidemical fevers. It cures colic pains and the bites of mad dogs. Made into a poultice with Garlic, Bay Salt and Bacon, it cures abscesses effectively; it assists in birth, expels the afterbirth and provokes menstruation. It is very good medicine for the eyes.

Take the leaves of Rue picked fresh from the stalks and bruise 6 oz, of Garlic, picked from the stalks, and bruised, Venice Treacle, and the scrapings of Pewter, 4 oz, boil all these over a slow fire, in 2 quarts of strong ale, until 1 pint of liquid has been consumed, then keep the remainder in a close stoppered bottle. Heat nine spoonfuls, and give seven mornings fasting.

This is an infallible cure for the bite of a mad dog if it is applied within nine days after a person has received the hurt.

WILD RUE
(Ruta sylvestris sive harmala)

It has three or four stalks growing upright, covered with long narrow leaves, smaller and more divided than Garden Rue. The flowers are white and appear on the tops of the branches.

It has a hot nature, therefore it disperses and dissolves viscous phlegm and provokes urination and menstruation.

RUPTURE WORT
or All Seed
(Millegrana minima)

It is a very small plant, having many small white flowers like little round grains. It is useful for ruptures, if it is applied in a poultice. Taken internally, it is good against colic pains.

COMMON CANDLE RUSH
(Juncus levis)

It has a dry nature. If the seed is parched and steeped in wine, it stops diarrhoea and menstrual flow and provokes urine.

S

SAFFRON
(Crocus verus sativus)

It is cultivated in gardens.

It is very good for fevers, smallpox and measles, for jaundice and for most disorders of the lungs. Saffron also opens obstructions of the liver and spleen, provokes menstruation, assists birth and expels the afterbirth.

BASTARD SAFFRON or
Safflower
(Carthamus sive cenicus)

The stalks are round, growing to 3 or 4 ft high and it is covered with long indented prickly leaves. On the tops of the branches are several round prickly heads, from which appear pleasant orange-coloured flowers. It grows in gardens, flowering in July.

The juice of the seed drunk with honey and water purges viscous phlegm. It is good against coughs and the cholic and disorders of the lungs. The flowers open obstructions of the liver and are useful against jaundice.

COMMON GARDEN SAGE
(Salvia hortensis major vulgaris)

It has a very hot, dry and astringent nature. If eaten, it can benefit pregnant women, and can also promote conception. The juice drunk with honey is very useful against spitting or vomiting of blood. A decoction of water taken internally cures coughs, dysentery and obstructions of the liver and spleen. It is commonly used in gargles for sore mouths.

SMALL SAGE
(Salvia minor)

This Sage has much the same virtues of the former, only it is commonly chosen to make Sage tea, being accounted best for that purpose. It is a good antidote to love potions.

WOOD SAGE or
Garlic Sage
(Salvia agrestis vel scorodonia)

It has several square hairy brown stalks; its leaves are not much unlike the leaves of Great Sage, only that they are broader, softer and shorter. The flowers grow in long spikes on the tops of the branches. It is found in hedges and shrubs, and flowers in July.

It has a hot dry nature. A decoction of it drunk dissolves congealed blood and cures internal wounds and bruises. It is also useful in provoking urination and menstruation.

MOUNTAIN SAGE
(Salvia alpinea)

The leaves are rough, like Garden Sage and it grows in mountains.

It is very good at removing obstructions and aids conception, and is especially useful in provoking menstrual flow.

BLACK SALTWORT or Sea Miltwort
(Glaux, Martima exigua)

It grows in low salt marshes, and moist places near the sea, and flowers in June and July.

If eaten while nursing, it increases the production of milk. It has the same properties as Polygala or Milkwort.

SAMPHIRE
(Crithmum faeniculum marinum, Herba St. Petri)

It grows on rocks by the sea, and is especially abundant in the Aran island and the west coast of Clare.

It has a warm dry nature. It provokes urine and menstruation, opens obstructions of the bowels, liver, spleen and kidneys, strengthens the stomach, and creates an appetite if it is picked and eaten or a decoction drunk in wine.

Samphire

SANICLE
(Sanicula seu diapentia)

The leaves are dark green, five-cornered and serrated about the edges. The stalks are about 1 ft high, and are bare of leaves to the top on which appear little clusters of five-leaved white flowers. It grows in woods and on stony banks, and flowers in May.

It stops dysentery, and all other flows of blood. It heals ulcers of the kidneys, ruptures, decayed lungs and rotten sores of the mouth, gums and throat. It is also exceedingly good against internal and external wounds and bruises.

SARACENS CONSOUND
(Solidago saracenica)

The stalks are round and brown, and about 5 or 6 ft high. The leaves are long, narrow and indented about the edges and the flowers have a pale yellow colour. Saracens Consound flowers in August.

It has a dry astringent nature. It heals all kinds of wounds and ulcers, both internal and external. A decoction is very good against obstructions of the liver, bladder and gall. A gargle made from it is useful against ulcers of the mouth, throat and gums.

SAVIN or the
Ordinary Savin tree
(Sabina)

It is planted in gardens, and has a very hot and dry nature. Drinking a decoction of the leaves in wine provokes urination and menstruation, causes abortion, and expels a stillborn child, and also the afterbirth. The crushed leaves applied with honey cures ulcers, scabby hands, spreading sores and warts. The juice of the leaves mixed with milk and sweetened with honey is a powerful remedy for destroying worms in children.

SUMMER SAVOURY
(Cunila hortensis aestiva)
WINTER SAVOURY
(Satureia hortensis vulgaris)

The winter variety grows wild and flowers in June.

Both varieties have a hot dry nature. They provoke menstrual flow, open obstructions, encourage flatulence, and are beneficial for the mouth, lungs and womb.

WHITE SAXIFRAGE or
Stone Break
(Saxifraga alba)

It has whitish green round leaves, notched about the edges; the stalks are round and hairy growing about 1 ft high, on which grow spikes of white five-leaved flowers. The root consists of several small reddish grains, mixed with a few small fibres. It grows in dry meadows and rough stony places and flowers in April and May.

It has a hot dry nature. Taken internally, a decoction of the granulated root is very good against obstructions of the kidneys, bladder and ureter.

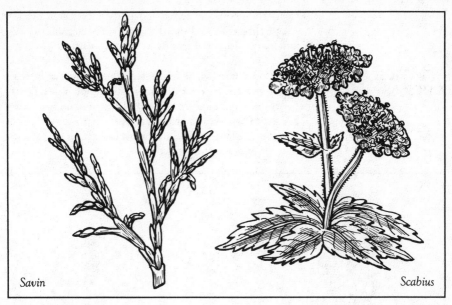

Savin   Scabius

**MEADOW
SAXIFRAGE**
*(Saxifraga vulgaris
pratensis)*

It has long channelled stalks over 2 ft high; the leaves are a dark green, and serrated about the edges, and the flowers are small and of a pale yellow colour. It grows in upland meadows and pastures, and flowers in August.

It is very good against obstructions of the kidneys, bladder and ureter. The crushed root taken with sugar aids digestion, eliminates flatulence and cures colic pains.

**GOLDEN
SAXIFRAGE**
(Saxifrage aurea)

It grows to about a span and a half high; the leaves are like those of Meadow Saxifrage; on the tops of the stalks grow small golden flowers, which are succeeded by round husks full of small red seed. It grows in moist places, and flowers in March and April.

Its properties are similar to those of Meadow Saxifrage.

SCABIUS or
Common Field
Scabious
(Scabiosa major vulgaris)

When it first appears, the leaves are long, rough and hairy, spreading on the ground. The stalks are round and hairy, 2 or 3 ft high, bearing jagged leaves like the Great Valerian, and on the tops of which appear round, flattish blue flowers. It grows in meadows and pastures, and flowers in June and July.

It has a hot dry nature. Drinking a decoction of the leaves

clears the chest and lungs and is therefore good against coughs, abscesses and sore throats. It is good against scabby and itchy skin, if it is made into an ointment.

SCIATICA CRESSES
(Iberis)

It is above 1 ft in height, and bears spikes of small white four-leaved flowers. It grows in gardens, flowering in June.

An ointment made from it with Foxglove and Rue, cures sciatica. The leaves and root beaten into a plaster with Hogs lard has the same effect, but it must be kept on the afflicted part for only four hours.

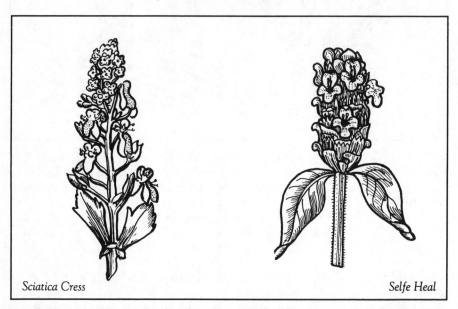

Sciatica Cress   *Selfe Heal*

SCORPION GRASS
or Mouse Ear
(Mysotis scorpioides arvensis)

It is a low herb, not much longer than a man's hand; the stalks are small, on which grow long narrow leaves, which are somewhat like a hare's ear and the flowers are small and yellow. It is planted in gardens, but often grows wild, and flowers in June and July. (There is also another kind called Water Scorpion Grass (Mysotis Scorpioides palustris), but its virtues are as Scorpion Grass.)

In properties, it is similar to Borage or Bugloss. The leaves and flowers infused in wine make the heart cheerful and merry. It is also good for the kidneys, and when nursing, helps increase the production of milk.

SCORZONERA or Viper's Grass
(Scorzonera seu vipravia hispanica)

It is planted in gardens, and flowers in July.

The root only is used. It works against poison and infection, induces perspiration and is good for the heart, and all kinds of fever.

GARDEN SCURVY GRASS
(Cochleria batava rotundifolia hortensis)

It grows in gardens, and flowers in April.

It cleanses and is exceedingly good to purify the blood, if the juice or an infusion of it is drunk. It is an excellent remedy for rotten ulcers of the mouth, if they are washed reguarly with a decoction. If it is applied with vinegar it cures scabs, itches, freckles and other eruptions of the skin.

SEA SCURVY GRASS
(Cochleria marina)

It grows in salt marshes, and flowers later than the garden kind.

It has much the same properties as the Garden Scurvy Grass.

WILD SCURVY GRASS
(Cochleria sylvestris)

It grows in fields and in shape and qualities it is similar to the Garden Scurvy Grass.

COMMON BROAD LEAVED SEA WRACK or Sea Weed
(Quercus marina sucus, Alga marina latifolia vulgatissima)

On the sea coast in the west of Ireland, the inhabitants dung or manure their land with it, and also burn it, in order to make ashes, which they transport to England, and there dispose of to good advantage as a fertilizer.

SEA THONGS
(Quercus marina secunda sucus longo angustoq folio)

These sea weeds are found upon our coasts, being cast up by the tide.

SELERY
(Apium dulce, Eleoselinum, Paludapium)

It has the same nature with Smallage and Parsley, and therefore partakes of their virtues and qualities.

SELFE HEAL
(Prunella major folio non dissecto)

It grows in meadows and pastures, and flowers in June and July.

It dissolves clotted and congealed blood, heals all internal and external wounds, removes obstructions of the liver and gall, and is therefore good for jaundice. It cures ulcers of the mouth and gums, if they are washed with a decoction; if applied to the head with oil of roses and vinegar, it cures a headache. It is also good against internal bleeding and pissing of blood.

SENNA TREE or Bastard Senna
(Colutea)

It grows in gardens.

The leaves and seed are violent purgatives, and should only be given to those with strong constitutions, and even then, they should be used with caution.

SHEPHERDS PURSE or Pickpurse or Caseweed
(Bursa pastoris)

It grows on banks, in streets and backyards, and flowers all summer.

It has a very hot, dry and binding nature. It stops diarrhoea, dysentery, the spitting and pissing of blood and menstrual and other flows of blood. It is so excellent for this purpose, that it will stop bleeding, if it is only held in the hand. It is also very good in preventing miscarriages. The juice is useful against a fever.

SKIRRET
(Sisarum)

It is planted in gardens, and flowers in June.

The roots have a hot and dry nature. They excite the appetite, provoke urine, stop diarrhoea, cure colic pains and also the hiccups.

SLAUKE or Sea Lettuce or Wrack or Laver
(Lichen marinus, Muscus marinus, Fucus marinus, Lactuca marina)

It is a plant without stalks, having wrinkled broad leaves, like the leaves of lettuce, only more wrinkled. It grows on rocks in the sea.

It is good against boils and gout, and when boiled and dressed, it is esteemed by some as a delicate dish.

SLOE BUSH or Black Thorn
(Prunus sylvestris)

Sloe trees grow in hedges and the fruit has a cold dry and astringent nature.

They stop diarrhoea, menstrual and all other flows of blood. It is used in gargles for sore mouths and gums and to fasten loose teeth. A decoction of the bark heals wounds and ulcers.

SMALLAGE
(Apium palustre vel eleoselinum)

It grows in moist marshy places, and flowers in summer.

In qualities it is similar to Garden Parsley. It provokes urine, opens obstructions of the liver, spleen and kidneys, and encourages flatulence. The juice cleanses rotten sores, especially those of the throat and mouth. The leaves purify and sweeten the blood.

SNEEZEWORT or Common Field Pellitory
(Ptarmica vulgaris pratensis)

The stalks are upright, about 1 ft high; the leaves are long and narrow, finely serrated about the edges, while the flowers appear in clusters of white petals. It grows in moist meadows, and flowers in July.

When chewed, the root is good for toothache; if crushed and sniffed up the nostrils, it causes sneezing and clears the head.

SOLOMONS SEAL
(Polygonatum seu sigillum Solomonis)

It is planted in gardens, but grows wild in dry woods and copses, and flowers in May and June.

It has a hot dry nature, which is cleansing and somewhat binding. If pounded and applied to wounds, it closes and heals them. The juice of the root removes spots, freckles and black and blue marks caused by bruising. It stops haemorrhages and all kinds of flow.

Sopewort

SOPEWORT or Bruisewort
(Saponaria)

It grows in gardens, moist places and near rivers, and it flowers in June.

It has a hot dry nature. It clears the chest and lungs and is also good against epilepsy, and general infections. A decoction can be used to wash out wounds and rotten ulcers.

ORDINARY MEADOW SORREL
(Acetosa vel oxalis)

It grows in cornfields and meadows, and flowers in May.

The leaves are cooling, able to quench the thirst and resist putrefaction and are good in fevers.

FIELD SORREL or Sheep's Sorrel or Spear-Pointed Sorrel
(Acetosa arvensis)

It is like the Great Sorrel only much smaller. It grows in dry barren soil, flowering in May.

In qualities, it is similar to the Great Sorrel, but it is not so strong in its operation. It suppurates abscesses and tumours. Taken internally, it removes obstructions, is beneficial for jaundice and quenches the thirst.

ROUND LEAVED or **ROMAN SORREL**
(Acetosa romana rotundifolia hortensis)

It grows in gardens and has the same virtues and qualities to the Common Sorrel.

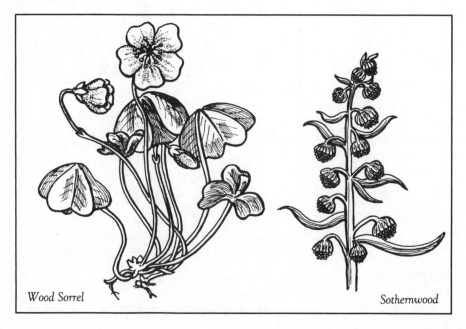

Wood Sorrel   *Sothernwood*

WOOD SORREL
(Acetosella lujula,
Trifolium acetosum
vulgare)

It grows in woody and shady places, and flowers in April.

It is more powerful than Common Sorrel. It is beneficial for the heart, mouth and liver and because it induces perspiration, it is also good against jaundice. It cleanses and heals rotten ulcers.

SOTHERNWOOD
or Male Common
Sothernwood
(Abrotanum mas)

It is planted in gardens, and flowers in July.

It has a very hot and dry nature. It provokes urination and menstruation, opens obstructions and breaks up stone in the bladder and kidneys, and kills worms. Applied externally, it is good against baldness and hair loss. It dissolves swellings, and can be put into an ointment that is generally strengthening.

PRICKLY SOW THISTLE
(Sonchus asper)

It grows by banks and by waysides, and flowers in May and June.

It has a cold dry nature and it is of much the same nature with Dandelion. Is good against the pain of the stomach, and provokes urine, and breaks up stone in the bladder. If a decoction is drunk when nursing it helps to increase the production of milk. The leaves are useful against boils, abscesses and inflammations. The leaves roasted in the embers cure piles, and the falling down of the anus.

SMOOTH SOW THISTLE or Hares
Lettuce
(Sonchus laevis)

This thistle grows in the same places with the former, and has the same virtues and qualities.

IVY LEAVED SOW THISTLE or Wild
Lettuce
(Sonchus laevis muralis)

It is similar to Prickly Sow Thistle as to its medicinal operations.

SOW BREAD
(Artanita vel cyclamen)

The leaves are round, dark green on top and reddish or purple underneath, and usually marked with white spots. The flowers are pale purple, and the root is round like a small turnip. It is planted in gardens, but also grows wild, and it flowers in September and October.

It has a very hot dry nature. A dram crushed and taken, it opens obstructions of the liver and spleen, cures jaundice, and expels the afterbirth. The juice mixed with honey and dropped into the eyes clears the sight, and removes any impediment. It also cures mangy and itchy skin. The root hung about a women's neck in labour assists delivery. However, it is very dangerous for pregnant women to make use of it or to step over it.

SPIGNEL or Mew
(Meum vulgatius)

The leaves are not very large and are divided into several fine segments. The stalk is about 1 ft high, but without many branches, and on the tops of the branches grow clusters of small white five-leaved flowers. It flowers in June and only the root is used.

It has a hot dry nature. It opens obstructions of the liver, spleen and kidneys, provokes urine and eliminates flatulence from the stomach. It also cures stomach and colic pains and catarrh. Being applied to young children's bellies, it will cause them to make water plentifully.

SPINAGE
(Spinachia)

It has a dry moist nature. It provokes urine and aids digestion. Applied externally it dissolves inflammatory tumours and boils.

SPINDLE TREE or
Common Prickwood
with Red Berries
(Euonymus vulgatis)

It is a kind of shrub, rather than a tree, for it is small and low, not growing to any height. It grows in moist woods. It is thought to be hurtful to cattle and especially goats.

It is called Spindle tree and Prickwood because spindles and skewers are commonly made from the wood.

SPLEENWORT or
Ceterach or Miltwast
*(Asplenium vel
scolopendria)*

The leaves are almost the length of a man's finger, and $\frac{1}{2}$ in wide, green on top and brownish underneath. It has neither stalk nor flower. It grows in shady and stony places and on old stone buildings.

It has a temperate nature. The juice of the leaves taken in vinegar for forty days every morning, cures all obstructions of the spleen and liver. It is also very good against painful urination, stone in the bladder, jaundice, fevers and rickets in children.

**ROUGH
SPLEENWORT**
(Lonchitis aspera minor)

The leaves are about 1 ft long, in shape like those of Polypodium, only much narrower and more finely divided. It grows along the sides of ditches, and in woody and low moist places.

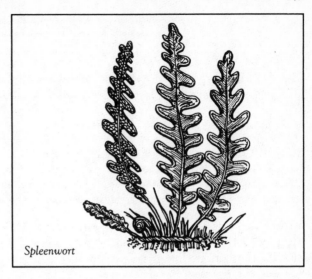

Spleenwort

It has a hot dry nature. Either internally or externally applied, it is very good for obstructions and swellings of the spleen. It is also beneficial for wounds, for it protects them from inflammation.

SPUNK or Touch Wood
(Fungus ignarus)

It grows on the stumps and trunks of trees in the shape of a horse's hoof.

SPUNGE
(Spongia)

This is an imperfect plant which grows on rocks and stone on the sea bed. It is never used internally in medicine, but can be used in applications externally to stop bleeding.

SPURGE or Laurel
(Laureola)

It grows in gardens, and flowers in March and April, with the berries ripening in September.

The leaves and the berries aid digestion and purge viscous substances. If the leaves are chewed, they draw out phlegmatic and clammy substances from the brain, and if sniffed into the nostrils, they cause sneezing. However, it is dangerous to take internally, for it can inflame the stomach.

PETTY SPURGE
(Esula rotunda sive paeplus)

This plant is fashioned like a small tree, like Sun Spurge, but far smaller.

It has a hot and dry nature, and it aids digestion, softens

hardness of the spleen, dissolves flatulence and expels viscous phlegm. It is dangerous in operation and should be used with great caution.

SEA SPURGE
(Tithymalus maritimus)

It produces six or seven red stalks. The leaves are like the leaves of flax, while the flowers are yellow, and are succeeded by triangular seed. The root is long and of a woody substance.

SUN SPURGE or
Wart Spurge
(Tithymalus helioscopium)

It has three or four stalks about 1 ft long which are reddish, the leaves are not as thick as garden Purslain, and the flowers are yellow and grow in tufts.

(It is called Helioscopium because it turns round with the sun.)

MOUNTAIN SPURGE or Knotted
Rooted Spurge
(Tithymalus hibernicus montanus)

All kinds of Spurge usually flower in June and July, with their seeds ripening in August, and they all have much the same properties.

They purge viscous phlegm, and the juice when put into hollow teeth, or the roots if boiled in vinegar and held in the mouth, alleviates the toothache. The juice also cures the roughness of the skin, itches, warts, decaying ulcers, and most eruption on the skin.

SPURRY
(Spergula)

It has round stalks, each having three or four joints, on which grow small narrow leaves in the shape of a star. On the tops of the stalks grow many small white flowers. It usually grows in fields and among corn. It is good fodder for cattle, for it increases their production of milk.

STONE BRAMBLE
or Raspis (The Juice of a Fair Woman)
(Rubus sanatilis, Alpinus, Chamerubus, Sanatilis, Rubus minimus)

It grows in moist woods, and bears red berries which are useful against scurvy.

SMALL STONE CROP or Wall Pepper
(Sedum parvum

It grows on old walls and buildings, and flowers in summer.

It has a hot dry nature. The juice taken with vinegar excites vomiting, and purges viscous phlegm. It is good

*vermicularis,
Illecebra minor acris)*

against fevers and poison, although it must be administered only to strong constitutions. The leaves mixed with lard dissolves lumps and swellings. If pounded and the juice drunk in beer, it is very good for fevers.

STRAWBERRIES
(Fragaria)

Drinking a decoction of strawberry leaves stops diarrhoea and menstrual flow and also cleanses the gums and cures sores and ulcers of the mouth. The juice of the leaves removes redness of the face. Strawberries quench the thirst, and are good for the heat of the stomach.

**GARDEN
SUCCORY**
(Cichoreum sativum)

It is planted in gardens, and flowers in June.
It has a cold dry nature. Drinking the juice eases the pain of the stomach, provokes urine, breaks up stone and cures jaundice. When nursing, it increases the production of milk.

**WILD BLUE
SUCCORY**
(Cichorium sylvestre)

It is like Garden Succory, only not so tall. It grows in lanes and by hedgesides, and flowers in July.
It has the same properties as the former. It opens obstructions and is good against scurvy.

SUN DEW
(Ros folis rota folis vel sponsa solis)

It has reddish rough round leaves about an inch long, shaped like spoons, growing on long stalks, bearing several

Sun Dew

small five-leaved flowers. It grows in bogs and moist bottoms and flowers in June and July. It has a strange nature, for the hotter the sun shines on it, the moister it is.

If bruised with salt and laid on the skin, it raises blisters. Being corrosive, it eats away at rotten sores.

SWALLOW WORT
(Asclepias vincetoxicum, Hirundinaria)

The stalks are smooth, round and small and about 2 ft high. The leaves are dark green, like ivy leaves, only longer and sharp pointed; on the tops of the stalks grow small bunches of five-leaved white flowers. It grows in gardens, and often in sandy and rocky mountainsides, and flowers in June.

The roots have a hot and dry nature, and are a useful antidote against poison. Drinking a decoction cures colic pains, and is good for the bite of a mad dog, used either internally or externally. Pounded leaves are good in applications to sore breasts. The roots are good in inducing perspiration and are useful against jaundice.

T

TAMARISK
(Tamariscus)

It is a small tree that grows in gardens.

The wood, bark and leaves are very good for all disorders of the spleen. Drinking a decoction opens obstructions and is good for coughs and catarrh.

COMMON YELLOW TANSY
(Tanacetum)

It grows near highways, and along the borders of fields, and flowers in July.

It has a hot dry nature, the seed and flowers are an approved remedy against worms. Bruised and mixed with Ox Gaul and applied to the region of the navel, it kills worms in children. Rubbing a mixture of Oil of Roses and the juice of Tansy to the body prevents a shivering fit. The juice drunk with wine provokes urine and opens all obstructions of the body. An ointment made of it cures scabby and itchy skin.

Common Yellow Tansy

WILD TANSY or Silver Weed
(Argentina vel potentilla)

It grows in moist barren places, and flowers in May and June.

Drinking a decoction is good against diarrhoea, dysentery, menstrual and other flows of blood. Taking a decoction in water and salt is good against bruising. It cures ulcers of the mouth and gums, heals wounds, secures loose teeth, eases a toothache and removes freckles, pimples and sun burn.

STRANGLE TARE or Wild Vetch
(Aracus seu cracca major)

The leaves, stalks and pods are like the Common Vetch, only much smaller. The leaves are Cloven at the ends into two or three clasping tendrils. The flowers are small and of a light purple colour, and the pods are long and narrow.

There is little of medicinal value in it, but cattle feed upon it.

MANURED TARE or Vetch
(Vicia sativa)

It is sown in fields, and flowers in May, with the seed ripening in August and September.

A decoction in milk drives out smallpox and measles, but in general it is not much used in medicine.

148

TARRAGON
*(Dracunculus hortensis
seu draco herba)*

It is planted in gardens, and flowers in July and August.

It has a hot dry nature. It provokes urination and menstruation, and expels flatulence.

GARDEN TEASEL
or Manured Teasel
*(Dipsacus sativus seu
carduus sullonum)*

The leaves are long and large, serrated about the edges; the stalks are about 3 ft high, divided into several branches, on the tops of which appear large heads, full of crooked pricklyhooks. It is cultivated in fields, flowering in July.

WILD TEASEL or
Great Shepherds Rod
or Venus Baton or
Carde Thistle
*(Dipsacus syvestris,
Labrum venaris,
Virga pastoris major)*

It is like the former, only the leaves are narrower, and it has purple flowers, and its hooks are neither so hard nor so sharp. It grows in moist places, near brooks and rivers, and flowers in July.

The roots boiled in wine and pounded into a smooth ointment heal anal ulcers, and take away warts, although this ointment must be retained in a copper box. The water

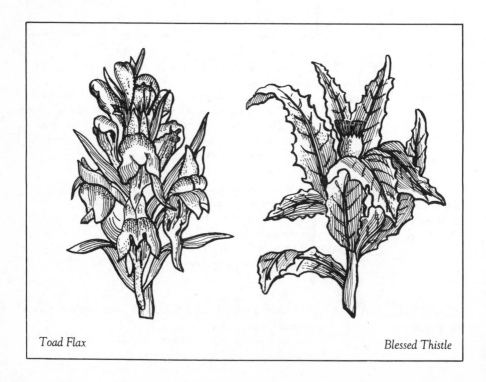

Toad Flax

Blessed Thistle

which is found in the cavities of the leaves is good for the eyes and face.

BLESSED THISTLE
(Carduus benedictus)

It grows in gardens, and flowers in June.

It has a hot and dry nature, and it provokes urination and menstruation, induces sweat, and is beneficial for the mouth, lungs and kidneys. Drinking a decoction in wine cures colic pains. In its powdered state it is exceedingly good against pestilence, but it must be taken within the space of twenty-four hours from the time a person is seized with it. The juice is a powerful antidote against poison if it is taken immediately. Drinking a decoction with water provokes a gentle vomit. It also destroys worms in the stomach.

LADY'S THISTLE
or Milk Thistle
(Carduus mariae)

The leaves are long, large, prickly and shiny green. The stalks are as thick as a man's finger, growing to 5 ft in height, and on the tops of the stalks appear large heads full of sharp prickles. It grows in uncultivated places on banks and along the borders of fields, and flowers in June.

The root is dry and astringent, and the seed is hot. Drinking a decoction of the root in wine is good for the spitting of blood and for weak stomachs. The seed may be profitably given to children who suffer from convulsions.

GARDEN THYME
(Thymus)

It is planted in gardens, and flowers in July.

It has a hot dry nature. It is good against coughs, shortness of breath and all disorders of the head and nerves. Two drams of its powder in vinegar and honey with a little salt, clears phlegm. If pounded with vinegar it dissolves swellings and removes warts. If pounded with barley meal and applied it is good for sciatica.

TOAD FLAX or
Great Toad Flax
(Linaria)

It has small slender blackish stalks; the leaves are long and narrow with sharp points, and have a bluish-green colour, and the flowers are yellow. It grows in uncultivated places and along the borders of fields, and flowers in July.

It has a hot dry nature. It provokes urine, and opens obstructions of the liver spleen and kidneys. It also breaks up stone in the bladder and is useful for jaundice. An ointment made with hogs lard mixed with an egg yolk is excellent for piles.

TOBACCO
(Nicotiana,
Petum,
Tabaccum,
Hyoscyamus peruvianus)

It grows in gardens, and flowers in July and August.

It is good for clearing the head and glands of the throat of phlegm, so preventing catarrh, apoplexy, migraine, inflammation of the throat and infection. It encourages sneezing and vomiting, and it's a good antidote to poison. Externally applied, it cures an itchy and scabby skin.

Tobacco

TORMENTIL or
Setfoil
(Tormentilla sylvestris)

It grows in moist meadows and commons, and flowers in June and July.

The root only is used in medicine. If crushed and drunk in wine or water, in which iron or steel has been quenched, it induces perspiration. It stops diarrhoea, dysentery, the spitting and pissing of blood, and menstrual and other flows of blood. It cures ulcers and other sores of the mouth if they are washed out with a decoction.

COMMON PURPLE MEADOW TREFOIL & WHITE FLOWERED MEADOW TREFOIL (Shamrock)
(Trifolium pratense purpureum minus, Trifolium pratense album)

They grow in fields and meadows, and flower in May and June.

They have a binding nature, good for all kinds of flow and for painful urination. Externally applied they are good against abscesses and inflammations.

TURNEP or Turnip
(Rapum)

It grows in gardens, and flowers in April.

It is a very wholesome nourishing root and is good for the chest, being useful against coughs and consumption.

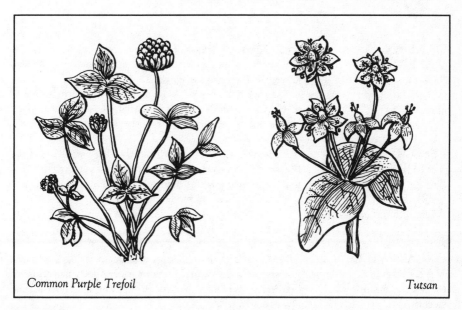

Common Purple Trefoil   *Tutsan*

TUTSAN or Park Leaves
(Androsaemum vulgare seu hypericum maximum)

It is very like St John's wort, except that its leaves and flowers are larger. It grows in hedges and thickets, and flowers in July.

This can be mixed with other medicines in treating

wounds, and is also good for the kidneys. Otherwise its properties are similar to those of St John's Wort.

TWAYBLADE
(Bifolium sylvestre)

It has a round smooth stalk which bears only two leaves, which are like the leaves of great Plantain. The flowers grow in spikes which have a dull green colour. It grows in thickets and moist meadows, and flowers in June.

It is good for wounds and ruptures.

GARDEN VALERIAN or Setwall
(Valeriana major hortensis)

It has broad oval leaves of a whitish-green colour; the stalks are knotty and channelled and on them grow whitish flowers. It is planted in gardens.

The root has a hot dry nature; it provokes urination and menstruation and induces sweating. It is an antidote to poison and it is beneficial for the nerves, head and mouth.

LESSER VALERIAN or Ladder to Heaven or Jacobs Ladder
(Valentina minor)

It is like the garden variety only that it is smaller and the flowers have a pale purple colour. It grows in marshy ground and moist meadows, and flowers in May.

It is seldom used in medicine.

GREAT WILD VALERIAN
(Valeriana major sylvestris)

The stalks are channelled and about 3 ft high, and the flowers are a pale purple colour and shaped like those of Garden Valerian. It grows in moist places, near ditches, and flowers in May.

It heals ulcers and blisters of the mouth and inflammations of the throat, if the mouth and throat are washed with a gargle. It is good for the head and nerves. The roots being pulverized and the quantity of half a spoonful taken at a time in a pleasing drink is exceeding good against epilepsy.

A decoction drunk every day for a month has the same effect.

VERVEIN or
Common Blue-
Flowered Vervein
*(Verbena communis flore
caeruleo)*

It grows in gardens, and is often found growing wild near walls, ditches and highways, flowering in July.

It is good for ulcers of the mouth and jaws if the mouth is washed with a decoction. Such a decoction will also secure loose teeth and alleviate the pain of a toothache if the liquid is held in the mouth for a while. If it is mixed with oil of roses and vinegar, it cures a headache. If the leaves are pounded with honey, they cure and heal fresh wounds. It is very good for all disorders of the brain and is excellent for strengthening the sight.

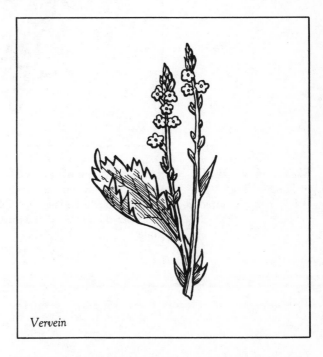

Vervein

VINE TREE
(Vitis vinisera)

In this country it is planted in some gardens, but it seldom comes to any great perfection.

The wine produced from the fruit, especially the red wine, aids digestion, strengthens the stomach and bowels and is good for the heart and is useful against infection.

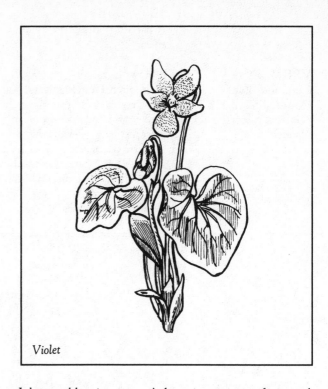

Violet

MARCH VIOLET
or Purple Violet
(Viola martina purpurea)

It has a cold moist nature. A decoction or syrup of it is good against fever, inflammations of the liver and lungs, and is useful for coughs and pleurisy. Externally applied, it is good for abscesses and inflammations. The seed breaks up kidney stone.

WALL FLOWER or
Ordinary Yellow
Wallflower
*(Keiri,
Cheiri,
Leucorum luteum
vulgare)*

It is planted in gardens and it is found growing wild on old walls and buildings, flowering in April and May.

It has a hot dry nature. It provokes urination and menstruation and expels a stillborn child, and the afterbirth if a decoction of the dried flowers , or a little seed is drunk in wine. A plaster made from the flowers with oil and wax closes up old ulcers. The juice dropped into the eyes strengthens the sight. It cures sores on the fingers and abscesses and is also good against apoplexy.

WALNUT TREE
(Juglans)

It is planted along walks, and in parks and fields.

Two or three walnuts eaten with a fig and a little Rue on an empty stomach, provide a good prevention against infection. The kernel oil will heal bruises and scabby and itchy skin, and taken internally will break up stone in the bladder and urinary crystals. A decoction of the green peel or husk of the walnut is useful against tumours and ulcers of the mouth and throat. The bark of the tree, either green, dried or crushed, encourages vomiting.

WHEAT
(Triticum)

A decoction of the flowers of wheat and honey and water dissolves tumours. A decoction of the bran in vinegar is good against itchy skin and boils. A piece of toasted bread dipped in wine and applied to the stomach stops vomiting. A poultice of the wheaten bread in milk will reduce tumours and a decoction of the flowers in vinegar and honey removes spots and freckles. It is advisable not to eat the crust of the bread especially if it is in the least bit burnt.

WILLOW TREE
*(Salix vulgaris alba
arborescens)*

A decoction of the leaves, bark, flowers and seed in wine, taken internally, stops vomiting, spitting of blood, excessive menstrual flow and all other flows of blood. The ashes of the bark mixed with vinegar causes warts to fall off, and softens hard skin. The sap that flows from the bark is good for inflammations of the eyes.

RUE LEAVED WHITLOW GRASS
(Paronychia rutaceo folio)

The leaves are thick, fat and divided into three parts; the stalks are hairy, and on their tops grow small, white five-leaved flowers. It is a small plant, about 3 or 4 in high. It grows on the tops of walls and low houses, flowering in April

It is beneficial against scrofulous tumours.

RED WINTER CHERRIES or Red Nightshade
(Alkekengi seu halicacabum)

It is planted in gardens, and grows wild in woods and moist places, and flowers in July and August, with the fruit ripening in September.

The leaves are cooling as with Common Nightshade. The berries provoke urine, and open obstructions of the bladder, liver and kidneys.

WINTER GREEN
(Pyrola vulgaris)

It has nine or ten green tender leaves, like those of Beet, but much smaller. The stalks are about 1 ft high, and on their tops appear several five-leaved white flowers. It grows in woods and shady places, and flowers in July.

The leaves are useful in healing internal and external wounds and ulcers. They stop haemorrhages, like the passing of blood in the urine and excessive menstrual flow.

WOAD
(Glasium sativum aut isatis sativa)

It is planted in fields and gardens, mainly as a principal ingredient in blue dyes. It is also found growing wild in uncultivated areas.

It is good when applied to wounds and decaying ulcers. It prevents bleeding and dissolves swellings. Drinking a decoction is useful against obstructions of the liver and spleen. It can also be applied to ruptures and dislocations.

WOLFE-BANE
(Aconitum)

It grows by riversides and near bogs and woods.

If made into a plaster and externally applied, it is very good in dissolving glandular tumours.

WOODROOF or Small, Sweet Scented Madder
(Asperula, Aspergula oderata, Rubeola montana odera)

The stalks are square and full of joints, at each of which grow seven or eight long narrow leaves, like a star. The flowers grow on the tops of the stalks in small clusters of little single-leaved white flowers. It grows in woods and shady places, and flowers in May.

It has a hot dry nature. It is good in healing wounds if

Wolfe-bane

bruised and then applied and also in curing boils and inflammations. If it is drunk with wine it is good for the heart and useful against inflammations of the liver and obstructions of the gall and bladder.

COMMON WORMWOOD
(Absinthium latifolium vulgare)

It strengthens the stomach, creates a good appetite, and can be useful for jaundice. It is good in stopping diarrhoea and vomiting. If applied externally, it dissolves swellings, and is good for dislocations, swelling of the tonsils and inflammation of the throat if a plaster is made from it with Rue, Sothernwood and hogs lard is applied.

SEA-WORMWOOD
(Absinthium tenuifolium vel seriphium marinum album)

If a decoction is drunk, or if applied externally to the belly or navel in a poultice it kills all kinds of worms.

YARROW or Milfoil
(Millefolium terrestre vulgare)

It commonly grows in fields and meadows, flowering in June and July.

It has a very dry astringent nature. Drinking a decoction stops dysentery, and excessive menstrual and other flows. If bruised and applied to wounds, it stops bleeding and prevents inflammations and swelling. A dram of it pulverized and taken in a glass of white wine is a perfect remedy for the cholic. Nothing is more effectual against the piles, either taken inwardly or outwardly applied. If applied to the pit of the stomach in a plaster with grated nutmeg, it is beneficial for fevers.

YEW TREE
(Taxus)

It is good neither as food nor as medicine, and can actually be dangerous to man. It is reported that if a man sleeps under the shadow of this tree, he will fall sick and will sometimes die. Birds that eat of the fruit either die or cast their feathers. Eating the fruit can provoke acute diarrhoea.

Of further interest . . .

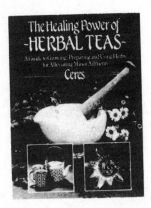

The Dictionary of
MODERN
HERBALISM
A Comprehensive Guide to Practical Herbal Therapy

Compiled and written by
Simon Y. Mills M.A., M.N.I.M.H.
President and Director of Research of the
National Institute of Medical Herbalism

Published in Conjunction with *Here's Health* Magazine

DICTIONARY OF MODERN HERBALISM

THE COMPLETE GUIDE TO HERBS

Simon Mills MNIMH. Herbal medicine is a healing art that has been practiced for thousands of years. In China it is held in equal esteem with acupuncture and Western medicine. Now, Simon Mills, the Director of Research and a past President of the National Institute of Medical Herbalists, has drawn upon his years of experience in herbal research to provide an up-to-date, concise reference book which is invaluable to both the general and professional reader.

It contains the latest information on the full range of herbs and herbal remedies and includes colour plates to assist in identification.

This title is being published by Thorsons in collaboration with Newman Turner Publications, publishers of HERE'S HEALTH magazine.

THE HEALING POWER OF HERBAL TEAS

Ceres. Colour photographs and line drawings. Lists common herbs, tells where and when to gather them and beautifully illustrates each one. Reveals in simple language the enormous potential of herbal teas as natural healers and tonics. Many of these easily obtained plants provide helpful alleviators of pain and simple discomforts where habit-forming drugs might previously have been used. Gives precise instructions for making infusions to relieve indigestion, cramp, insomnia, and sunburn, as an aid to slimming and as a general bodily tonic. Also gives directions for growing herbs either in an outdoor garden or an easily maintained window box, and for companion planting with non-edible species to enhance the appearance of the plot. A veritable cornucopia of refreshing and soothing drinks and lotions. A Thorsons publication.

Few cities have been so cel
from Smollett to Jane Austen, ...
Burney, and from Sheridan to Georgette Heyer. Many other famous writers have passed through as well – Mary Shelley wrote *Frankenstein* in a house in the Abbey Church Yard, Coleridge met his wife in the city, and in the twentieth century John Betjeman championed its architectural heritage. Even Shakespeare – or so it is believed – turned up to take a dip in the hot springs.

These eleven walks look at Bath through their eyes, creating a vivid social history of the city over the last 300 years and bringing the past alive with unparalleled immediacy. Fully illustrated, and including in-depth accounts of the writers and works featured, they can either be followed on foot or – with the aid of historic maps of the city – read as a series of essays.

Andrew Swift and Kirsten Elliott are Bath-based writers and broadcasters, who between them have over 35 years experience of leading walking tours around the city. They have devised walks for the Bath Literature Festival, the Bath International Music Festival and numerous other organisations. Their company, Bath Walks, was established in 1992, and in 2003 they founded Akeman Press to publish a range of local books. This is the fourteenth title to appear under the Akeman Press imprint. Andrew Swift also writes walks for *The Bath Magazine* and *The Bristol Magazine*, while Kirsten Elliott has written an illustrated history of Bath published by Frances Lincoln and Yale University Press, and produced a DVD on Bath – *Glorious History, Majestic Beauty*.

LITERARY WALKS IN BATH

Eleven Excursions in the Company
of Eminent Writers

Andrew Swift & Kirsten Elliott

AKEMAN
PRESS

Published by AKEMAN PRESS
www.akemanpress.com

© Andrew Swift & Kirsten Elliott 2012

ISBN 978-0-9560989-3-1

Cover: The High Street, Bath, 1829, by Thomas Shepherd

Printed by HSW Print, Tonypandy

CONTENTS

LIST OF MAPS

FOREWORD
by Peter Lovesey

Before reading this book, I was conceited enough to believe I had a sound knowledge of Bath's literary history. What complacency! I have now been re-educated, but in the best possible way, through surprise, amusement, fascination and sometimes being moved to tears. I have learned about writers I neglected to read and characters I'm delighted to engage with for the first time. Their link to Bath is the starting point. A book of literary walks has been turned into a logical reason to get close to people of genius, sample their work and gain an insight into their eventful lives.

So this is much more than a programme of suggested walks by the two people who know more about the topography of the city than anyone I know, estimable as that undoubtedly is. Andrew Swift and Kirsten Elliott are the guides you would most want to be led by, but they are also superb researchers and authoritative historians. *Literary Walks in Bath* is, I suggest, their crowning achievement because they have also presented the history of Bath in an accessible, entertaining form. And what a surprising history it is.

Forget the travel-brochure images. Bath was not always a joy to stroll around taking in the magnificent Georgian architecture. In its time, the place has been hellish. Read the chapter on poor Tom Paine who was treated as a latter-day Guy Fawkes, with his likeness burned in effigy all over the area because he had the temerity to advocate republicanism in *The Rights of Man.* Read the account of the mob hounding Philip Thicknesse – a far less worthy character, it has to be said – and you will think twice about stepping into a time machine.

This is not to say that the story is all shocks and horrors. For the favoured few at the right points in history, Bath was the best place to be. It inspired great writing from the likes of Smollett, Sheridan, Austen, Burney and Dickens. You will be treated to sizeable extracts from their work and may discover, as I did, that revered writers can be more subversive than ever you suspected. And you will chance upon some in unguarded moments, such as Coleridge, high on laudanum, walking in driving rain from Box to Bath; Sheridan placing secret letters to his lover in Delia's Grotto, beneath North Parade; Fanny Burney encountering an eagle at Bathwick Villa; and

Boswell taking tea for hours on end with Dr Johnson at the Thrales' house in South Parade.

I particularly enjoyed the minor characters, fictional and historical, who appear incidentally in these pages. Who could resist Kitty Crocodile, Miss Snapper and – I kid you not – Rear Admiral Balderick? There is even a Captain Mainwaring, author, not of a Home Guard manual, but *Annals of Bath* (1838).

I have to admit that, as a crime writer who often uses Bath as a setting, I have frequently gone to books written previously by Andrew and Kirsten for the kind of detail that enriches a plot. The current volume will, I must warn them, be plundered without restraint. I have noted the duel on Claverton Down between Count Rice and the Vicomte du Barry and the murderous tendencies of James Quin, the actor. I would dearly like to solve the mystery of the Merlin swing in Sydney Gardens. Perhaps most intriguing of all is the American lady, Patience Wright, residing in Abbey Church Yard, who was modelling celebrities in wax before Tussaud's opened. She charmed everyone who sat for her, including George III and William Pitt. All the while she was gathering information about the British preparations for the War of Independence, for Patience was a spy.

I hope some of this has whetted the appetite. You may also want to whet the whistle. If so, you couldn't do better than start the walk recommended in Chapter One, 'The Lost Inns of Bath: a Literary Odyssey'. Enjoy!

Peter Lovesey
February 2012

INTRODUCTION

Bath's literary heritage is as rich as its architectural one, and as important in understanding the culture that created it. The eleven walks in this book introduce an array of remarkable writers – from the famous, such as Jane Austen, Mary Shelley and Charles Dickens, to those whose star has faded, such as Philip Thicknesse, Fanny Burney and Catherine Macaulay. All, though, provide us with unforgettable insights into what it was like to live in Bath at various times in its history. Taken together, these insights form a vivid social history of the city over the last 300 years.

Bath's fortunes, during its eighteenth-century heyday, were founded on, and inextricably linked with, the coaching trade, and the first walk sets the scene by going in search of the literary associations of Bath's lost coaching inns.

The second walk looks at the development of the theatre in eighteenth-century Bath, showing how it held the mirror up to a society every bit as artificial and contrived as that presented on stage.

The third walk features Tobias Smollett, who first came to the city in the 1740s when it was a mecca for gamblers, card sharps and adventurers, but lived to see it transformed into the epitome of polite society. Although his last novel, *Humphrey Clinker*, which celebrates that transformation, is well known, his earlier novels, chronicling often overlooked aspects of eighteenth-century society, are largely forgotten. Our walk round Smollett's Bath revives these neglected works to create a portrait of a rough-and-tumble city as it stumbled towards respectability.

There is nothing respectable about the subject of our fourth walk. Philip Thicknesse is not a name many will be familiar with, but, if you had lived in eighteenth-century Bath, you would not have been able to avoid him. The author of two guidebooks to the city – one of which led to him nearly being lynched – he was one of the most unpleasant, opinionated – and entertaining – characters to end up in Bath during its golden age. He also makes a splendid companion on a walk that seeks to get beneath the veneer of polite society.

In total contrast is the subject of our fifth walk, the ultra-respectable Fanny Burney. Despite her gentility, she was an acute observer of human nature and mingled with some of the most fascinating people of the age, many of whom we meet as we follow her around the city.

The sixth walk introduces several writers not normally associated with Bath – Catherine Macaulay, Samuel Taylor Coleridge, Mary Shelley and Percy Bysshe Shelley. Entitled 'Rebels and Romantics', it demonstrates that not all of Bath's visitors were devoted to the pleasure principle. As the eighteenth century drew to a close, and radical ideas took hold, Bath was caught up in the political and ideological ferment. Catherine Macaulay, a celebrated historian who inspired revolutionaries in America and France, was fêted in Bath, until an ill-advised marriage led to her being ostracised by polite society; Coleridge, fired with Utopian idealism, met his future wife in Bath, preached in the city's Unitarian chapel, and nearly died of an opium overdose in an upstairs room at the Greyhound Inn; Mary Shelley wrote part of *Frankenstein* in Bath, while the radical fervour of her husband, Percy Bysshe Shelley, would have been roused by a mass political rally less than a hundred yards from their lodgings.

The seventh walk continues this theme, looking at the impact Tom Paine's writings had in Bath, with a handful of brave souls standing up to the arbitrary power of the city corporation and the national government as the country slid ever further into recession and political turmoil.

Among those living in Bath at this time was Jane Austen, and the eighth walk follows in the footsteps of the city's most celebrated novelist – visiting not only sites routinely associated with her, but many out-of-the-way spots as well. With optional excursions to Lyncombe Vale, Beechen Cliff, Charlcombe and Weston, this may well be the most exhaustive Jane Austen walk yet published – an appropriate tribute to one who was not only a great walker but is too often hijacked by those intent on seeing the past through rose-tinted spectacles. As demonstrated by the two preceding walks, which serve as an introduction to it, Jane Austen's Bath was a more troubled and edgier place than the Bath of today.

Jane Austen's two Bath novels, written some 17 years apart, capture Bath's transformation from the most fashionable place in the country to a city whose star was fading, as the beau monde followed the Prince Regent to Brighton. By the time Charles Dickens first visited Bath in the mid-1830s, its decline was well advanced. Snobbery and a desperate gentility had replaced the gaiety of an earlier age. The coaching era had but a few years to run. When the railway arrived in the 1840s, it was not just the coaching trade that collapsed; Bath, designed as a playground for the most fashionable in the land, became a retirement home for distressed gentlefolk. All of which explains why Dickens regarded it with undisguised contempt.

The city did eventually struggle free from its nineteenth-century nadir, but it took a long time, and the whiff of that Miss Haversham-like existence can still be caught in out-of-the-way places. Bath's twentieth-century reinvention as a World Heritage city is reflected in the last two walks, whose subjects – unlike the earlier writers featured – concentrated not on the present but the past. First comes Georgette Heyer, whose Regency romances are informed by meticulous research and an encyclopaedic knowledge of the period – a sort of literary archaeology. Finally, we take a walk around Bath in the company of someone who not only opened people's eyes to its architectural heritage but also fought to preserve it – John Betjeman. Over a quarter of a century after his death, we look at what has happened to Betjeman's Bath and at the legacy he has bequeathed us.

Most of these walks had their genesis in walks devised for the Bath Literature Festival between 2002 and 2012, and are designed so that they can be either followed on foot or read as essays. Three of them – on Smollett, Thicknesse, and the Rebels and Romantics – are preceded by extended essays, as this was felt to be the best way of presenting them; the others have short introductions, with the various writers and their works discussed in the course of the walks.

Although the walks follow a chronological sequence and follow on from each other, they can be undertaken individually or in any order you choose. If you decide to tackle them all, you will become aware of a certain amount of duplication, at least as regards their itineraries. The Smollett and Thicknesse walks, for example, follow much the same route through the old city, while the Fanny Burney and Tom Paine walks both end in an old cemetery well off any recognised tourist trail. Certain places, such as the Pump Room and Queen Square, feature in most of the walks, as do long-lost buildings such as Bath's original Assembly Rooms on Terrace Walk and the White Hart Inn in Stall Street. Although you will find yourself covering the same ground in the course of several of the walks, however, you will be looking at it through different – sometimes very different – eyes. And, while we have pointed out some of the more illuminating correspondences between various writers' views of the city, we have left many more for you to discover for yourself on this series of literary trails round an endlessly fascinating city.

A summary of the distances covered in each walk and whether or not steps are encountered en route can be found on page 316.

Note: Although the wording of quotations from earlier writers has not been altered, spelling, capitalization and punctuation have been edited, where this does not affect the sense of the original, to conform with modern usage.

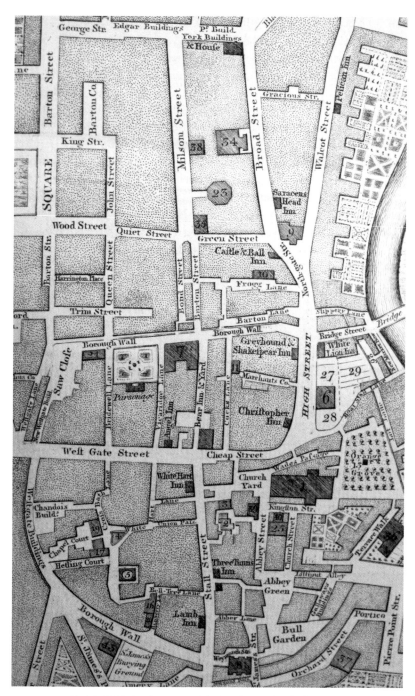

Bath in 1786 showing some of the inns featured in the first walk

1

THE LOST INNS OF BATH
A Literary Odyssey

This walk follows in the footsteps of Dr Johnson, Coleridge, Jane Austen, Dickens and others in search of Bath's lost coaching inns. It is very much a taster of the walks that follow, familiarising you with the city and introducing some of the writers you will meet later.

Although there have been inns in Bath from earliest times, the first regular stagecoach service between London and Bath only started in 1667. It ran to the White Lion in the High Street and the journey took three days. London was 108 miles away, which meant that the average speed was a mere 36 miles a day. This was largely due to the appalling state of the roads, which improved as coaching traffic increased, so that by the time mailcoaches were introduced in 1784 they could accomplish the journey in 13 hours. Mailcoaches, incidentally, were the idea of a Bath theatre manager, but to find out how his theatrical endeavours led to the introduction of the mailcoach you will have to wait till the second walk.

Coaching traffic grew as Bath grew. In 1740, 23 coaches a week ran between London and Bath; by the end of the century there were over 150. But it all came to an abrupt end when the railway between London and Bath opened in 1841. The inns that relied for most of their business on the coaching trade either closed or went into rapid decline. Most were demolished a century or more ago; none survive in anything like their original form.

In the heyday of Bath's coaching inns, several of them were celebrated in a popular rhyme that indicated the rivalry that existed between the various stagecoach operators:

> May the White Hart outrun the Bear
> And make the Angel fly,
> Turn the Lion upside down
> And make the Three Tuns fly.

That did not exhaust the list of inns, however – there was the Greyhound, the Christopher, the Packhorse, the Unicorn, the George, the Pelican, the Three Cups, the Lamb ... many of them with literary connections.

We start at the southern end of the High Street where All Bar One, just along from the corner of Cheap Street, occupies the old Christopher Inn. This dates from the sixteenth century. Latterly it was known as the Christopher Hotel, and its old name can still be seen above the second-floor windows. In the eighteenth century, the landlord, Mr Hadden, was a staunch supporter of John Wesley and the inn became a meeting-place for Bath's Methodists. John Wesley, who described Bath as 'that Sodom of our land', stayed at the Christopher over 80 times.

Walk along the High Street to the corner of Bridge Street, where the northern extension of the Guildhall stands on the site of the White Lion. Isambard Kingdom Brunel, the man associated more than any other with the demise of Bath's coaching trade, stayed here for long periods during the building of the Great Western Railway. Charles Dickens also stayed here in 1869 when he came to give readings at the Assembly Rooms. It was while looking through a window of the inn at the rain falling outside that he made his most damning condemnation of Bath, which can be found in the ninth walk. Five years later, the diarist Francis Kilvert visited Bath and found an unusual variety of street entertainer outside the White Lion:

> At the door of the White Lion Hotel in Bath we found a large crowd gathered round the donkey and cart of the nobleman organ grinder. The disguised nobleman and his organ were putting up at the hotel and the people were waiting for him to finish breakfast and come out. No one knows who he is.

There are many reports. Some say he is an Irish baronet, some say that he is a lord. It is believed that he has made a wager for £30,000 that he will go about

for three years with the same donkey, and live by his earnings. People give him gold in the street and some days it is said he makes as much as £15. Perhaps he has run through one fortune and taken this means of getting another. Or perhaps a fortune of £30,000 was left him to be inherited on this condition.

Opposite the White Lion, on the west side of the High Street, was the Greyhound. The poet Samuel Taylor Coleridge turned up here unannounced on the night of 5 December 1813. He already knew the city fairly well. In 1794 he had proposed to his wife at the house of Robert Southey's mother in Westgate Buildings, and in 1796 he had travelled over from Bristol to give a sermon at the Unitarian Chapel in Frog Lane (now New Bond Street). By 1813, he was in his early forties and hopelessly

Looking south along the High Street, with the White Lion on the left and the Greyhound on the right

addicted to opium. He had left his wife and spent much of his time as the guest of various friends who could tolerate his addiction. One set of benefactors were the Morgans. In late 1813, he moved into a cottage at Ashley, near Box, with Mary Morgan and her sister Charlotte. He was not the easiest of house guests, and on the evening of 5 December things came to a head. Although the details of what happened are unclear, he ended up swallowing a massive dose of laudanum and storming out of the house.

He set off for Bath, trudging along the muddy, unlit road into the driving rain, as the effects of the drug began to take hold. When he arrived in Bath, he went to the Greyhound and persuaded the innkeeper, William May, to take him in. He was consigned to a small garret room and a doctor was called. He lay seriously ill for several days and it was two weeks before he was sufficiently recovered to take a post-chaise to Bristol to stay with friends and continue his convalescence.

Head north into Northgate Street and carry on across the lights at the end of New Bond Street to the old post office, which stands on the site of the Castle Inn, sometimes known as the Castle & Ball. It was here that the Rev James Woodforde, a celebrated diarist, stayed in June 1786:

> June 29 ... We all got safe to Bath (thank God) this morning about ten o'clock, to the Castle Inn, where we made a second breakfast, and there also dined, supped and slept ... After breakfasting at Bath we took a walk over the city till dinner to show Nancy [his niece] the public rooms etc, she being

The Castle on the corner of Northgate and New Bond Streets was demolished in the 1920s to make way for the post office

never at Bath before – gave for seeing them one shilling. We had very good accommodation at our inn.

In 1826, Charles Westmacott, under the pseudonym Bernard Blackmantle, featured the Castle in *The English Spy*, a Pickwickian journey around Britain. He included a song written in praise of the Castle and its landlord, Matthew Temple:

> Come all you gay fellows, so merry and witty,
> Ye Somerset lads of the elegant city,
> Ye sons of the turf who delight in a race
> And ye Nimrods of Bath, who are fond of the chase;
> Come join us, and pledge us, like true brothers all,
> At old Matthew Temple's, the Castle & Ball.

Cross to the Podium and turn left along Walcot Street. At the far end of the Hilton Hotel, stop on the corner of the road leading down to the car park. This is the site of the Pelican Inn, where James Boswell stayed in 1776. He recorded the visit in his *Life of Johnson*:

The Pelican was renamed the Three Cups in the nineteenth century. It was demolished in 1956

Soon after this day, [Dr Johnson] went to Bath with Mr and Mrs Thrale. I had never seen that beautiful city, and wished to take the opportunity of visiting it, while Johnson was there. On the 26th of April, I went to Bath; and on my arrival at the Pelican Inn, found lying for me an obliging invitation from Mr and Mrs Thrale, by whom I was agreeably entertained almost constantly during my stay. They were gone to the Rooms; but there was a kind note from Dr Johnson, that he should sit at home all the evening. I went to him directly, and before Mr and Mrs Thrale returned, we had by ourselves some hours of tea-drinking and talk.

Although Boswell made it quite clear that, while he stayed at the Pelican, Dr Johnson stayed with the Thrales at 14 South Parade, it soon became part of Bath folklore that Dr Johnson had stayed at the inn – so much so that in 1923 GK Chesterton unveiled a plaque on the building commemorating his visit.

Cross Walcot Street, go through an archway between Nos 33 and 35, up the steps to Broad Street Place and on into Broad Street.[1] **Cross Broad Street and turn left downhill, past the old King Edward's School** (where Thomas de Quincey was a pupil). **Four doors further down, stop by the archway leading to the Côte restaurant.** The building to the left of the archway was the King's Arms Inn. The archway led through to the inn yard; the Côte restaurant was originally its stables. On 23 May 1765, the Rev James Woodforde recorded in his diary that 'we got into Bath this evening about seven o'clock, and we put up at the King's Arms in Broad Street, where I supped and spent the evening and laid.'

On the opposite side of the road is the Saracen's Head, famous for its connection with Charles Dickens, who, so it is claimed, stayed there in 1835. The evidence for this piece of Bath folklore is examined in the ninth walk.

Continue down Broad Street and turn right into Green Street. On the left-hand side of Green Street is the Old Green Tree, built around 1716. Its three small, wood-panelled rooms are redolent of days long gone, as is this tale which appeared in the *Bath Journal* on 22 July 1899:

> A well-known purveyor, who lived not far from the Green Tree, and sometimes disbursed a deal of his money and his time at that hostelry, on one occasion backed himself for a ten-pound note, although upwards of 60 years of age, to walk to Wells in four hours. The feat was accomplished with time to spare, but it took Jacob more than four days to get back, for after arriving at the cathedral city and partaking of sundry drops with friends, he, to adopt his own phrase, donned his 'sitting breeches', and the whole of the ten-pound note he had won and a little besides was expended before he turned his head homeward.

Carry on along Green Street, cross Milsom Street, continue along Quiet Street and turn left into Queen Street. The Raven, on your left, is not only one of Bath's finest real ale pubs, but is home to some splendid pokerwork

---

1 For a step-free alternative, walk up Saracen Street to Broad Street, cross and turn left downhill.

pictures executed by the landlady, Jill Forsey, reviving the eighteenth-century tradition of satirical cartoons.

Carry on along Queen Street, under St John's Arch and straight on along Trim Bridge. Cross Upper Borough Walls and continue along Bridewell Lane. At the end, turn left along Westgate Street and cross the bottom of Parsonage Lane. A little further along you come to the Westgate Inn, originally known as the Angel and dating from the seventeenth century. The Rev James Woodforde recorded a visit here in February 1775:

> I put up at the Angel in Westgate Street where I supped and slept ... The Bath coach for tomorrow for Oxford [is] quite full, so that I forfeit my half guinea that I paid some time back, and must go to Oxford some other way, as I did not come last week. However I met with a young gentleman from Devon at my inn, who is going to Oxford, by name Coleridge of Ottery St Mary, and we agreed to take a chaise tomorrow between us for Oxford ... He spent the evening with us at the Angel Inn.

This was not Samuel Taylor Coleridge, who was only two years old at the time, but his brother William, who died five years later in 1780 at the age of 22.

Carry on along Westgate Street to the corner of Union Street. Union Street was built in 1806 on the site of one of Bath's biggest inns, the Bear, which dated from the sixteenth century. Prior to its demolition, the yard of the Bear was the principal route from the old city centre to Queen Square and the new streets to the north. Matthew Bramble, in Tobias Smollett's *Humphrey Clinker*, commented scathingly on this arrangement:

> The avenues to [Queen Square] are mean, dirty, dangerous, and indirect. Its communication with the baths is through the yard of an inn, where the poor trembling valetudinarian is carried in a chair, betwixt the heels of a double row of horses, wincing under the curry-combs of grooms and postilions, over and above the hazard of being obstructed, or overturned by the carriages which are continually making their exit or their entrance – I suppose after some chairmen shall have been maimed, and a few lives lost by those accidents, the corporation will think, in earnest, about providing a more safe and commodious passage.

Turn right along Stall Street and stop opposite the entrance to the Abbey Church Yard. The shops set back behind a colonnade on the right-hand side of the street stand on the site of the Bear's great rival, the White Hart, which was open by 1503. The satirical writer Ned Ward stayed here in 1700 during a visit to the city described in *A Step to the Bath*. The White Hart also features in Jane Austen's *Persuasion* and Charles Dickens' *The Pickwick Papers*, making it the most significant inn, in literary terms, in the city. That did not save it, however, from being demolished in 1867.

Carry on along Stall Street to the corner of Beau Street. Opposite, on the left-hand side of Stall Street, stood another important inn, the Three Tuns. Although long gone, a lodging house at the back, which formed part of the inn, survives as the Crystal Palace on Abbey Green. It was at the Three Tuns that the great Shakespearian actor, James Quin, held court between 1751, when he retired to Bath, and his death in 1766. You will find a fictionalised account of one of his legendary drinking sessions, from Tobias Smollett's *Humphrey Clinker*, on pages 29-30.

The Three Tuns closed in 1804 and was demolished eight years later, just another of Bath's long lost coaching inns. Contemplating the fate that overtook them is, if not enough to drive you to drink, at least deserving of a gentle stroll to a nearby hostelry. A walk back up Stall Street, on – through the yard of the Bear – along Union Street and up Burton Street will bring you to Milsom Street and a tantalising choice – left along Quiet Street to the Raven or right along Green Street to the Old Green Tree. Cheers!

2

'LIKE MIRRORS MADE, FOR MEN TO SEE'
The Bath Stage in the Eighteenth Century

In the afternoon there is generally a play, tho' the decorations are mean, and
the performances accordingly; but it answers, for the company here (not the
actors) make the play, to say no more.

Daniel Defoe, *A Tour Through the Whole Island of Great Britain*, 1724

It was a pleasure city that was improvised here, and its sumptuous aspect has
outlived its fortune … The spectacle of modern life in this setting … comes
upon one with something of a shock. The eye instinctively wanders over the
wide pavements, seeking the costumes of a bygone age … On this stage,
prepared for a very different society, it is the present occupants and their habits
that seem out of place. Only the eighteenth century, we feel, could ever be at
home here; these scenes were a theatre it arranged according to its own taste,
for its use and pleasure, and in which it figured in its utmost brilliance … The
theatre is empty; the actors have long deserted it, the play already forgotten,
can never be revived. But literature makes it possible to resuscitate some of the
former, to reconstitute the main lines of the latter, and by means of this dual
memory to animate scenery that has remained almost intact.

A Barbeau, *Life & Letters in Bath in the Eighteenth Century*, 1904

Theatre was the lifeblood of eighteenth-century Bath, holding up the
mirror to a society every bit as mannered as that portrayed on stage. In this
walk we take a theatrical stroll around the city to see how life reflected art
and art reflected life on the stage that was Georgian Bath.

**We start at the south end of the High Street, near the Rebecca
Fountain**. The venue for most theatrical performances until the beginning
of the eighteenth century was the room above the town hall, which
stood on columns in the middle of the High Street. Between 1569 and
1612, 30 companies of travelling players visited Bath, giving around
100 performances. The companies included several that Shakespeare was
associated with, and it is possible that he visited and performed in the city.
Although there is no way of proving this, it has been suggested that the last
two of his sonnets – Nos 153 and 154 – indicate that he knew the city and
bathed in the hot springs.

Theatrical performances ceased in Bath, as elsewhere, during the
Cromwellian interregnum, but were revived thereafter. Facilities were

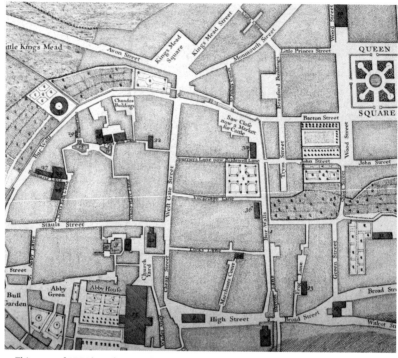

This map of 1736 by John Wood (with north oriented to the right) shows the Town Hall (indicated by No 8) in the middle of the High Street. It was here that the Drury Lane Company performed *Sir Courtly Nice* for Queen Anne in 1702. Bath's first purpose-built theatre (No 36), which opened in 1705, can be seen on 'Bur-Walls'.

rudimentary in the extreme – somewhat of an embarrassment for a city that was now looking to attract sophisticated visitors. In 1702, Queen Anne visited Bath, accompanied by the Drury Lane Theatre Company. Despite being the most acclaimed troupe of actors in the country, they only managed to provide 'an entertainment of sorts' for the queen. The play chosen was John Crowne's comedy *Sir Courtly Nice*, with Colley Cibber and Anne Oldfield in the lead roles. The play's subtitle was *It Cannot Be*, a sentiment many of the company must have echoed as they attempted to stage a royal command performance in a cramped upstairs room.

As a result of this debacle, several of Bath's leading citizens decided that the city needed a theatre. A subscription soon raised £1,300 for a new theatre in Parsonage Lane, which opened in 1705. No trace of it remains nor have any pictures of it survived. The only detailed description we have of it appears in Captain Rowland Mainwaring's *Annals of Bath*, published in 1838:

The first regularly built theatre in Bath was ... on the ground where the General Hospital now stands. It was the property of Widow Poore, and under the management of Hornby, a comedian. But as gaming was the prevailing rage at the time, the theatre met with very indifferent encouragement, and the performers were hardly able to support themselves. Lady Hawley afterwards became the purchaser of the property, but that did not mend the condition of the actors. The theatre was under her ladyship's ballroom, and the seats were placed one above the other, until they reached within four feet of the ceiling; there was only one box, placed above the door, which held four persons, and the price of admittance was half-a-crown to every part of the house. Thirty pounds was the receipt of the fullest house, and her ladyship was entitled to a third share of the profits, and one-fourth for the use of scenes and dresses. The standing expense was £2.10s. per night, which included music, attendants, bills, and tallow candles; the remainder was divided among twelve performers.

This was the theatre Defoe described as 'mean'; comments by other visitors confirm the impression of a distinctly lacklustre enterprise. In 1716, Dudley Ryder recorded in his diary:

Went to the play, where Mrs Marshall and her sister were gone before in chairs. It was a play called *Love Makes a Man*. The plot and dialogue of the play put me in a very grave humour and I found myself more in love with Mrs Marshall than ever. There were one or two of the low comic parts acted pretty tolerably well but the rest were acted very ill.

Not surprisingly, the theatre was poorly attended. In 1721 Lady Bristol wrote that 'for plays, there is hardly ever company enough to make it warm,' and when Lord Chesterfield visited in 1734, 'the audience consisted of 17 souls, of which I made one.'

One production was an undoubted hit, however. On 11 May 1728, *Farley's Bristol Newspaper* carried the following report:

We hear from Bath, that last week all the quality were at the playhouse, to hear the rehearsal of *The Beggar's Opera*, collected a handsome sum and presented the actors with it. And that on Monday and Wednesday last, notwithstanding the pit and boxes were laid together, they were so full, that they turn'd away as many as they took in: 'tis evident, they were pleas'd with the performance, because there was a purse of gold made up at the Pump House, and presented to Lucy Locket, and Polly Peachum, to buy each of them a new dress in which they are each to perform their part this evening ... We don't indeed much wonder at the performing of it well, when we hear that Mr Gay hath taken so much pains to instruct them, [he being] the author of that humorous piece.

Although we do not know what the theatre looked like, inside or out, we can get an idea what *The Beggar's Opera* looked like from Hogarth's painting of the London production – one of the earliest paintings of an English stage performance. In it, Macheath stands chained, under sentence of death, between his two lovers, Lucy Lockit and Polly Peachum, both pleading for his life. At either side of the stage sit members of the audience. Among them is the Duke of Bolton, the lover of the actress Lavinia Fenton, who played Polly Peachum. This correspondence or blurring of distinctions between drama and real life characterised the eighteenth-century attitude to the theatre – and, as we will see, having the audience on the stage was only one of its more obvious manifestations.

Among those who saw the Bath production was Princess Amelia, the daughter of George II. The *Caledonian Mercury* reported on 25 June 1728 that she had attended *The Beggar's Opera* in Bath. A few months later, the same journal reported that she had paid another visit to the Parsonage Lane Theatre to see a play called *The Busy Body* on 14 September.

Despite the success of *The Beggar's Opera*, the Parsonage Lane Theatre continued to struggle for a few more years until it closed in 1736. This was partly because of plans to introduce a new law suppressing unlicensed playhouses, but mainly because the land was needed for the General Hospital – the pet project of Beau Nash and other leading citizens.

Head east past the Abbey and along the south side of the Orange Grove, before turning right into Terrace Walk, crossing the end of York Street and stopping outside the Huntsman pub, built in the 1740s as the Parade Coffee House. The fountain on the traffic island stands on the site of Bath's first Assembly Rooms, known as Simpson's Rooms, which opened in 1705. After the closure of the Parsonage Lane Theatre, a new theatre opened in the cellar of Simpson's Rooms. Despite the shortcomings of the Parsonage Lane Theatre, this was something of a retrograde step – as the use of the word 'cellar' indicates. Although the law suppressing unlicensed playhouses came into force in 1737, this theatre operated, according to John Wood, 'without the least molestation for more than ten years'. Plays seem to have been few and far between, however – although a French visitor managed to catch one when he visited Bath in 1750. He was not impressed:

> I have never told you how astonished I was to see your little theatre 40 feet under the ground. It is quite a pretty little catacomb, though naturally somewhat stunted in its proportions. But when the curtain went up, and the stage began to vomit forth the actors, I was reminded of the band of robbers in Gil Blas' cavern. Their manner of acting did not break the spell, nor even the young actress in male attire who appeared between the two pieces, and recited a complimentary address. Everything that the coarsest affectation could invent in the way of offensive grimaces to spoil a pretty face was successfully made use of by the little person; I was never more shocked.

There was an even less well-equipped theatre on Kingsmead Street where performances were staged sporadically from around 1723 to 1751. It later became a synagogue before being demolished in the nineteenth century. Kingsmead Street itself has virtually disappeared as well, being largely destroyed during bombing raids on 25-26 April 1942.

The reason these theatres were so rudimentary and so badly supported was that they were largely incidental to social life in Bath in the early eighteenth century – and not just because of competition from gambling. Defoe's observation – that 'the company here (not the actors) make the play' – takes us to the heart of what eighteenth-century Bath was like – and what makes it so alien to anything we would recognise today. Defoe's comment was true on several levels. On the most obvious level it meant that people showed off – in dress, in behaviour, by conspicuous consumption, and so on – as they still do today. The culture of celebrity is nothing new. On a more profound level, however, Defoe was alluding to the way in which society was governed by a series of codes and rituals to an almost unimaginable degree. While they may not have flocked to the theatre, they participated in what we would regard today as a series of highly ritualised charades. And within these charades was an astonishing range of theatrical or coded behaviours – in dress, deportment, speech and so on. People hired dancing masters to show them not only how to dance, but how to walk, how to hold their hats, and so on – and when they went to a ball, walked on the parades or attended the Pump Room they put what they had learned into practice.

Choreographing all this activity was Richard 'Beau' Nash. Barbeau describes how he 'arranged a succession of pleasures and pastimes which awaited the visitor when he rose in the morning, and led him on without fatigue to the end of the day. Every hour had its appointed occupation ... Private parties were voted unfashionable, and discontinued ... Occupations and amusements being thus established, the Master of the Ceremonies made them subject to a severe etiquette ... A reform in costume next engaged his attention.'

The most theatrical occasions were the balls in the Assembly Rooms. These started with minuets – the assembled company watched as the first couple danced; the lady was then conducted to her seat and the Master of Ceremonies led forth another lady for the man to dance with; then a second couple danced, and so it went on. This lasted about two hours – two hours of people watching other people performing. Only later, after a break, would the company reassemble to join in a series of country dances. Although this may sound unutterably tedious and repetitive – with the same procedure and often the same dancers featuring at every ball – the daily routine was no less rigid. Some found it tedious at the time – Fag, for example, in Sheridan's *The Rivals*:

> 'Tis a good lounge. In the morning we go to the Pump Room (though neither my master or I drink the waters); after breakfast we saunter on the parades or play a game at billiards; at night we dance but damn the place, I'm tired of it: their regular hours stupefy me.

The Rivals, though, was first performed in 1775. Beau Nash had been dead 14 years and attitudes were changing. In the first half of the century the rigid code of behavioural etiquette Nash imposed on Bath was almost universally welcomed. And it was because he was so successful in regulating Bath society that Bath became so popular.

Richard 'Beau' Nash

The reason people voluntarily submitted to being cast in what we might regard as a series of elaborate charades was because they saw themselves as being at the cutting edge of a social revolution – a revolution to create a 'polite society'. Although this may be a somewhat anachronistic term these days – and not one likely to be used without irony – there was nothing ironic about what Nash and his cohorts were up to.

The word 'polite' came from the word 'polished' and was, in the eighteenth century, interchangeable with it. The Earl of Shaftesbury explained that, in Bath, 'we polish one another and rub off our corners and sides by a sort of amicable collision.' The aim was conversation without constraint between people of different rank, religion, occupation or politics. At the beginning of the eighteenth century, this was a revolutionary idea. The barriers between different groups and classes of people were enormous. Within living memory, society had been torn apart by religious and political strife. Society was still very violent. Men wore swords as a matter of course and were only too ready to challenge each other to duels. Nash's ban on the wearing of swords in Bath was only part of his campaign to make Bath the epitome of polite society – a template for what could be done elsewhere. And in this he was, of course, helped because Bath was in many ways a blank canvas – an old and rather run-down city ripe for redevelopment and reform. He was also helped by it being a spa, a place where people were removed from their familiar environment and more likely to be open to new ideas. Lady Luxborough summed up Nash's aims succinctly: 'To promote society, good manners, and a coalition of parties and ranks; to suppress scandal and late hours, are his views.'

This belief in the value of good manners as the bedrock of civilised society continued long after Nash's death. In 1796, Edmund Burke wrote that:

> Manners are of more importance than laws … Manners are what vex or soothe, corrupt or purify, exalt or debase, barbarize or refine us, by a constant, steady, uniform, insensible operation like that of the air we breathe in.

The artificiality of Nash's 'polite kingdom' may to us appear shallow and superficial, but that superficiality was driven by conviction. It was important for people to get on with each other, by observing predetermined codes of conduct and having superficial conversations – the alternative was for them to have conversations that were not superficial, fall out with each other and spread dissension and dismay through the ranks.

It did not always work – there were plenty of unenlightened individuals around – but, when it did, Bath became what Nash intended, the epitome of polite society, with himself as director, and with stage sets provided by John Wood.[1] Nash was the greatest actor of all, so it is hardly surprising that when Dr Oliver wrote his obituary he should have ended it thus:

> His existence … was spun out to so great an age, that the man was sunk, like many former heroes, in the weakness and infirmities of exhausted nature; the unwilling tax all animals must pay for multiplicity of days. Over his closing scene, charity long spread her all covering mantle, and dropped the curtain, before the poor actor, though he played his part, was permitted to quit the stage.

Although the theatre was not a major part of the social scene during the early years of Nash's reign, by the mid-1740s attitudes were changing. This may have been partly due to the growing popularity of the London stage, but it was also due to a growing awareness of the role theatre could play in society. John Gay had shown what could be done in *The Beggars Opera*, using low-life characters to hold the mirror up to those at the other end of the social spectrum. At the end of the opera, a beggar tells the audience:

> Through the whole piece you may observe such a similitude of manners in high and low life, that it is difficult to determine whether (in the fashionable vices) the fine gentlemen imitate the gentlemen of the road, or the gentlemen of the road the fine gentlemen.

---

1 The stage-set analogy is pertinent – it was generally only the frontages of buildings that were designed by John Wood, like film sets, with the backs left to jobbing builders. What was important was the façade, not what lay behind it.

The realisation that the theatre could be a moral force had an obvious attraction for social reformers. One of the dominant eighteenth-century beliefs was that life and society could be improved by reason and intelligence. Just as rational architecture could inspire people to think more rationally, so watching plays in which the characters were rewarded or punished according to their actions could make them behave better themselves. This moral imperative became increasingly important as the century wore on. One of the most popular playwrights in the second half of the eighteenth century was Hannah More, who lived in Great Pulteney Street. She was an evangelical who campaigned against slavery and worked to improve the morals of the working classes. Another popular playwright was Hannah Cowley who turned the distinction between real life and the theatre on its head, claiming in the epilogue to *The Belle's Stratagem* of 1780, that, while people in society took refuge behind masks, on the stage they appeared as they really were:

> Should I show your features to each other,
> Not one amongst ye'd know his friend or brother.
> 'Tis plain, then, all the world, from youth to age,
> Appear in masks – Here, only, on the stage,
> You see us as we are: Here trust your eyes;
> Our wish to please, admits of no disguise.

To summarise – in the first half of the eighteenth century, people adopted quasi-theatrical personae to help create a polite society; in the latter half of the century, the theatre increasingly became a moral force, setting standards for thought, behaviour and conduct. That, at any rate, was the idea. As we shall see, things did not always work out like that in practice.

Walk along North Parade Passage (to the left of the Huntsman) and turn left into North Parade Buildings. Go down the ramp at the end and turn left through the covered alleyway by Marks & Spencer. Turn left at the end and left again into Old Orchard Street.[1] On the right-hand side of the street, you will see a large plaque indicating that this was Bath's first Theatre Royal. The idea for this theatre came from a Bristol actor called John Hippisley, who was fed up with the facilities on offer at Simpson's Rooms. In 1747, he sent a proposal 'to the nobility & gentry at Bath', asking for their support. He opened his appeal with an epigram –

> Plays are like mirrors made, for men to see
> How bad they are, how good they ought to be

– before going on to explain why Bath needed a new theatre:

1 If the alleyway by Marks & Spencer is closed, carry on along Abbeygate Street, turn left into Stall Street, left again into New Orchard Street and then left into Old Orchard Street.

Theatrical performances, when conducted with decency and regularity, have always been esteem'd the most rational amusements, by the polite and thinking part of mankind. Strangers, therefore, must be greatly surpris'd to find at Bath entertainments of this sort in no better perfection than they are, as it is a place, during its seasons, honour'd with so great a number of persons, eminent for politeness, judgement and taste; and where might reasonably be expected (next to London) the best theatre in England … The present playhouse, or rather play room, is so small and incommodious, that 'tis almost impossible to have things better done in it than they are … And nothing can be more disagreeable, than for persons of the first quality, and those of the lowest rank, to be seated on the same bench together, which must be the case here, if the former will honour and the latter have an inclination, to see a play.

The proposal was received enthusiastically, with Beau Nash among its main supporters. Unfortunately, Hippisley died a few months later, but John Palmer, a wealthy brewer from Southgate Street, stepped in to bring the plans to fruition.

The theatre opened on 27 Oct 1750 with a performance of *Henry IV Part 1*. The theatre in Simpson's Rooms limped on for another five years in unequal competition, until Beau Nash weighed in on the side of the

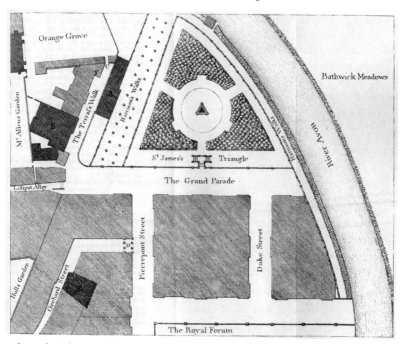

A map by John Wood from around 1750 showing the theatre in Orchard Street and the two sets of Assembly Rooms on either side of Terrace Walk. Those on the right had a theatre in the cellar.

THE BATH STAGE IN THE EIGHTEENTH CENTURY

new theatre and the old one was bought out and closed. In 1764, John Palmer handed over the management of the theatre to his son, John Palmer Jr, who remodelled it with a magnificent dome featuring Apollo and the muses in relief. Unfortunately, this had an adverse effect on the acoustics, while the lack of ventilation made the building stifling. Nevertheless, he was determined to make it the best provincial theatre in England, scouring the country for talented actors and persuading them to come to Bath. In 1768, he applied for a royal warrant and it became the first Theatre Royal outside London.

On play nights, the theatre opened at around four o'clock when servants arrived to reserve seats for their employers. This was not only sanctioned but encouraged by the management. Playbills announced that 'ladies and gentlemen are desired to send their servants to keep places by half an hour after four o'clock'. There was a pub across the road called the Pineapple (now a Spiritualist church), and no doubt the servants took full advantage of it, sending each other across for drinks while they looked after their seats.

John Brewer, writing of the London stage in the eighteenth century, gives an idea of the shenanigans that preceded the performance:

> During the hour before the curtain rose, the theatre was filled by what a bemused German visitor, von Archenholz, called 'noise and bombardment'; the audience chatted, cheered and sang, threw fruit at one another, flirted and preened themselves. A few years earlier James Boswell, waiting with a Scottish friend for a Drury Lane performance to begin, 'entertained the audience prodigiously by imitating the lowing of a cow'. As he later proudly remarked, 'I was so successful in this boyish frolic that the universal cry of the galleries was "Encore the cow! Encore the cow!"'

Theatres were also associated with vice and prostitution. As late as 1819, when society was a good deal more refined than it was in the mid-eighteenth century, Walter Scott explained why he did not want to write for the stage:

> I do not think the character of the audience in London is such that one could have the least pleasure in pleasing them. One half come to prosecute their debaucheries, so openly that it would degrade a bagnio [while] another set snooze off their beef-steaks and port wine.

In the green room, at the side of the stage, actors and their guests would mingle before the performance began. When it was about to start, these favoured guests would take their seats at the side of the stage. Richer members of the audience, with reserved boxes, would also begin to turn up, although many of them would continue to trickle in, with all the disruption this entailed, long after the start of the performance.

Hogarth's *Laughing Audience* of 1733

Some of the servants who had been sent on early to keep seats for their employers were still there when the play started. When, as generally happened, they got bored, they would act up, shouting to their friends or making a nuisance of themselves. When their employers eventually turned up, they would often make an impressive entrance, upstaging the actors and making sure they were seen.

It was a much more intimate – and much more public – space than we are used to today. People went to the theatre as much to be seen as to see – take, for instance, the description of Catherine Morland's visit to the Orchard Street Theatre in *Northanger Abbey*, where she sits in a box opposite Henry Tilney. The theatre was lit by candles, which dripped tallow onto members of audience and could not be dimmed during the performance, so the audience was as brightly lit as the actors. The atmosphere was like that of a comedy club, with people entering and leaving. Actors often ad-libbed, and banter and heckling were commonplace. Sometimes things turned nasty. On 20 November 1788, for example, a notice appeared in the *Bath Chronicle* offering a reward for information on the persons who had thrown stones from the gallery onto the stage and into the pit 'by which two gentlemen were materially injured'.

An evening's performance lasted for three or four hours. First there would be an overture played by the orchestra, then came the main play

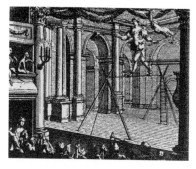

or opera. This was followed by an interlude (music or dancing), then a shorter afterpiece. Afterpieces were generally comic and included circus-style tricks. Although many actors and managers disliked this lighter fare, they had to bow to commercial pressures. On occasion, some of them did draw the line, however. Garrick, for example, refused to allow tightrope walkers to perform at Drury Lane. At Bath, however, tightrope walking was staple fare. On New Years Day 1784, the play *The*

Earl of Essex, was followed by an interlude called *The Enchanted Wood* and 'rope dancing and tumbling'. In January 1786, Massinger's *A New Way to Pay Old Debts* was followed by *Tom Thumb the Great* – and tightrope dancers and tumblers. In November 1783, a tragedy called *Mahomet* was followed by rope dancing and tumbling and the musical farce *Rosina*. A few weeks later both *Macbeth* and *King Lear* were followed by rope dancing and tumbling.

Christopher Anstey in his *New Guide to Bath* included a description of a typical playgoer about town:

> What sends Peter Tewksbury every night
> To the play with such infinite joy and delight?
> Why Peter's a critic, with true attic salt,
> Can damn the performers, can hiss, and find fault,
> And tell when we ought to express approbation,
> By thumping, and clapping, and vociferation;
> So he gains our attention, and all must admire
> Young Tewksbury's judgement, his spirit and fire.

A letter from Richard Graves to Robert Dodsley on the reception of Dodsley's play *Cleone* in Bath in March 1759 gives an idea what the actors were up against:

> It was represented to a crowded audience – and I think the principal parts were well performed. I fixed myself ... in the centre of the pit – in the midst of young milliners & abigails – where I had the pleasure of observing the effect of your genius upon undisguis'd humanity ... I had the satisfaction of silencing (with a single hiss) one or two fellows who ... were clamorously rallying Mrs Bri..as & two or three more very pretty women upon their amiable sensibility.

Despite these distractions, the actors who won the public's affection came to enjoy celebrity status, and intense interest in their private lives. Theatrical biography became a major genre. The attitude towards actresses was often similar to that towards high-class courtesans, and they were pursued, often successfully, by rakes and roués. In the 1760s, James Boswell took advantage of a Covent Garden actress who was down on her luck and in need of a 'friend'. 'A more voluptuous night I never enjoyed,' he wrote later in his diary, 'five times was I fairly lost in supreme rapture.' He soon came to regret his night on the town, however, when he discovered that he had been 'clapped', and demanded the return of the money he had – he claimed – loaned to the unfortunate woman.

There are many anecdotes about actors at Bath's Theatre Royal in the eighteenth century – here are just a couple that catch the flavour of the times:

On 21 November 1778, John Henderson, one of the most celebrated actors in eighteenth-century Bath, was playing Falstaff in *Henry IV Part I*. On the previous Wednesday, in the early hours of the morning, the Vicomte du Barry, a French nobleman who was staying in the Royal Crescent, had fallen out with his friend Count Rice over a game of cards. They hired a coach from the Three Tuns in Stall Street and went to Claverton Down, where Rice shot du Barry dead in a duel. At the end of Act 5 Scene 1 of *Henry IV Part I*, on the eve of the Battle of Shrewsbury, Prince Hal addresses Falstaff:

> *Prince:* Say thy prayers, and farewell.
> *Falstaff:* I would 'twere bedtime, Hal, and all well.
> *Prince:* Why, thou owest God a death.   *[Prince exits]*
> *Falstaff:* 'Tis not due yet: I would be loath to pay him before his day. What need I be so forward with him that calls not on me? Well, 'tis no matter; honour pricks me on. Yea, but how if honour prick me off when I come on? How then? Can honour set to a leg? No. Or an arm? No. Or take away the grief of a wound? No. Honour hath no skill in surgery then? No. What is honour? A word. What is in that word honour? What is that honour? Air – a trim reckoning! Who hath it? ...

Henderson paused and turned to the audience before continuing …

> He that died a Wednesday ... Doth he feel it? No. Doth he hear it? No. 'Tis insensible then? Yea, to the dead.

The effect on the audience can be imagined. Many people thought he had adapted Shakespeare's words. He had not. They were the original words – used to devastating effect.

In 1776, Henderson was performing at Birmingham alongside a young actress called Sarah Siddons. She had already appeared at Drury Lane, but had not gone down well. Her contract had been terminated and she joined a company touring the provinces. Henderson was so impressed with her, however, that he persuaded Palmer to take her on. Palmer was initially reluctant, and it was two years before she made her Bath debut in 1778 at the age of 23. A few weeks later, when she appeared in *Percy* by Hannah More, the review in the *Bath Chronicle* declared that 'Mrs Siddons' performance in the tragedy of *Percy* has established her, in the judgement of the town, as the most capital actress that has performed here these many years.' She never looked back, and four years later left Bath to make a triumphant return to the London stage.

Her farewell performance was on 21 May 1782 in *The Distressed Mother*. At the end of the performance she delivered a speech composed especially for the occasion:

The time draws nigh when I must bid adieu
To this delightful spot – nay ev'n to you –
To you, whose fost'ring kindness rear'd my name,
O'erlooked my faults, but magnified my fame ...
Why don't I here, you'll say, content remain,
Nor seek uncertainties for certain gain?
What can compensate for the risks you run;
And what your reasons? – Surely you have none.
To argue here would but your time abuse:
I keep my word – my reason I produce –

At which point, her three small children walked onto the stage. She continued:

These are the moles that bear me from your side;
Where I was rooted – where I could have died.
Stand forth, ye elves, and plead your mother's cause;
Ye little magnets, whose soft influence draws
Me from a point where every gentle breeze
Wafted my bark to happiness and ease –
Sends me adventurous on a larger main,
In hopes that you may profit by my gain.
Have I been hasty? – am I then to blame;
Answer, all ye who own a parent's name? ...

Farewell speeches do not come more powerful than that – and there is unlikely to have been a dry eye in the house. Sarah Siddons was not only a great actress; she also managed to resist the stereotyping many other actresses succumbed to. She achieved this by giving her family life – and her role as a mother – a high profile, as well as by refusing roles likely to compromise her image. In the process, she also became a model for virtuous womanhood, turning the customary view of actresses on its head. Not only was the theatre coming to be seen as a morally edifying force, its more illustrious practitioners were being held up as paragons of virtue.

Gainsborough's portrait of Sarah Siddons

The Orchard Street Theatre was redesigned and enlarged by another John Palmer, a Bath-based architect, in 1774. The original theatre was set a little way back from the street – the frontage you see today dates from the 1774 rebuilding. The auditorium was also enlarged and 25 feet were added at the rear to provide an entrance lobby and seven new boxes. The stage was remodelled in classical style, and new boxes built on either side, replacing the seats on the stage. An orchestra pit was added, creating a 'buffer zone' of several feet between the actors and the audience.

Some years later, Palmer persuaded the council to build a coach road from St James's Street to the theatre, with parking for around 50 coaches. This was necessary because the fashionable new developments in the upper town were a considerable distance from the theatre. The new road was at a lower level than the theatre and was reached by a flight of steps.

Despite all these improvements, the size of the theatre and its distance from the upper town led to plans for a new and much grander theatre on the other side of town, which opened in 1805. Four years later, the old theatre was converted to a Catholic chapel. The Catholics stayed until 1863 when St John's church opened. Two years later the old theatre became a Masonic lodge, which it still is today. There are regular guided tours of the building – one of the most fascinating in the city – and, despite not having been a theatre for over two centuries, the stage still survives, together with one of the boxes.

A sedan chairman waits for custom outside the Theatre Royal in Orchard Street around 1790. The steps down to the coach park can be seen on the right.

Carry on along Old Orchard Street, following it round to the right and stopping just before the archway outside Linley House. The story that follows will demonstrate how blurred the distinction between real life and that portrayed on the stage could become in the eighteenth century.

By the late 1760s, Thomas Linley, who lived in this house, was the most influential musician and impresario in Bath. Like Leopold Mozart, he drove his children to become child prodigies, and his daughter Elizabeth, although still in her teens, was already a celebrated singer.

In September 1770, Thomas Sheridan, a former actor and elocutionist arrived in Bath and settled in Kingsmead Street. With him was his son Richard. On 13 October 1770, Richard Sheridan wrote to a friend:

> There is a Mr Linley here, a music master, who has a daughter that sings like an angel … the father too sings in a particular natural style … The public concerts do not begin till after Xmas, but we heard them at a private one in Mr Linley's House.

That December, Elizabeth became engaged to a Mr Long, a wealthy landowner. He was 60 years old – she was 16. A few months later, she broke off the engagement, but despite this Mr Long presented her with

money and jewels – possibly in the hope she would change her mind. At this stage a married man called Captain Mathews appeared on the scene in hot pursuit of Elizabeth, and spreading the rumour that she was his mistress. It was a rumour many were prepared to accept. Elizabeth was distraught.

The intrigue surrounding her was soon the hottest piece of celebrity gossip not only in Bath but in London as well. She was often known as the Maid of Bath and on 26 June 1771 a play with that title opened at the Little Theatre in the Haymarket. Written by Samuel Foote, with a prologue by Garrick, it portrayed

Elizabeth Linley by Gainsborough

a Miss Linnet being pursued by a rich old man (played by Foote) and a Captain Mathews figure. And, in case anyone was in any doubt as to what the play was about, that week's *Bath Chronicle* carried an announcement assuring readers that it was 'based on fact'. Three weeks later, the Lord Chamberlain applied to prevent any further performances of the play because of its 'personality', but by then the harm had been done.

On 18 March 1772, Elizabeth Linley fled to France with Richard Sheridan. She planned to enter a convent, believing at this stage that Sheridan was merely rescuing her from an impossible situation. Among those vexed by this turn of events was Thomas Gainsborough. 'Miss Linley is walk'd off sure enough with young Sheridan,' he wrote, 'but he is not at the bottom of the mischief ... Mathews is the scoundrel supposed (and with much reason) to have undone the poor girl – it vexes me much ... because I was just finishing her picture for the exhibition.'

Mathews attempted to save his reputation, such as it was, by placing a notice in the *Bath Chronicle*:

> Mr Richard S having attempted, in a letter left behind him for that purpose, to account for his scandalous method of running away from this place, by insinuations derogating from my character, and that of a young lady, innocent as far as relates to me, or my knowledge, since which he has neither taken any notice of letters, or even informed his own family of the place where he had hid himself; I can no longer think he deserves the treatment of a gentleman, than in this public method, as a L[iar] and a treacherous S[coundrel].

Sheridan, meanwhile, waited until he got to France to inform Elizabeth of his true intentions. According to his sister,

> he told her he could not be content to leave her in a convent unless she consented to a previous marriage, which all along had been the object of his hopes, and she must be aware that after the step she had taken, she could not appear in England but as his wife.

She consented, but, as they were both minors, the marriage was invalid.

Her father tracked the couple down and persuaded them to return to England. When they arrived back, they went their separate ways – Elizabeth to Bath and Sheridan to London – and the marriage was kept secret. When Sheridan learned what Mathews had printed in the *Chronicle*, however, he challenged him to a duel. They met in Hyde Park, but found it too crowded and changed the venue to a tavern in Covent Garden. After dropping his sword, Mathews was forced to beg for his life. He agreed to apologise and signed a retraction of the article. After this was published, however, Mathews challenged Sheridan to another duel, which was fought at Kingsdown near Bath on 1 July. Despite breaking their swords, both men carried on fighting 'in a desperate struggle for life and honour'. This time, Sheridan came off worst, being 'borne from the field with a portion of his antagonist's weapon sticking through an ear, his breast-bone touched, his whole body covered with wounds and blood, and his face nearly beaten to jelly with the hilt of Mathews' sword'. He was taken to the White Hart Inn in Stall Street and lay seriously ill for some days.

He eventually recovered and, staying in Bath, continued his clandestine courtship of Elizabeth. If you look over the southern parapet of North Parade Bridge, you can see the seat – known as Delia's Grotto – where, so legend has it, they left hidden messages for each other. In the eighteenth century, it was in a secluded spot at the end of a riverside walk.

On 13 April 1773, Elizabeth and Sheridan married in London with her father's consent. Sheridan decided to try his hand at playwriting and, on 17 January 1775, *The Rivals* was premiered at Covent Garden. It was a disaster, with the audience showing its disapproval in the way only eighteenth-century audiences could. The actor playing Sir Lucius O'Trigger, on being hit by a well-aimed apple, exclaimed, 'By the powers. Is it personal?' The play was withdrawn, rewritten and restaged to become one of the best-known comedies in the repertoire.

The Rivals is imbued with the spirit of Bath in the late eighteenth century. Barbeau's assessment of it, written in 1904, underlines how blurred were the borders between life and art in the world Sheridan moved in:

> The very artificiality of the characters brings them into harmony with the essentially artificial society they represent. If sometimes they seem to reflect the brilliance of the footlights rather than that of the sun, to be playing a part rather than living, this does not make them false and unreal. For the candles of the Assembly Rooms were a good deal like footlights, and the actual Bath was a stage on which a perpetual comedy was enacted. To transfer it to the boards, Sheridan had no need to falsify it; he simply sketched the outline, and filled in the colours of his original.

The marriage of Sheridan and Elizabeth Linley, and the success of *The Rivals*, might seem a fitting conclusion to this tale of intrigue and tribulation. But just as the happy ending of *The Barber of Seville* is a curtain raiser to the intrigues of *The Marriage of Figaro*, this is not the end of the story. And this is where things get really bizarre.

In 1774, Thomas Linley – Elizabeth's father – moved from Bath to take up an appointment at Drury Lane. After the success of *The Rivals*, Linley agreed to provide some of the music for a comic opera called *The Duenna* with a libretto by Sheridan. Sheridan, however, did not let Linley see the libretto – fobbing him off with various excuses – but only the words to some of the songs. The reason for this became clear when the opera was eventually performed in November 1775 – its theme was the duping of two fathers whose plans to marry their daughters off to rich suitors were frustrated when they ran off with their lovers. *The Duenna* was an instant hit. Over the next 25 years, it became England's most performed opera. Byron declared it the 'best opera ever written' and Dr Johnson called it 'one of the two best comedies of the age'.

It is at this point that Samuel Foote comes back into the story. Sheridan's newly-found celebrity prompted Foote to return to the subject of Elizabeth Linley and her elopement with Sheridan in a play called *The Trip to Calais*. This included a character called Kitty Crocodile, based on one of the eighteenth century's most notorious celebrities, Elizabeth Pierrepont, Duchess of Kingston. One of her most outrageous publicity stunts was attending a masquerade ball in the character of Iphigenia. Elizabeth Montagu commented that her 'dress, or rather undress, was remarkable, she was Iphigenia for the sacrifice, but so naked, the high priest might easily inspect the entrails of the victim'. Her husband, the Duke of Kingston, owned the whole of this part of Bath, and gave his name to Pierrepont Street. He also gave his name to his wife, although she was generally known by her maiden name, Elizabeth Chudleigh – and with good reason.

When Foote wrote *The Trip to Calais* she was facing trial for bigamy, which is why he included her in the play. When she found out, a venomous exchange of letters between Foote and the Duchess appeared in the press, and eventually she persuaded the Lord Chamberlain to ban the play. The Duchess's case was not helped by Foote's intervention. She was convicted of bigamy in April 1776 and, only managing to evade corporal punishment because of her rank, fled to the continent. Her cause was taken up by the Rev William Jackson, her personal secretary and the editor of a publication called *The Public Ledger*. He included attacks on Foote in the *Ledger*, alluding to his alleged homosexuality, and published a satirical pamphlet entitled *Sodom & Onan*. This was a thinly-veiled account of Foote's homosexual encounters, and, in case anyone was in any doubt who Jackson was referring to, he placed a picture of Foote on the cover. Foote sued for libel and won, but then the Duchess re-entered the fray by instituting legal proceedings against him for sodomy. Although several witnesses – including one of Foote's servants – testified against him, his connections led to his acquittal. During his trial, he rewrote the banned *Trip to Calais* as *The Capuchin*, taking out Kitty Crocodile but including a new character based on Jackson, called Dr Viper.[1] The play was subsequently performed to great acclaim before members of the royal family.

But to return – briefly – to Mr and Mrs Sheridan, and to that unhappy ending hinted at earlier. Sheridan quickly tired of Elizabeth. He forbade her from singing in public and was serially unfaithful to her. She died of tuberculosis on 28 June 1792 after 'a long and lingering

---

1 At one time it was believed that Dr Viper was a portrait of Philip Thicknesse, the subject of our fourth walk – a biography of Thicknesse by Philip Gosse published in 1952 was actually called *Dr Viper* – but recent research indicates that Foote had Jackson in mind.

illness' at Hotwells in Bristol. She was just 38 years old. Sheridan lived for another 24 years, giving up the theatre to become a successful politician, before dying in poverty. His obituary in the *Times*, after listing his achievements, ended with an extraordinary attack:

> Never were such gifts as those which Providence showered upon Mr Sheridan so abused – never were talents so miserably perverted. The term 'greatness' has been most ridiculously applied to one who, to speak charitably of him, was the weakest of men.

He was spared a pauper's grave, however. His funeral in Westminster Abbey was attended by dukes, earls, lords, viscounts and luminaries of the theatrical and political worlds. He was laid to rest in Poets' Corner, between the monuments to Shakespeare and Addison and near the grave of Garrick.

As you **walk under the archway into Pierrepont Street**, look across to Century House, where a plaque commemorates the actor James Quin, who lived here between 1751 and 1766. It was unveiled in 1905 by Sir Henry Irving. **Turn left along Pierrepont Street and left again along North Parade. Continue along North Parade Passage to the Crystal Palace pub on Abbey Green.** Quin may have lived in Pierrepont Street, but – as you will recall from the first walk – he held court at the Three Tuns Inn in Stall Street. The Crystal Palace, once a lodging house attached to the inn, is all that is left of it. Quin retired to Bath after a glittering career in London and is buried in the abbey. Although he never performed on stage in Bath, his larger-than-life personality made him one of the best-known celebrities in the city.

Sir Henry Irving unveiling the plaque to James Quin in Pierrepont Street

He was born in London in 1693 to an Irish father, and educated in Dublin. From the start, he was something of an eighteenth-century Oliver Reed, except that Oliver Reed would not have got away with half the things Quin did. In 1718 he was convicted of manslaughter for killing another actor in a duel. As he had been provoked, however, he was acquitted. In 1735, he killed another actor by stabbing him in the eye with a cane during a quarrel over a wig. This time he was charged with murder. After several well-connected character witnesses came forward, the charge was reduced to manslaughter and again he was acquitted. On another occasion, John Rich, the manager of the theatre he was performing in, was attacked by a drunken nobleman sitting at the side of the stage. Quin stepped in and saved his life, but a riot subsequently ensued. He had a gargantuan appetite for both food and drink and allegedly topped the scales at over 20 stone, but turned this to his advantage by becoming the most celebrated Falstaff of his generation.

After a quarrel with John Rich, the story goes that he came down to Bath in a pique, expecting to be quickly recalled. He sent Rich a terse letter: 'I am in Bath – Quin'. The reply came back: 'Stay there and be dead – Rich'. Which he did – although he was determined to enjoy his early retirement as much as possible first. It was he who came up with the immortal line, 'I know of no better place than Bath for an old cock to roost in.' A semi-fictionalised reminiscence of Quin appears in Tobias Smollett's *Humphrey Clinker*, in a letter written by Jeremy Melford, whose uncle, Matthew Bramble, is an old friend of Quin's:

> My uncle ... has discovered some old friends, among the invalids of Bath; and, in particular, renewed his acquaintance with the celebrated James Quin, who certainly did not come here to drink water ... My uncle and he are perfectly agreed in their estimate of life; which Quin says, would stink in his nostrils, if he did not steep it in claret ... I took the liberty to differ in opinion from Mr Bramble, when he observed, that the mixture of people in the entertainments of this place was destructive of all order and urbanity; that it rendered the plebeians insufferably arrogant and troublesome, and vulgarized the deportment and sentiments of those who moved in the upper spheres of life. He said such a preposterous coalition would bring us into contempt with all our neighbours; and was worse, in fact, than debasing the gold coin of the nation. I argued, on the contrary, that those plebeians who discovered such eagerness to imitate the dress and equipage of their superiors, would likewise, in time, adopt their maxims and their manners, be polished by their conversation, and refined by their example; but when I appealed to Mr Quin, and asked if he did not think that such an unreserved mixture would improve the whole mass? 'Yes (said he) as a plate of marmalade would improve a pan of sirreverence' [1]

1 So much for Nash's vision of a polite society – 'sirreverence' was a euphemism for excrement.

James Quin by Hogarth

I had hopes of seeing Quin, in his hours of elevation at the tavern which is the temple of mirth and good fellowship, where he, as priest of Comus, utters the inspirations of wit and humour – I have had that satisfaction. I have dined with his club at the Three Tuns, and had the honour to sit him out. At half an hour past eight in the evening, he was carried home with six good bottles of claret under his belt; and it being then Friday, he gave orders that he should not be disturbed till Sunday at noon – You must not imagine that this dose had any other effect upon his conversation, but that of making it more extravagantly entertaining – He had lost the use of his limbs, indeed, several hours before we parted, but he retained all his other faculties in perfection; and as he gave vent to every whimsical idea as it rose, I was really astonished at the brilliancy of his thoughts, and the force of his expression.

All this is put into the mouth of an impressionable and rather naïve young man, and not everyone was so charitably disposed towards Quin. Samuel Derrick, who was Bath's Master of Ceremonies from 1761 to 1769 – and appears as such in *Humphrey Clinker* – lampooned him in a vitriolic poem that proposed an alternative reason for his retirement to Bath:

> When Quin of all grace and all dignity void,
> Murdered Cato the Censor, and Brutus destroyed,
> He strutted, he mouth'd; you no passion could trace
> In his action, delivery, or plum-pudding face;
> When he massacred Comus the gay god of mirth
> He was suffered because we of actors had dearth.
> But when Foote with strong judgment, and true genuine wit
> Upon all his peculiar absurdities hit;
> When Garrick arose, with those talents and fire,
> Which nature and all the nine muses inspire,
> Poor Guts was neglected, or laughed off the stage
> So bursting with envy and tortured with rage;
> He damn'd the whole town in a fury and fled,
> Little Bayes[1] an extinguisher clapp'd on his head.
> Yet we never shall Falstaff behold so well done,
> With such character, humour, such spirit, such fun,
> So great that we knew not which most to admire,
> Glutton, parasite, pander, pimp, lecher, or liar;
> He felt as he spoke, nature's dictates are true
> When he acted the part, his own picture he drew.

1 One of Garrick's most celebrated roles was as Bayes in *The Rehearsal* by Buckingham.

But, as Quin had opposed Derrick's appointment as Master of Ceremonies, he was hardly impartial.[1] The epitaph on Quin's memorial in Bath Abbey, written by Garrick, offers a mellower view of one of Bath's more colourful characters:

> That tongue which set the table on a roar
> And charmed the public ear is heard no more.
> Closed are those eyes, the harbingers of wit,
> Which spake before the tongue what Shakespeare writ.
> Cold is that hand which living was stretched forth
> At friendship's call to succor modest worth.
> Here lies James Quin, deign readers to be taught
> Whate'er thy strength of body, force of thought,
> In Nature's happiest mood however cast,
> To this complexion thou must come at last.

The Three Tuns has another – albeit somewhat indirect – theatrical connection. In 1778, John Palmer Jr, who held the lease of the Theatre Royal, obtained the lease of the theatre in King Street, Bristol, applied and was granted a royal warrant for it, and operated it in tandem with the theatre in Bath. This stretched the resources of both theatres, and, to expedite the transfer of actors, stagehands, musicians and props, he established a private stagecoach service between the two. He also ran coaches between Bath and London as required, to take him up to town on business or to bring actors down to Bath. This dedicated coach service worked so well, it occurred to him that perhaps the idea could be adapted for the Royal Mail. He presented the idea to the government, it was adopted, and the first mailcoach between Bristol and London called at the Three Tuns in Bath on 2 August 1784. Like Ralph Allen before him, John Palmer Jr went on to make a fortune from revolutionising the postal service. He sold his interest in the theatre two years later, in 1786, before going on to become Mayor and MP for Bath.

Go through the archway on the south side of Abbey Green and turn right along Abbeygate Street. At the end, turn right into Stall Street and then left along Beau Street to the Hot Bath. During the period between the demolition of Bath's first theatre in Parsonage Lane and the building of the Orchard Street Theatre, the inadequacies of the cellar under Simpson's Rooms led to at least two inns being used to stage plays. One of them, the George, stood where Hot Bath Street now runs. On 4 April 1748, the *Bath Journal* announced that:

---

1 Quin was not the only one opposed to the appointment of Derrick, a somewhat insalubrious character best known as the editor of *Harris's List of Covent Garden Ladies*, an annual directory of prostitutes working in the capital.

This evening *The Fair Penitent* with *Miss in her Teens* will be acted at the George for the benefit of Mr & Mrs Kennedy, being the last time of performing here.

This was not lightweight entertainment. *The Fair Penitent* by Nicholas Rowe was a tragedy praised highly by Dr Johnson, while *Miss in her Teens*, although a farce, was by none other than David Garrick. The George closed in 1798 and was demolished four years later.

Head north along Hot Bath Street, past the Cross Bath and on through St Michael's Place into Westgate Street. Cross the street, turn right, take the second left along Parsonage Lane and stop under the archway at the end. The site of the Parsonage Lane Theatre was on the right. It was built by George Trim, a wealthy clothier and member of the corporation, who also built Trim Street, which you can see ahead of you. In the early eighteenth century, this was the unfashionable end of town, at some distance from the Grove and the Pump Room. Although Queen Square had been built by the time the theatre closed in 1736, raising the profile of this area considerably, the site was needed for the General Hospital. The theatre that eventually replaced it, in Orchard Street, was much closer to the heart of what had been fashionable Bath in the early part of the eighteenth century. Even by 1750, however, it was losing ground to the Upper Town. Two decades later, the building of the Royal Crescent and the opening of the New Assembly Rooms shifted the balance decisively, leaving the theatre at the wrong end of town. When a new theatre was opened in 1805 it was only a stone's throw from the one that had stood in Parsonage Lane.

Cross the road and head down Trim Street, following it round to the left and carrying on to Beauford Square. This square, dating from the 1730s, was chosen as the site of the new Theatre Royal. There were buildings on only three sides – the fourth looked across to Beau Nash's old house on the corner of the Sawclose, which had come down in the world somewhat since he lived there, making the site ideal for a major building project. The façade of the new Theatre Royal was designed by George Dance, a London architect, but the work, along with much of the internal design, was carried out by John Palmer, the local architect who had redesigned the old Theatre Royal in 1774.

The new Theatre Royal opened on 12 October 1805, with a performance of *Richard III*. Bizarrely, the leading role was taken not by one of the top actors of the day but by someone who appeared on the playbill simply as 'a gentleman' – and proved sadly unfit for the task. There were three entrances to the theatre – the entrance for those arriving by carriage was in the Sawclose (where the main entrance is now), the entrance for those arriving by sedan chair was here in Beauford Square, and the entrance to the pit and gallery was in St John's Place. A century after its first theatre had opened in Parsonage Lane, the city now had one of the finest and most up-to-date theatres in the country, but by the time it opened Bath's star was already on the wane. As this walk deals with the Georgian theatre, what was to happen to the Theatre Royal later in the nineteenth century is another story – a story of declining audiences, crises and eventual renaissance. There is one part of the story that we cannot ignore, however – and for that we need to **head west out of Beauford Square, left into Princes Street and left again along Monmouth Street to the Egg Theatre on the corner of St John's Place.**

At one time, there was a pub on this corner. Originally known as the Bolt & Tun, it was renamed the Theatre Tavern when the Theatre Royal opened in 1805. In 1843 it was described as a 'well-accustomed, home-brewed inn & tavern with spacious yard and stabling'. On the morning of Good Friday 1862, the landlord of the Theatre Tavern heard a peculiar crackling sound outside, which he took to be rain. When the noise grew more persistent, he went into the yard to investigate, and was horrified to see smoke billowing from a window in the theatre. He raised the alarm, but, by the time the fire brigade arrived, it was too late. Before long, the theatre was gutted. The cause of the blaze was never established, but, as the building had not been used since the previous Wednesday, it was thought that a spark from a flue in the brewery, which backed onto the theatre, was almost certainly to blame.

Ironically, the Theatre Tavern was largely untouched by the fire and stayed open till 1888, when its licence was revoked. Shortly afterwards it was pulled down to make way for St Paul's Parish Hall and Church House – now home to the Egg Theatre.

Walk along St John's Place to the Sawclose and the entrance to the Theatre Royal. The last play to be performed at the Theatre Royal before it burned down was *Peep O'Day*. This was about a member of a band of Irish Protestant rebels (known as 'peep o'day men' because of their habit of visiting the houses of their enemies at dawn). It was the first time a play had been staged at the Theatre Royal during Holy Week, and many saw the fire as a judgement by the Almighty on its blasphemous proprietors.

Be that as it may, the theatre was rebuilt and reopened less than a year later with a production of *A Midsummer Night's Dream*, starring a 16-year-old Ellen Terry as the Queen of the Fairies. But, if the proprietors

The Peep O'Day which once stood opposite the Theatre Royal

thought that Shakespeare's magic would dispel the memory of the terrible fire, they had not counted on the tenant of the building at the top of New Westgate Buildings who, to celebrate the reopening of the theatre, opened a beerhouse called the Peep O'Day. To have had your theatre burnt down by one pub was bad enough. To have the event celebrated by the opening of another was really rubbing salt into the wound. Although the Peep O'Day beerhouse closed in 1906, the Peep O'Day fish and chip shop continued to operate from the premises for several more years.

The entrance and façade of the Theatre Royal was completely revamped, as part of a £3M refurbishment in 2010. It is not the only theatre on the Sawclose, however. Opposite, the Gala Bingo Hall occupies the former Palace Theatre, built in 1886 as the Pavilion Music Hall. A little further down is the back entrance to Komedia, a comedy, music and cabaret venue which opened in 2008 in the former Beau Nash Cinema.

Although that brings us right up to date, we will finish with one last look at the past. Just down from the corner where the Peep O'Day once stood, **go through an archway to the courtyard at the heart of the Seven Dials development**. Although it is modern, its ground plan replicates with uncanny accuracy the layout of an inn that once occupied the site. The first reference to it dates from 1717, when it was known as the Londonderry Inn. It was later renamed the Globe and, prior to the opening of the Orchard Street Theatre, plays were staged here. In 1747, for example, the *Bath Journal* announced that

> the Bath Company of Comedians have taken the Great Room at the Globe, without Westgate ... They intend to perform on Monday next the tragedy of *Theodosius, or the Force of Love*; with the entertainment of *Miss in her Teens, or the Medley of Lovers*, as it is now at the Theatre Royal, Covent Garden, London.

Other plays given at the Globe that season included *The Distressed Mother, Oroonoko, The Lying Valet, Jane Shore, Tamerlane, An Old Man Taught Wisdom, Othello* and *The Honest Yorkshireman*. The Globe closed around 1770 although part of it later reopened as the Seven Dials. The Seven Dials closed in 1926 and was demolished in 1931, only for its name to be resurrected when the site was redeveloped. The new Seven Dials has another connection with the theatre – a fountain (now filled with soil) installed in 1990 and encircled by sixteen bronze plaques, each bearing the palm prints, signatures and names of actors who appeared at the Theatre Royal while it was being installed. They include Derek Jacobi, Frank Finlay, Lionel Blair, Juliet Mills, Pauline Collins, Susan Hampshire, Joan Collins, Peter Ustinov, Richard Briers, Nigel Hawthorne, Michael Horden, Hayley Mills, Edward Fox, Maureen Lipman, Paul Eddington and Penelope Keith. One day, perhaps – assuming this monument to transience survives – a latter-day literary pilgrim may look at these names, as remote from him or her as Henderson, Garrick, Quin, Siddons and Sheridan are from us, and try to imagine what it was like to visit the theatre in Bath in the late twentieth century. For the moment, though, in the words of Prospero,

> Our revels now are ended. These our actors,
> As I foretold you, were all spirits and
> Are melted into air, into thin air:
> And, like the baseless fabric of this vision,
> The cloud-capp'd towers, the gorgeous palaces,
> The solemn temples, the great globe itself,
> Yea all which it inherit, shall dissolve
> And, like this insubstantial pageant faded,
> Leave not a rack behind. We are such stuff
> As dreams are made on, and our little life
> Is rounded with a sleep.

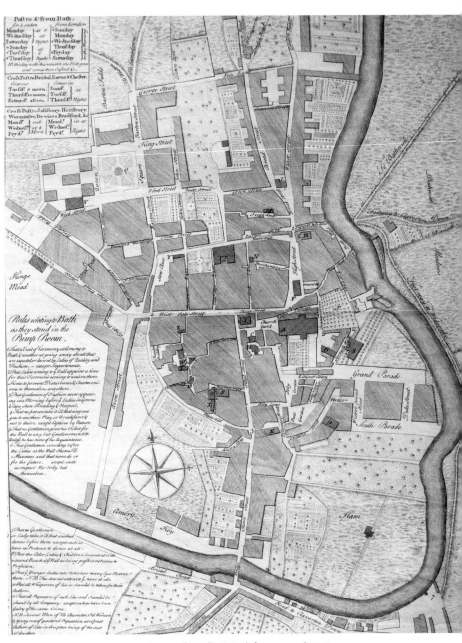

A map of Smollett's Bath from around 1755

3

'A SINK OF PROFLIGACY AND EXTORTION'
Tobias Smollett in Bath

Tobias Smollett was the John Wood of Bath letters. Like Wood, he had great plans for Bath; like Wood, he failed to achieve them. Like Wood, he was an outsider who saw that many at the top of his chosen profession – in Smollett's case medicine – were dullards or imposters. Like Wood, he had a massive chip on his shoulder, spending vast reserves of energy trying to establish his own superiority and expose the weaknesses of others. Like Wood, he suffered from chronic and severe asthma, exacerbated by overwork and stress. Like Wood he died, worn out and embittered, at the age of 50. And, like Wood, he only produced his greatest work within months of his death.

Wood and Smollett both loved Bath, saw the city's potential, and tried to help it achieve that potential. Both, though, fell foul of the all-powerful Bath corporation. When Smollett published an essay in 1752, laying out his proposals for making the hot baths 'more safe, agreeable and efficacious', he knew that the chances of them being accepted were slim. Smollett rightly saw that the corporation did not represent the city; they represented the vested interests opposed to any changes that threatened their stranglehold over the life of the city:

> Narrow minds will ever have narrow views. The corporation of Bath seems to have forgot that the ease and plenty they now enjoy, and to which their fathers were strangers, are owing to their waters; and that an improvement upon their baths would, by bringing a greater concourse of company to their town, perpetuate these blessings to them and their posterity. How little is to be expected from them, in this particular, might have been guessed by their conduct to Mr Wood, the architect, to whose extraordinary genius they are indebted for a great part of the trade and beauty of the place: yet they have industriously opposed his best designs, which, had they been executed, would have rendered Bath, in point of elegant architecture, the admiration of the whole world. It is, therefore, to be hoped there are still some among us whose exalted station, superior sense, and public spirit, will be sufficient to interest the legislature in an affair which is truly national, that the public may no longer suffer from the private claims, sordid passions, or selfish views of any particular set of men.

Tobias Smollett

Unfortunately, his call for the baths to be, in effect, nationalised, fell on deaf ears.

Smollett is remembered today, not for his proposals to improve the baths, but for one book, *The Expedition of Humphrey Clinker*, which was published in 1771 as he lay dying in Italy. While it is unquestionably his greatest work, there is, among the millions of words he published, much that is worth rediscovering. Undoubtedly, he wrote far too much, but he wrote for fame and money, not for posterity. The speed at which he wrote did have one benefit, however. He did not allow himself the luxury of meticulous revision or self-censorship, and so, in his writings, we get a real sense of what living in the mid-eighteenth century was like. He seems often to be writing at white heat, and his novels often read like diaries rather than works of fiction. We find out about the minutiae of everyday life – all the trivia that a more considered writer would have cut as inessential. And we also get a vivid sense of what Smollett himself was like, not only because he based many of the incidents he described on his own experiences, but also because he constantly intruded his own opinions and personality into his works.

He was born in Scotland in 1721. From an early age, he wanted to be a writer. He wrote his first play, *The Regicide*, at the age of 18. But he needed to get a proper job, and, after studying medicine at Edinburgh University, he travelled to London where he ended up as a surgeon's mate in the navy. Practising any sort of medicine in the eighteenth century was not for the faint-hearted, but working as a surgeon's mate on board a fighting ship was just about the toughest option of the lot. A few months after taking the job he saw action at the Siege of Cartagena under Admiral Vernon. He was just 20 years old.

Back in London, he continued to try to establish himself as a writer, publishing satirical poems and a masque called *Alceste* – never performed and now lost – for which Handel provided the incidental music. In his mid-twenties he married a Jamaican heiress with an income from sugar plantations.

He must also have visited Bath around this time, because the city featured in his first novel, *Roderick Random*, published in 1748. The book contained a memorable picture of an extremely unpleasant Beau Nash, plus a description of the rough and tumble life of the city at that time.

Bath also featured in Smollett's second novel, *Peregrine Pickle*, published three years later. The following year, 1752, he published his proposals for improving the baths as part of a campaign to establish himself as a physician in Bath. When the establishment closed ranks against him, he returned to London and threw himself into a regime of hack writing so punishing that his health soon began to suffer. In 1759, at the age of just 38, he wrote to a friend:

> I would not wish my greatest enemy a greater curse than the occupation of an author, in which capacity I have toiled myself into an habitual asthma, and been baited like a bear by all the hounds of Grub Street. Some people have flourished by imputed wit, I have suffered by imported dullness. I have been abused, reviled, and calumniated for satires I never saw; I have been censured for absurdities of which I could not possibility be guilty ... I perceive myself going downhill apace, and promise myself but a few years of enjoyment.

As his health deteriorated, he made frequent trips to Bath to take the waters. Although he never lost his interest in medicine – and in particular the medicinal use of water – it was as a patient rather than as a physician that he now visited the city. This letter, written from Bath in 1762, is typical of several he wrote in the last decade of his life:

> I have been at Southampton and crossed the country from the New Forest to Bath, where I am now settled in private lodgings. My health was so indifferent during the whole journey that I was obliged to get out of bed every night and sit two hours until the difficulty of breathing abated. Since my arrival in Bath I have, in spite of a fresh cold, slept very well, without any interruption from the asthma. I drink moderately of the water, ride out every day on the downs, eat like a horse, and if I could recover a little flesh I should think myself already cured; but the truth is I am thinner than when I last saw you, and begin to be afraid of looking in the glass of a morning. I believe my breathing so easily is owing to the warmth and moisture of the air at Bath, which seems to be peculiarly adapted to my lungs. Yet I can feel a very sensible effect from the waters. I have no sooner drank a large glass of them hot from the pump than my face, my hands and feet begin to glow; and this sensation is succeeded by an itching and tingling all over the surface of my body, resembling what is called the prickly heat in the West Indies. I think I can plainly perceive these mineral waters opening up the obstructed capillaries, and restoring the perspiration which in the extremities had been in a great measure lost. I intend in a few days to bathe with a view to open still more effectually the strainer of the skin.

The King's Bath as Smollett would have known it. Stall Street is in the foreground, the Queen's Bath is on the right and the original Pump Room is on the left.

Despite his failing health, he maintained a prodigious workload. His political and critical writings were savage in their condemnation of those he thought worthy of his scorn and he received a three-month jail sentence for libel in 1758. Nevertheless, these writings are almost totally forgotten – as are his major works from these years: *The Adventures of Ferdinand Count Fathom*, *The Life and Adventures of Sir Lancelot Greaves*, *The Complete History of England*, and *The Adventures of an Atom*. Only his *Travels through France and Italy*, two slim volumes of letters written during a continental tour in the early 1760s, are still remembered today. Despite all the setbacks and disappointments he encountered, despite his chronic ill-health, these *Travels* are filled with enthusiasm and *joie de vivre*. A rueful acceptance of life with all its imperfections pervades them, and this attitude also characterises his last and most famous work, *The Expedition of Humphrey Clinker*.

Totally different from his other novels, *Humphrey Clinker* consists of a series of letters from six imaginary people travelling around the country together – four members of a somewhat dysfunctional family and two servants. It may have been influenced by Richardson's *Pamela*, but a more likely inspiration is Christopher Anstey's *New Bath Guide*, a hugely popular set of humorous poetical epistles supposedly written by various members of one family and published in 1766. Smollett may also have had in mind Samuel Derrick's *Letters Written from Leverpoole, Chester, Corke, the Lake of Killarney,*

Tunbridge-Wells, Bath, published in 1767. Derrick, who was also the editor of *Harris's List of Covent Garden Ladies*, had succeeded Nash as Bath's Master of Ceremonies and was a former colleague of Smollett's. Smollett, however, far transcended these models, producing a novel that, in its use of letters to produce a series of different impressions, looks forward to writers such as William Faulkner, while its mingling of high and low life, and its delight in scatological puns and comic twists, foreshadows James Joyce.

Smollett wrote much of *Humphrey Clinker* in Italy, where he went for the sake of his health in 1768. Despite being seriously ill, he managed to complete it a few months before his death at his villa near Livorno on 17 September 1771. His wife wrote later that, 'it galls me to the soul, when I think how much that poor dear man suffered when he wrote that novel.' She stayed on at Livorno, living off the meagre revenues from her Jamaican estates. In 1782, however, disaster struck. On 24 October that year an appeal appeared in the *Bath Chronicle*:

> Ann Smollett, widow of the late Dr Tobias Smollett, humbly begs leave to represent, that by a letter received from her agent, Mr Angus MacBean, dated Kingston, March 6th, 1782, she is informed of the melancholy misfortune befallen her, by the late dreadful fire, which has entirely consumed her tenements and property at that place, and reduced her into the most deplorable state, being in a foreign country, at a great distance from her native island Jamaica, in a very infirm state of health, far advanced in years, and now deprived of every means of support. Thus oppressed with grief, which such a dire and most unexpected stroke of providence has caused her, she is under the necessity to recur to the known humanity and benevolence of her country, and hopes she shall receive from their generosity such support as may enable her to finish with decency the few days which God may be pleased to spare her, and which will be employed in offering her prayers to the Supreme, for the protection and happiness of her humane benefactors.

The appeal raised enough for her to continue living in Livorno until her death, seven years later, at the age of 70.

*

Roderick Random, Smollett's first novel, presents a vivid picture of Bath in the 1740s. The eponymous hero, who narrates the story in the first person, visits Bath not because of his health, but in pursuit of an advantageous marriage. Finding Roderick down on his luck, a friend of his called Banter comes up with a scheme to make them both rich:

> I have a relation [he tells Roderick] who is to set out for Bath next week, with an only daughter, who being sickly and decrepit, intends to drink the waters for the recovery of her health. Her father, who was a rich Turkey merchant, died about a year ago, and left her with a fortune of twenty thousand pounds,

under the sole management of her mother, who is my kinswoman. I would have put in for the plate myself, but there is a breach at present between the old woman and me. You must know, that some time ago I borrowed a small sum of her and promised, it seems, to pay it before a certain time; but being disappointed in my expectation of money from the country, the day elapsed without my being able to take up my note; upon which she wrote a peremptory letter, threatening to arrest me, if I did not pay the debt immediately. Nettled at this precise behaviour, I sent a d--d severe answer, which enraged her so much that she actually took out a writ against me. Whereupon, finding the thing grow serious, I got a friend to advance the money for me, discharged the debt, went to her house, and abused her for her unfriendly dealing. She was provoked by my reproaches, and scolded in her turn. The little deformed urchin joined her mother with such virulence and volubility of tongue, that I was fain to make a retreat, after having been honoured with a great many scandalous epithets, which gave me plainly to understand that I had nothing to hope from the esteem of the one, or the affection of the other. As they are both utter strangers to life, it is a thousand to one that the girl will be picked up by some scoundrel or other at Bath, if I don't provide for her otherwise. You are a well-looking fellow, Random, and can behave as demurely as a Quaker. If you will give me an obligation of five hundred pounds, to be paid six months after your marriage, I will put you in a method of carrying her in spite of all opposition.

Accordingly, Roderick sets off for Bath, contriving to take a place in the same coach as the lady in question – Miss Snapper – and her mother. He ingratiates himself with them by various stratagems, including the capture of a highwayman who attempts to hold up the coach. On their arrival at Bath, they invite him to call and accompany them to the Assembly Rooms.[1]

From the outset, it is plain that Roderick's only interest in Miss Snapper is monetary. He describes his first impressions of her thus:

I had the good fortune to find my mistress not quite so deformed nor disagreeable as she had been represented to me. Her head, indeed, bore some resemblance to a hatchet, the edge being represented by her face; but she had a certain delicacy in her complexion, and a great deal of vivacity in her eyes, which were very large and black; and, though the protuberance of her breast, when considered alone, seemed to drag her forwards, it was easy to perceive an equivalent on her back which balanced the other, and kept her body in equilibrio. On the whole, I thought I should have great reason to congratulate myself if it should be my fate to possess twenty thousand pounds encumbered with such a wife.

However, after spending a few hours in her company, he begins to have second thoughts. He finds, in particular, that she labours 'under such a

---

1 Smollett does not distinguish, in his earlier novels, between the two sets of Assembly Rooms, which faced each other across Terrace Walk, as can be seen on the map on page 17.

profusion of talk, that I dreaded her unruly tongue, and felt by anticipation the horrors of an eternal clack!'

Miss Snapper's unruly tongue stands her in good stead, however, when, with Roderick in tow, she enters the Assembly Rooms. He describes their reception there as follows:

> We no sooner entered, than the eyes of everybody present were turned upon us, and, when we had suffered the martyrdom of their looks for some time, a whisper circulated at our expense, which was accompanied with many contemptuous smiles and tittering observations, to my utter shame and confusion. I did not so much conduct as follow my charge to a place where she seated her mother and herself with astonishing composure notwithstanding the unmannerly behaviour of the whole company, which seemed to be assumed merely to put her out of countenance. The celebrated Mr Nash, who commonly attends in this place, as master of the ceremonies, perceiving the disposition of the assembly, took upon himself the task of gratifying their ill-nature further, by exposing my mistress to the edge of his wit. With this view he approached us, with many bows and grimaces, and, after having welcomed Miss Snapper to the place, asked her in the hearing of all present, if she could inform him of the name of Tobit's dog. Miss was so much incensed at his insolence, that I should certainly have kicked him where he stood without ceremony, had not the young lady prevented the effects of my indignation, by replying with the utmost vivacity, 'his name was Nash, and an impudent dog he was.' This repartee, so unexpected and just, raised such a universal laugh at the aggressor, that all his assurance was insufficient to support him under their derision; so that, after he had endeavoured to compose himself by taking snuff and forcing a smile, he was obliged to sneak off in a ludicrous attitude, while my Dulcinea was applauded to the skies for the brilliancy of her wit, and her acquaintance immediately courted by the best people of both sexes in the room.

All goes well with Roderick's pursuit of Miss Snapper until another lady called Narcissa turns up at a ball in the Assembly Rooms. Roderick is madly in love with Narcissa, and, as soon as he sees her, all thought of Miss Snapper goes out of the window. Although Roderick's feelings are reciprocated, Narcissa's brother (who is also her guardian) considers him a low-born adventurer. The brother is a loutish, moronic country squire, whose main pleasures are foxhunting and drinking port. To Roderick's relief, he is also so dim that he fails to recognise him from a previous encounter. He remains ignorant of Roderick's identity even after Roderick has inveigled himself into his company and joined him in a couple of bouts of heavy drinking. Despite a rival for Narcissa's affections turning up in the person of Lord Quiverwit, Roderick is soon well on his way to winning Narcissa's brother round, as well as bringing matters with Narcissa to a head. At this stage, however, Melinda, a former lover of Roderick's, turns up and starts spreading 'scandalous aspersions' about him. Roderick tries to brazen it out:

> When I went into the Long Room, I observed several whispers circulate all of a sudden, and did not doubt that Melinda had been busy with my character; but I consoled myself with the love of Narcissa, upon which I rested with the most perfect confidence; and going up to the rowly-powly table, won a few pieces from my suspected rival, who, with an easy politeness, entered into conversation with me, and, desiring my company to the coffee-house, treated me with tea and chocolate … He artfully turned the discourse upon Narcissa, and endeavoured by hinting at an intrigue he pretended to be engaged in elsewhere, to learn what connection there was between her and me. But all his finesse was ineffectual, I was convinced of his dissimulation, and gave such general answers to his inquiries, that he was forced to drop the subject, and talk of something else.

Melinda's stories finally reach the ear of Narcissa's brother, and when Roderick goes to the Assembly Rooms the following day he has an unpleasant surprise:

> I was met at the door by a servant, who presented a billet to me without a subscription, importing that my presence was disagreeable to the company, and desiring I would take the hint without further disturbance, and bestow myself elsewhere for the future. This peremptory message filled me with indignation. I followed the fellow who delivered it, and, seizing him by the collar in presence of all the company, threatened to put him instantly to death, if he did not discover the scoundrel who had charged him with such an impudent commission, that I might punish him as he deserved. The messenger, affrighted at my menaces and furious looks, fell upon his knees, and told me, that the gentleman who ordered him to deliver the letter was no other than Narcissa's brother, who, at that time, stood at the other end of the room, talking to Melinda. I went up to him immediately, and in the hearing of his inamorata, accosted him in these words; 'Lookee, squire, were it not for one consideration that protects you from my resentment, I would cane you where you stand, for having had the presumption to send me this scurrilous intimation'; which I tore to pieces and threw in his face: at the same time darting an angry regard at his mistress, I told her, I was sorry she had put it out of my power to compliment her upon her invention, but at the expense of her good nature and veracity. Her admirer, whose courage never rose, but in proportion to the wine he had swallowed, instead of resenting my address in what is called an honourable way, threatened to prosecute me for an assault, and took witnesses accordingly: while she, piqued at his pusillanimous behaviour, and enraged at the sarcasm I had uttered against her, endeavoured to make her quarrel a public cause, and wept aloud with spite and vexation.

The tears of a lady could not fail of attracting the notice and concern of the spectators to whom she complained of my rudeness with great bitterness, saying, if she were a man, I durst not use her so. The greatest part of the gentlemen, already prejudiced against me, were offended at the liberty I had taken, as appeared from their looks; though none of them signified their disgust any other way except my Lord Quiverwit, who ventured to say, with a sneer, that I was in the right to establish my own character, of which he had now no longer any doubt. Nettled at this severe equivocation, which raised a laugh at my expense, I replied with some warmth, 'I am proud of having in that particular got the start of your lordship.' He made no answer to my repartee, but with a contemptuous smile walked off, leaving me in a very disagreeable situation. In vain did I make up to several people of my acquaintance, whose conversation, I hoped, would banish my confusion; everybody shunned me like a person infected, and I should not have been able to bear my disgrace, had not the idea of the ever faithful and fond Narcissa come to my relief. I quitted the scene of my mortification, and, sauntering about the town, happened to wake from my contemplation, when I found myself just opposite to a toy-shop, which I entered, and purchased a ring set with a ruby in the form of a heart, surrounded by diamond sparks, for which I paid ten guineas, intending it for a present to the charmer of my soul.

That night, Roderick visits Narcissa in her chamber and consummates his relationship with her. Creeping back to his lodgings in the early light of dawn, he goes to bed for a well-earned rest, only to be woken a couple of hours later by his servant with a message. Lord Quiverwit saw him leaving Narcissa's, and this, combined with Roderick's insolence the day before, has left him with no choice but to challenge him to a duel. The description of the duel is superb, shorn of all the gallantry and derring-do that many a lesser writer would have used. The fight – like that between Sheridan and Captain Mathews described in the previous walk – is bloody, messy, and rather sordid. Roderick becomes so confused during the contest that, when he receives a minor wound under his shoulder, he thinks one of his lungs has been pierced. Grabbing Lord Quiverwit's sword so that he cannot withdraw it from his body, he turns his sword on him to inflict a mortal blow. Unfortunately, he only manages to wound him in the arm:

> Disappointed at this expectation, and afraid still that death would frustrate my revenge, I grappled with him, and, being much the stronger, threw him upon the ground, where I wrested his sword out of his hand, and, so great was my confusion, that instead of turning the point upon him, struck out three of his foreteeth with the hilt. In the meantime, our servants, seeing us fall, ran up to separate and assist us; but before their approach I was upon my feet, and had discovered that my supposed mortal wound was only a slight scratch. The knowledge of my own safety disarmed me of a good deal of my resentment, and I began to inquire with some concern into the situation

of my antagonist, who remained on the ground bleeding plentifully at his mouth and arm. I helped his footman to raise him, and, having bound up his wound with my handkerchief, assured him it was not dangerous; I likewise restored his sword, and offered to support him to his house. He thanked me with an air of sullen dignity: and whispering that I should hear from him soon, went away, leaning on his servant's shoulder.

Lord Quiverwit, frustrated in his desire to teach him a lesson, tells Narcissa's brother of Roderick's relationship with Narcissa. Her brother immediately whisks her away from Bath and Roderick turns to the gaming table for solace:

Melancholy and despondence took possession of my soul; and, repining at that providence which, by acting the stepmother towards me, kept me from the fruition of my wishes, I determined, in a fit of despair, to risk all I had at the gaming table, with a view of acquiring a fortune sufficient to render me independent for life; or of plunging myself into such a state of misery, as would effectually crush every ambitious hope that now tortured my imagination.

Actuated by this fatal resolution, I engaged in play, and, after some turns of fortune found myself, at the end of three days, worth a thousand pounds; but it was not my intention to stop there … and continued my career until I was reduced to five guineas, which I would have hazarded also, had I not been ashamed to fall from a bet of two hundred pounds to such a petty sum.

And so he returns to London. The picture Smollett paints of Bath in *Roderick Random* is, despite the absence of any topographical details, a remarkably vivid one. We get a real sense of what Bath was like in the 1740s, where sexual politics were fuelled by gossip and intrigue, and where violent passions and rivalries meant that you had to have a hide like a rhinoceros to survive. The episode in which Miss Snapper wins over those sniggering at her disability by being more abrasive than Beau Nash gives an idea of what you had to do to hold your own in Bath society. And the ignominious end of Roderick's career as a gambler was played out time and again at the city's gaming tables.

Smollett's next novel, *Peregrine Pickle*, appeared three years later. Unlike *Roderick Random*, it is not narrated in the first person, and overall it is far less accomplished. Two-dimensional figures take the place of the fully rounded characters of *Roderick Random*, and, while there is a good deal of knockabout humour in the Bath episodes, there is a far less compelling sense of what the city was like.

Neither Roderick nor Peregrine come to Bath because of their health – although Roderick does come in pursuit of an invalid. Peregrine's ambition is even more straightforward. He wants to make his mark in the most fashionable city in the land outside London:

Our hero, panting with the desire of distinguishing himself at that resort of the fashionable world, communicated his design of going thither to his friend Godfrey, whom he importuned to accompany him in the excursion; and leave of absence from his regiment being obtained by the influence of Peregrine's new quality friends, the two companions departed from London in a post-chaise, attended, as usual, by the valet-de-chambre and Pipes, who were become almost as necessary to our adventurer as any two of his own organs.

On the way to Bath, they stop at an inn, where Peregrine's companion meets a professional gambler he knows from Tunbridge Wells. He is on his way back from Bath, having been taken to the cleaners by a company of sharpers. Peregrine treats him to dinner, where he is 'fully informed of all the political systems at Bath':

> He understood that there was at London one great company of adventurers, who employed agents in all the different branches of imposition throughout the whole kingdom of England, allowing these ministers a certain proportion of the profits accruing from their industry and skill, and reserving the greatest share for the benefit of the common stock, which was chargeable with the expense of fitting out individuals in their various pursuits, as well as with the loss sustained in the course of their adventures. Some whose persons and qualifications are by the company judged adequate to the task, exert their talents in making love to ladies of fortune, being accommodated with money and accoutrements for that purpose, after having given their bonds payable to one or other of the directors, on the day of marriage, for certain sums, proportioned to the dowries they are to receive. Others versed in the doctrine of chances, and certain secret expediences, frequent all those places where games of hazard are allowed: and such as are masters in the arts of billiards, tennis, and bowls, are continually lying in wait, in all the scenes of these diversions, for the ignorant and unwary. A fourth class attend horse-races, being skilled in those mysterious practices by which the knowing ones are taken in. Nor is this community unfurnished with those who lay wanton wives and old rich widows under contribution, and extort money, by prostituting themselves to the embraces of their own sex, and then threatening their admirers with prosecution. But their most important returns are made by that body of their undertakers who exercise their understandings in the innumerable stratagems of the card table, at which no sharper can be too infamous to be received, and even caressed by persons of the highest rank and distinction. Among other articles of intelligence, our young gentleman learned, that those agents, by whom their guest was broke, and expelled from Bath, had constituted a bank against all sporters, and monopolized the advantage in all sorts of play.

They decide to teach the sharpers a lesson, and, with Godfrey's skill at billiards and Peregrine's talent for acting, are soon successful. They then seal their place in the affections of Bath society by making 'a handsome benefaction to the hospital' out of their winnings.

Before they have been in Bath a fortnight, Peregrine has 'set all the ladies by the ears and furnished all the hundred tongues of scandal with full employment'. However, the object of his affections is elsewhere and he remains unmoved by the attention paid to him. He becomes bored, and decides to follow up his success with the sharpers by teaching the physicians of the city a lesson. These worthies have, rather unwisely, incurred his displeasure by spreading malicious rumours about him. By this time, Smollett had had plenty of experience of Bath's doctors and Peregrine's hatred of them reflects the author's own:

> Among the secret agents of scandal, none were so busy as the physicians, a class of animals who live in this place, like so many ravens hovering about a carcase, and even ply for employment, like scullers at Hungerford-stairs. The greatest part of them have correspondents in London, who make it their business to inquire into the history, character, and distemper of every one that repairs to Bath, for the benefit of the waters, and if they cannot procure interest to recommend their medical friends to these patients before they set out, they at least furnish them with a previous account of what they could collect, that their correspondents may use this intelligence for their own advantage. By these means, and the assistance of flattery and assurance, they often insinuate themselves into the acquaintance of strangers, and, by consulting their dispositions, become necessary and subservient to their prevailing passions. By their connection with apothecaries and nurses, they are informed of all the private occurrences in each family, and therefore enabled to gratify the rancour of malice, amuse the spleen of peevish indisposition, and entertain the eagerness of impertinent curiosity.

Peregrine sends a message to all the doctors in Bath informing them that a splenetic and arthritic colonel, who hates the medical profession with a passion, wishes to see them urgently. They turn up, with predictable results, and before long the story of their slapstick eviction from the colonel's lodgings has gone round the town.

His next escapade is the humbling of a card-sharping bully who bears more than a passing resemblance to Beau Nash:

> Among those who never failed to reside at Bath during the season, was a certain person, who, from the most abject misery, had, by his industry and art at play, amassed about fifteen thousand pounds; and though his character was notorious, insinuated himself so far into the favour of what is called the best company, that very few private parties of pleasure took place in which he was not principally concerned. He was of a gigantic stature, a most intrepid countenance; and his disposition, naturally overbearing, had, in the course of his adventures and success, acquired a most intolerable degree of insolence

and vanity. By the ferocity of his features, and audacity of his behaviour, he had obtained a reputation for the most undaunted courage, which had been confirmed by divers adventures, in which he had humbled the most assuming heroes of his own fraternity; so that he now reigned chief Hector of the place with unquestioned authority.

Peregrine, after playing cards with him for a while, accuses him of cheating. Peregrine is unmoved by his bluster and, after refusing to withdraw the accusation, accepts his challenge to a duel. The outcome is a good more comic than the duel in *Roderick Random*:

> When they arrived next morning upon the field, the gamester, arming his countenance with all its terrors, advanced with a sword of a monstrous length, and, putting himself in a posture, called out aloud in a most terrific voice, 'Draw, d--n ye, draw; I will this instant send you to your fathers.' The youth was not slow in complying with his desire; his weapon was unsheathed in a moment, and he began the attack with such unexpected spirit and address, that his adversary, having made shift with great difficulty to parry the first pass, retreated a few paces, and demanded a parley, in which he endeavoured to persuade the young man, that to lay a man of his character under the necessity of chastising his insolence, was the most rash and inconsiderate step that he could possibly have taken; but that he had compassion upon his youth, and was willing to spare him if he would surrender his sword, and promise to ask pardon in public for the offence he had given. Pickle was so much exasperated at this unparalleled effrontery, that, without deigning to make the least reply, he flung his own hat in the proposer's face, and renewed the charge with such undaunted agility, that the gamester, finding himself in manifest hazard of his life, betook himself to his heels, and fled homewards with incredible speed, being closely pursued by Peregrine, who, having sheathed his sword, pelted him with stones as he ran, and compelled him to go, that same day, into banishment from Bath, where he had domineered so long.

Peregrine Pickle is a good deal more knockabout than *Roderick Random*, although it includes a contrasting section entitled 'Memoirs of a Lady of Quality'. This comes shortly after the Bath chapters, and tells the true story of Lady Vane. This contains a memorable portrayal of Bath's sexual politics, with the thirteen-year heiress taking Bath by storm and receiving several offers of marriage. A couple of years later she elopes with Lord Hamilton, and, although their union is soon accepted by both sets of parents, her happiness is short-lived and she is left a widow by the age of 18.

Like *Roderick Random*, *Peregrine Pickle*, while it paints a vivid picture of the type of people who came to Bath, gives little idea what the city looked like. Not so Smollett's last novel, T*he Expedition of Humphrey Clinker*, which appeared in 1771. The novels which appeared in the interim did not feature Bath to any significant extent, a reflection of Smollett's absorption in the literary and political milieu of London during this period. *Ferdinand, Count Fathom*, published in 1753, however, is of indirect interest because the eponymous hero sets up as a medical expert at Hotwells in Bristol. Here he explodes the pretensions of an esteemed doctor at the spa by declaring that his theory as to why the water is hot is nonsense and putting forward his own explanation, which he makes up on the spur of the moment. The funny thing is that, apart from the odd detail, what he says is what we know to be true today:

> He alleged, that fire was the sole vivifying principle that pervaded all nature; that, as the heat of the sun concocted the juice of vegetables, and ripened those fruits that grow upon the surface of this globe, there was likewise an immense store of central fire reserved within the bowels of the earth, not only for the generation of gems, fossils, and all the purposes of the mineral world, but likewise for cherishing and keeping alive those plants which would otherwise perish by the winter's cold. The existence of such a fire he proved from the nature of all those volcanoes, which in almost every corner of the earth are continually vomiting up either flames or smoke. 'These,' said he, 'are the great vents appointed by nature for the discharge of that rarefied air and combustible matter, which, if confined, would burst the globe asunder; but, besides the larger outlets, there are some small chimneys through which part of the heat transpires; a vapour of that sort, I conceive, must pass through the bed or channel of this spring, the waters of which, accordingly retain a moderate warmth.'
>
> This account, which totally overthrew the other's doctrine, was so extremely agreeable to the audience, that the testy doctor lost his temper, and gave them to understand, without preamble, that he must be a person wholly ignorant of natural philosophy, who could invent such a ridiculous system, and they involved in worse than an Egyptian fog, that could not at once discern its weakness and absurdity. This declaration introduced a dispute, which was unanimously determined in favour of our adventurer.

Ferdinand Fathom also contains an observation on the peculiar social mores that applied not only at Hotwells but also at Bath and other spa towns. Having won over Bristol society, Ferdinand considers how he may repeat his success in London:

> He foresaw, that he should find great difficulty in transplanting his reputation, so as to take root in London, which was the only soil in which he could propose to rise to any degree of prosperity and independence; and this reflection was grounded upon a maxim which universally prevails among the English people, namely, to overlook and wholly neglect, on their return to the metropolis, all the connexions they may have chanced to acquire during their residence at any of the medical wells. And this social disposition is so scrupulously maintained, that two persons who lived in the most intimate correspondence at Bath or Tunbridge, shall in four-and-twenty hours

so totally forget their friendship, as to meet in St. James's Park, without betraying the least token of recognition; so that one would imagine these mineral waters were so many streams issuing from the river Lethe, so famed of old for washing away all traces of memory and recollection.

Humphrey Clinker is remembered today, not only as Smollett's masterpiece, but also as the book in which he dealt most fully with Bath. He wrote another book, however, which deals almost exclusively with Bath – the *Essay on the External Use of Water in a Letter to Dr **** with Particular Remarks upon the Present Method of Using the Mineral Waters at Bath in Somersetshire, and a Plan for Making them more Safe, Agreeable, and Efficacious*. Published in 1752, it was, as indicated earlier, Smollett the physician's attempt to take Bath by storm. Its failure was unfortunate not only for Smollett, but also for the city, because his proposals would have made the baths a good deal more pleasant.

Smollett failed to establish himself as a physician in Bath for two reasons: first, he was not well connected; second, he was a man of principle, who spoke out against corruption and incompetence, both rife among Bath's physicians in the mid-eighteenth century. Fortunes could be made from quack cures, if their authors greased the right palms.

Smollett – and his *Essay* – represented a threat in two ways. First, he disputed the claim that Bath's waters were efficacious because of the minerals in them. It was, he believed, the temperature of the waters which benefited patients and nothing else. This not only took away much of their mystery, it also meant that their effect could be replicated elsewhere simply by heating water up. His second claim was even less welcome. He declared that bathing in hot water, while it was good for some ailments, was positively harmful for others. For most conditions, bathing in cold water – and especially sea water – was more beneficial. This was not what Bath wanted to hear. Bath's position as England's top resort depended on people believing that it provided the best possible range of treatments for the sick, and that, while up and coming seaside resorts like Scarborough and Margate – and warm-water spas like Buxton and Clifton – were all right as far as they went, they simply could not compete with the hot springs of Bath.

In the event, of course, Smollett's view carried the day. Bath tried to cash in on the growing enthusiasm for sea bathing by establishing Weymouth as a sort of mini-Bath-on-Sea, but when the Prince Regent turned his back on Bath and started patronising Brighton, Bath's fate was sealed. Smollett, however, did not live to see this falling off. Although he predicted in 1752 that, if the baths were not improved, the corporation would live to see 'their springs deserted and their town utterly impoverished and ruined', as late as 1771 he has Matthew Bramble say that Bath is the one spa which has so far been unaffected by changes in fashion.

Smollett was spurred into writing his *Essay* by the treatment meted out to a friend of his, Dr Cleland, who had made certain recommendations as to how the baths could be improved. Despite the backing of the Prince of Wales and Beau Nash, the corporation turned them down. A campaign of vilification was launched against Cleland, and it was in response to this that Smollett weighed in on his side, reiterating his proposals and making some of this own. Many of these later found their way into *Humphrey Clinker* as the views of Matthew Bramble.

Bramble and his entourage arrive in Bath late in the season – towards the end of March – and take rooms on the first floor of a lodging house on the South Parade, a situation chosen 'for its being near the Bath, and remote from the noise of carriages'. However, it proves to be a poor choice and what Bramble hopes will be a quiet retreat turns out to be very noisy. No sooner has his sister Tabitha's screaming fit at the lack of towels subsided than a dog fight breaks out. Hard on the heels of this there is a visit from the city waits. Then comes a thumping and bouncing from above, as a dancing master puts a pupil through his paces. Finally, two negroes belonging to a Creole gentleman decide to practise their French horns on the landing. Surprisingly, Smollett does not end this catalogue of cacophonies, as he could have done, with a firework display. Spring Gardens was just across the river and firework displays there regularly disturbed the tranquillity of this part of town.

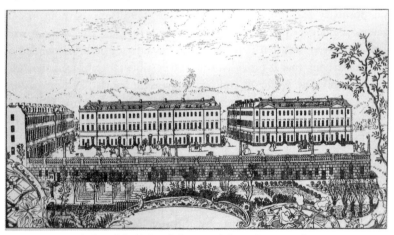

A view of South Parade from an eighteenth-century fan

LITERARY WALKS IN BATH

Even without a firework display, however, Matthew Bramble abandons South Parade and takes a 'small house in Milsham Street'. Milsom Street had only just been built, and was still a quiet backwater. It did not remain quiet for long, however, and, as the streets leading to it were opened up, lodging houses were converted to shops. Within a few years, it was the most fashionable shopping street in the city.

Milsom Street was not the only newly-built street in Bath at the time of Matthew Bramble's visit. Indeed, he complains that the city is 'so altered, that I can scarcely believe it is the same place that I frequented about thirty years ago'. It was not just the look of Bath that had changed. We need only go back just over 20 years to find Roderick Random and Peregrine Pickle walking the streets of the city, along with all the card sharpers, duellists and gossipers of those early novels. The Bath portrayed in *Humphrey Clinker* is a city where, for all its imperfections, a lot of the rougher edges have been knocked off, a city that Jane Austen would have recognised; it is unlikely that she would have felt at home in the rakish Bath of Smollett's earlier novels.

It is ironic, then, that Matthew Bramble recalls the Bath of 30 years earlier as a sort of pastoral idyll:

> This place, which Nature and Providence seem to have intended as a resource from distemper and disquiet, is become the very centre of racket and dissipation. Instead of that peace, tranquillity, and ease, so necessary to those who labour under bad health, weak nerves, and irregular spirits; here we have nothing but noise, tumult, and hurry; with the fatigue and slavery of maintaining a ceremonial, more stiff, formal, and oppressive, than the etiquette of a German elector. A national hospital it may be, but one would imagine that none but lunatics are admitted; and truly, I will give you leave to call me so, if I stay much longer at Bath.

It is not only the noise of the place which irritates him. There is all that ghastly modern architecture as well:

> The rage of building has laid hold on such a number of adventurers, that one sees new houses starting up in every outlet and every corner of Bath; contrived without judgment, executed without solidity, and stuck together with so little regard to plan and propriety, that the different lines of the new rows and buildings interfere with, and intersect one another in every different angle of conjunction. They look like the wreck of streets and squares disjointed by an earthquake, which hath broken the ground into a variety of holes and hillocks; or as if some Gothic devil had stuffed them altogether in a bag, and left them to stand higgledy-piggledy, just as chance directed. What sort of a monster Bath will become in a few years, with those growing excrescences, may be easily conceived: but the want of beauty and proportion is not the worst effect of these new mansions; they are built so slight, with the soft crumbling stone found in this neighbourhood, that I should never

sleep quietly in one of them, when it blowed (as the sailors say) a cap-full of wind; and, I am persuaded, that my hind, Roger Williams, or any man of equal strength, would be able to push his foot through the strongest part of their walls, without any great exertion of his muscles.

Matthew Bramble's niece, Lydia Melford, however, sees Bath through very different eyes:

Bath, to be sure, is an earthly paradise. The Square, the Circus, and the Parades, put you in mind of the sumptuous palaces represented in prints and pictures; and the new buildings, such as Princes-row, Harlequin's-row, Bladud's-row, and twenty other rows, look like so many enchanted castles, raised on hanging terraces.

She also has a rather different view of the company:

All is gayety, good-humour, and diversion. The eye is continually entertained with the splendour of dress and equipage; and the ear with the sound of coaches, chairs, and other carriages. The merry bells ring round, from morn till night … We have music in the Pump-room every morning, cotillons every forenoon in the Rooms, balls twice a week, and concerts every other night, besides private assemblies and parties without number.

It is through her eyes that we are introduced to the delights of Bath in the early 1770s:

Hard by the Pump-room, is a coffee-house for the ladies; but my aunt says, young girls are not admitted, insomuch as the conversation turns upon politics, scandal, philosophy, and other subjects above our capacity; but we are allowed to accompany them to the booksellers' shops, which are charming places of resort; where we read novels, plays, pamphlets, and newspapers, for so small a subscription as a crown a quarter; and in these offices of intelligence (as my brother calls them) all the reports of the day, and all the private transactions of the Bath, are first entered and discussed. From the bookseller's shop, we make a tour through the milliners and toymen; and commonly stop at Mr Gill's, the pastry-cook, to take a jelly, a tart, or a small bason of vermicelli. There is, moreover, another place of entertainment on the other side of the water, opposite to the Grove, to which the company cross over in a boat – It is called Spring-garden [sic]; a sweet retreat, laid out in walks and ponds, and parterres of flowers; and there is a long-room for breakfasting and dancing. As the situation is low and damp, and the season has been remarkably wet, my uncle won't suffer me to go thither, lest I should catch cold: but my aunt says it is all a vulgar prejudice; and, to be sure, a great many gentlemen and ladies of Ireland frequent the place, without seeming to be the worse for it. They say, dancing at Spring-gardens, when the air is moist, is recommended to them as an excellent cure for the rheumatism.

Part of the humour of *Humphrey Clinker* comes from the imprecise command of written English by the family's servants in their letters home.

Jenkins, the maid, echoes Lydia's description of Bath, for example, but fails to get it quite right:

> Dear girl, I have seen all the fine shews of Bath; the Prades, the Squires, and the Circlis, the Crashit, the Hottogon, and Bloody Buildings, and Harry King's row.

Jeremy Melford, Matthew Bramble's nephew, also sees Bath as a place of wonder, although he takes a somewhat different view to his sister:

> I am ... amazed to find so small a place so crowded with entertainment and variety. London itself can hardly exhibit one species of diversion, to which we have not something analogous at Bath, over and above those singular advantages that are peculiar to the place. Here, for example, a man has daily opportunities of seeing the most remarkable characters of the community. He sees them in their natural attitudes and true colours; descended from their pedestals, and divested of their formal draperies, undisguised by art and affectation – Here we have ministers of state, judges, generals, bishops, projectors, philosophers, wits, poets, players, chemists, fiddlers, and buffoons ... Another entertainment, peculiar to Bath, arises from the general mixture of all degrees assembled in our public rooms, without distinction of rank or fortune. This is what my uncle reprobates, as a monstrous jumble of heterogeneous principles; a vile mob of noise and impertinence, without decency or subordination. But this chaos is to me a source of infinite amusement.

In *Humphrey Clinker*, Smollett sets conflicting views alongside each other, tacitly acknowledging that each – although it may be muddle-headed, misinformed or naïve – is in its own way as valid as the others. Although he puts many of his own views into the mouth of Matthew Bramble, he is aware of Bramble's misanthropy – and the prickliness implied by his name – and opposes to them the innocent enthusiasms of his niece and nephew.

Much of Matthew Bramble's misanthropy is due to age and infirmity, as he himself comes close to admitting on several occasions. His description of a visit to the coffee house, which starts off as a comic yet wistful meditation on old age, ends up as a grumpy diatribe on the wickedness of the times:

> Going to the coffeehouse one forenoon, I could not help contemplating the company, with equal surprise and compassion – We consisted of thirteen individuals; seven lamed by the gout, rheumatism, or palsy; three maimed by accident; and the rest either deaf or blind. One hobbled, another hopped, a third dragged his legs after him like a wounded snake, a fourth straddled betwixt a pair of long crutches, like the mummy of a felon hanging in chains; a fifth was bent into a horizontal position, like a mounted telescope, shoved in by a couple of chairmen; and a sixth was the bust of a man, set upright in a wheel machine, which the waiter moved from place to place.

Being struck with some of their faces, I consulted the subscription-book; and, perceiving the names of several old friends, began to consider the group with more attention. At length I discovered Rear-admiral Balderick, the companion of my youth, whom I had not seen since he was appointed Lieutenant of the Severn. He was metamorphosed into an old man, with a wooden leg and a weatherbeaten face, which appeared the more ancient from his grey locks, that were truly venerable – Sitting down at the table, where he was reading a newspaper, I gazed at him for some minutes, with a mixture of pleasure and regret, which made my heart gush with tenderness; then, taking him by the hand, 'Ah, Sam (said I) forty years ago I little thought' – I was too much moved to proceed. 'An old friend, sure enough! (cried he, squeezing my hand, and surveying me eagerly through his glasses) I know the looming of the vessel, though she has been hard strained since we parted; but I can't heave up the name' – The moment I told him who I was, he exclaimed, 'Ha! Matt, my old fellow cruizer, still afloat!' And, starting up, hugged me in his arms. His transport, however, boded me no good; for, in saluting me, he thrust the spring of his spectacles into my eye, and, at the same time, set his wooden stump upon my gouty toe; an attack that made me shed tears in sad earnest – After the hurry of our recognition was over, he pointed out two of our common friends in the room: the bust was what remained of Colonel Cockril, who had lost the use of his limbs in making an American campaign; and the telescope proved to be my college chum, Sir Reginald Bently; who, with his new title, and unexpected inheritance, commenced fox-hunter, without having

The Parade Coffee House, seen here around 1900 when it was the Institution Wine Vaults. Today it is the Huntsman pub.

served his apprenticeship to the mystery; and, in consequence of following the hounds through a river, was seized with an inflammation of his bowels, which has contracted him into his present attitude ... I cannot express the half of what I felt at this casual meeting of three or four companions, who had been so long separated, and so roughly treated by the storms of life. It was a renovation of youth; a kind of resuscitation of the dead, that realized those interesting dreams, in which we sometimes retrieve our ancient friends from the grave. Perhaps my enjoyment was not the less pleasing for being mixed with a strain of melancholy, produced by the remembrance of past scenes, that conjured up the ideas of some endearing connexions, which the hand of death has actually dissolved.

The spirits and good humour of the company seemed to triumph over the wreck of their constitutions. They had even philosophy enough to joke upon their own calamities; such is the power of friendship, the sovereign cordial of life – I afterwards found, however, that they were not without their moments, and even hours of disquiet. Each of them apart, in succeeding conferences, expatiated upon his own particular grievances; and they were all malcontents at bottom – Over and above their personal disasters, they thought themselves unfortunate in the lottery of life. Balderick complained, that all the recompence he had received for his long and hard service, was the half-pay of a rear-admiral. The colonel was mortified to see himself over-topped by upstart generals, some of whom he had once commanded; and, being a man of liberal turn, could ill put up with a moderate annuity, for which he had sold his commission. As for the baronet, having run himself considerably in debt, on a contested election, he has been obliged to relinquish his seat in parliament, and his seat in the country at the same time, and put his estate to nurse; but his chagrin, which is the effect of his own misconduct, does not affect me half so much as that of the other two, who have acted honourable and distinguished parts on the great theatre, and are now reduced to lead a weary life in this stew-pan of idleness and insignificance. They have long left off using the waters, after having experienced their inefficacy. The diversions of the place they are not in a condition to enjoy. How then do they make shift to pass their time? In the forenoon they crawl out to the Rooms or the coffeehouse, where they take a hand at whist, or descant upon the *General Advertiser*; and their evenings they murder in private parties, among peevish invalids, and insipid old women – This is the case with a good number of individuals, whom nature seems to have intended for better purposes.

About a dozen years ago, many decent families, restricted to small fortunes, besides those that came hither on the score of health, were tempted to settle at Bath, where they could then live comfortably, and even make a genteel appearance, at a small expense: but the madness of the times has made the place too hot for them, and they are now obliged to think of other migrations – Some have already fled to the mountains of Wales, and others have retired to Exeter. Thither, no doubt, they will be followed by the flood of luxury and extravagance, which will drive them from place to place to the very Land's End; and there, I suppose, they will be obliged to ship themselves to some other country. Bath is become a mere sink of profligacy and extortion. Every article of house-keeping is raised to an enormous price; a circumstance no longer to be wondered at, when we know that every petty retainer of fortune piques himself upon keeping a table, and thinks it is for the honour of his character to wink at the knavery of his servants, who are in a confederacy with the market-people; and, of consequence, pay whatever they demand.

Jeremy Melford introduces us to one of these spendthrifts in tones of hushed admiration:

> Jack Holder, who was intended for a parson, has succeeded to an estate of two thousand a year, by the death of his elder brother. He is now at the Bath, driving about in a phaeton and four, with French horns. He has treated with turtle and claret at all the taverns in Bath and Bristol, till his guests are gorged with good chear: he has bought a dozen suits of fine clothes, by the advice of the Master of the Ceremonies, under whose tuition he has entered himself. He has lost hundreds at billiards to sharpers, and taken one of the nymphs of Avon-street into keeping.[1]

This paragon of conspicuous consumption has been advised by his 'counsellor' to give a 'general tea drinking at Wiltshire's room':

> In order to give it the more éclat, every table is to be furnished with sweet-meats and nosegays; which, however, are not to be touched till notice is given by the ringing of a bell, and then the ladies may help themselves without restriction.

Jeremy and his uncle, who have failed to resolve an argument over how refined Bath society is, decide to use this event as a touchstone. Jeremy insists it will be marked by the utmost decorum, Bramble that it will be an unseemly scrum. Not surprisingly, Bramble is proved right:

> The tea-drinking passed as usual, and the company having risen from the tables, were sauntering in groups, in expectation of the signal for attack, when the bell beginning to ring, they flew with eagerness to the dessert, and the whole place was instantly in commotion. There was nothing but justling, scrambling, pulling, snatching, struggling, scolding, and screaming. The nosegays were torn from one another's hands and bosoms; the glasses and china went to wreck; the tables and floors were strewed with comfits. Some cried; some swore; and the tropes and figures of Billingsgate were used without reserve in all their native zest and flavour; nor were those flowers of rhetoric unattended with significant gesticulation. Some snapped their fingers; some forked them out; some clapped their hands, and some their back-sides; at length, they fairly proceeded to pulling caps, and every thing seemed to presage a general battle; when Holder ordered his horns to sound a charge, with a view to animate the combatants, and inflame the contest; but this manoeuvre produced an effect quite contrary to what he expected.

---

1 Avon Street was notorious as Bath's red-light district; its 'nymphs' were the prostitutes who plied their trade there.

It was a note of reproach that roused them to an immediate sense of their disgraceful situation. They were ashamed of their absurd deportment, and suddenly desisted. They gathered up their caps, ruffles, and handkerchiefs; and great part of them retired in silent mortification.

By 17 May, however, the season has come to an end and Jeremy Melford reflects that

all our gay birds of passage have taken their flight to Bristol-well, Tunbridge, Brighthelmstone [Brighton], Scarborough, Harrowgate, etc. Not a soul is to be seen in this place but a few broken-winded parsons, waddling like so many crows along the North Parade.

A SHORT WALK ROUND SMOLLETT'S BATH

And so, even all though the gay birds of passage have long since flown to that great aviary in the sky, we will **waddle along South Parade** to see how much of Smollett's Bath is still left. We do not know where he stayed on his early visits to Bath, but in October 1765, when he came to Bath with Dr Macaulay and his wife Catharine (who features in the sixth walk), he stayed on South Parade. This is also where Matthew Bramble takes lodgings in *Humphrey Clinker* before decamping to Milsom Street.

Walk to the west end of South Parade, turn left along Manvers Street, cross at the pedestrian lights, turn right and then left along Henry Street, before turning right along Old Orchard Street to the old Theatre Royal. This had not been built when Smollett first visited Bath, but in 1757 he wrote a comedy called *The Reprisal, or The Tars of Old England* which received several performances here. Lydia Melford came here twice while staying in Bath and declared that 'the excellence of the performers, the gayety of the company, and the decorations of the theatre ... are very fine.'

Carry on along Old Orchard Street, turn left into Pierrepont Street and left again into North Parade. This was the hub of fashionable Bath in Smollett's day. North Parade, like South Parade, was a cul-de-sac which ended high above the river, and was designed for wealthy visitors to parade up and down. The Huntsman was built in the 1740s as the Parade Coffee House, so it was brand new when Smollett – and Roderick Random – first visited the city. The 1755 *Bath & Bristol Gu*ide informed visitors that Bath's 'two principal coffee houses are that kept by Mr Morgan in the Grove, called Morgan's Coffee House, the other kept by Mr Richard Stephens, called the Parade Coffee House, on account of its fronting the Grand Parade'. Morgan's, built against the east wall of the Abbey, has long gone, but the Parade survives. It may have been the one that Smollett had in mind when he described the rival for Narcissa's affection taking Roderick to a coffee house for a little chat. It may also have been the coffee house

North Parade at the height of the season around 1770

Matthew Bramble visited and found full of sick old men. Perhaps this was a reflection of the coffee houses' changing role – and also of Bath's gradual transformation from sin city to Saga-style holiday destination.

There were two Assembly Rooms nearby – Simpson's (later known as Gyde's) was roughly where the fountain is, Wiltshire's stood where York Street now runs.[1] 'The great scenes of entertainment at Bath,' writes Lydia in *Humphrey Clinker*, 'are the two public rooms; where the company meet alternately every evening. They are spacious, lofty, and, when lighted up, appear very striking. They are generally crowded with well-dressed people, who drink tea in separate parties, play at cards, walk, or sit and chat together, just as they are disposed. Twice a week there is a ball; the expense of which is defrayed by a voluntary subscription among the gentlemen; and every subscriber has three tickets. I was there Friday last. The place was so hot, and the smell so different from what we are used to in the country, that I was quite feverish when we came away. Aunt says it is the effect of a vulgar constitution, reared among woods and mountains; and, that as I become accustomed to genteel company, it will wear off.'

Head to the left of the Huntsman along North Parade Passage (originally known as Lilliput Alley) **and turn right along Church Street to Kingston Parade** (the open space south of the Abbey). This was the site of the Duke of Kingston's Baths. Although these were the most expensive and exclusive baths in the city in the eighteenth century, when Matthew

---

1 Wiltshire's Rooms had closed by the time the New Assembly Rooms opened in September 1771, however, shortly after *Humphrey Clinker* was published, thus rendering the book almost immediately out of date.

Bramble visited them, he was 'almost suffocated for want of free air; the place was so small, and the steam so stifling'.

Matthew Bramble was not impressed by the Abbey either:

The west front of the Abbey, with Gill's pastrycook's on the left

For my part, I never entered the Abbey church at Bath but once, and the moment I stept over the threshold, I found myself chilled to the very marrow of my bones. When we consider, that in our churches, in general, we breathe a gross stagnated air, surcharged with damps from vaults, tombs, and charnel-houses, may we not term them so many magazines of rheums, created for the benefit of the medical faculty? and safely aver, that more bodies are lost, than souls saved, by going to church, in the winter especially, which may be said to engross eight months in the year.

Head to the left of the Abbey, into the Abbey Church Yard. Gill's pastrycook's, where Lydia would 'commonly stop ... to take a jelly, a tart, or a small bason of vermicelli' stood in the alleyway leading to the High Street, and was built against the wall of the Abbey.

Turn left into the Pump Room, built in the 1790s to replace the one Smollett knew. Lydia Melford describes her visits there as follows:

At eight in the morning, we go in dishabille to the Pump-room which is crowded like a Welsh fair; and there you see the highest quality, and the lowest trades folks, jostling each other, without ceremony, hail-fellow well-met. The noise of the music playing in the gallery, the heat and flavour of such a crowd, and the hum and buzz of their conversation, gave me the head-ach and vertigo the first day; but, afterwards, all these things became familiar, and even agreeable. – Right under the Pump-room windows is the King's Bath; a huge cistern, where you see the patients up to their necks in hot water. The ladies wear jackets and petticoats of brown linen with chip hats, in which they fix their handkerchiefs to wipe the sweat from their faces; but, truly, whether it is owing to the steam that surrounds them, or the heat of the water, or the nature of the dress, or to all these causes together, they look so flushed, and so frightful, that I always turn my eyes another way.

Although the Pump Room has been rebuilt since Smollett's day, he would recognise the King's Bath, which the Pump Room overlooks, although the water level is now much lower and there are none of the bathers who so distressed Lydia. If Matthew Bramble's fears about cross-contamination were correct, it is just as well:

After a long conversation with the doctor, about the construction of the pump and the cistern, it is very far from being clear with me, that the patients in the Pump Room don't swallow the scourings of the bathers. I can't help suspecting that there is, or may be, some regurgitation from the bath into the cistern of the pump. In that case, what a delicate beverage is each day quaffed by the drinkers! medicated with the sweat, and dirt, and dandruff, and the abominable discharges of various kinds from twenty different diseased bodies, parboiling in the kettle below.

Kings Bath & Central Spring. Bath. 1442.

He had similar concerns about the King's Bath:

Two days ago, I went into the King's Bath, by the advice of our friend Ch--, in order to clear the strainer of the skin, for the benefit of a free perspiration; and the first object that saluted my eye, was a child full of scrophulous ulcers, carried in the arms of one of the guides, under the very noses of the bathers. I was so shocked at the sight, that I retired immediately with indignation and disgust.

Despite putting such comments into the mouth of Matthew Bramble, Smollett drank and bathed in the waters himself. On one visit he wrote that

I saw one of the guides at Bath, the stoutest fellow among them, who recovered from the last stage of a consumption, by going into the King's Bath, contrary to the express injunction of his doctor. He said, if he must die, the sooner the better, as he had nothing left for his subsistence. Instead of immediate death, he found instant ease, and continued mending every day, till his health was entirely re-established. I myself drank the waters of Bath, and bathed, in diametrical opposition to the opinion of some physicians there settled, and found myself better every day, notwithstanding their unfavourable prognostic.

Having taken the waters (or not, as your fancy takes you), **head out of the Pump Room into Stall Street.** This was where a friend of Matthew Bramble who had fallen on hard times lived:

> Serle lodges in Stall-street, up two pair of stairs backwards, walks a-foot in a Bath-rug, eats for twelve shillings a week, and drinks water as preservative against the gout and gravel.

A little way along Stall Street on the left (where Thornton's and Whittard's now stand) was the Three Tuns Inn (demolished 1812). It was here that Jeremy Melford, in *Humphrey Clinker*, recalled spending an evening with the actor James Quin.

If you **head up to the north end of Stall Street** you will come to the site of another inn, the Bear, which stood where Union Street is today. In Smollett's day, the main route from the baths and Pump Room to Queen Square and the upper town was through the yard of this inn. Matthew Bramble's tirade on the inadequacy of this arrangement can be found on page 7. An Act of Parliament had actually been passed in 1766 – five years before *Humphrey Clinker* was published – authorising the corporation to pull down the Bear and build a thoroughfare on the site. Because of vested interests, however (a member of the corporation held the lease of the inn), it was not demolished until 1806.

Walk up Union Street, cross Upper Borough Walls and carry on up to Milsom Street. When Milsom Street was built in the late 1760s it was a quiet backwater, and the buildings were let as lodging houses. It was here that Matthew Bramble found a quiet retreat after South Parade proved too much for him. The 'small house' he rented cost five guineas a week.

Head left along Quiet Street and Wood Street to Queen Square, which Matthew Bramble considered 'pretty well laid out, spacious, open, and airy; and, in my opinion, by far the most wholesome and agreeable situation in Bath'. It is curious, however, that he includes Queen Square among the 'new buildings' he sets out to see when he arrives in Bath, which implies that he has not seen it before. As it was built between 1728 and 1734 it would, of course, have been there when he visited 30 years earlier.

Head up the east side of Queen Square, cross at the lights and walk up the left-hand side of Gay Street. As you pass the turning on the right into George Street (where most of the traffic also turns right) you can look along to Princes Buildings, at the far end on the left). This is one of the terraces that Lydia found so enchanting, describing 'Princes-row, Harlequin's-row, Bladud's-row … and twenty other rows' as looking like

'so many enchanted castles, raised on hanging terraces'.[1] Gay Street, which continues uphill to the Circus, was where Smollett stayed in the winter of 1766-67. Matthew Bramble's description of it suggests the choice may not have been a felicitous one:

The only entrance to [the Circus] through Gay-street, is so difficult, steep, and slippery, that in wet weather, it must be exceedingly dangerous, both for those that ride in carriages, and those that walk a-foot; and when the street is covered with snow, as it was for fifteen days successively this very winter, I don't see how any individual could go either up or down, without the most imminent hazard of broken bones. In blowing weather, I am told, most of the houses in this hill are smothered with smoke, forced down the chimneys, by the gusts of wind reverberated from the hill behind, which (I apprehend likewise) must render the atmosphere here more humid and unwholesome than it is in the square below; for the clouds, formed by the constant evaporation from the baths and rivers in the bottom, will, in their ascent this way, be first attracted and detained by the hill that rises close behind the Circus, and load the air with a perpetual succession of vapours: this point, however, may be easily ascertained by means of an hygrometer, or a paper of salt of tartar exposed to the action of the atmosphere.

Smollett was seriously ill while staying in Gay Street, as he explained in a letter to John Moore in February 1767:

1 Harlequin Row and Bladud's Buildings can be found on the Paragon. Harlequin Row is the terrace between Lady Huntingdon's Chapel and the Star Inn; Bladud's Buildings is the row on the east side between the junction of Broad Street and the steps down to Walcot Street. Lydia's description may seem fanciful, but you can get some idea of what she meant if you take the steps down to Walcot Street, look back up at Bladud's Buildings and try to imagine what they were like when newly built, unobscured by vegetation and gleaming white in the sunshine.

At my return to Bath, I caught cold, in consequence of which my rheumatic pains retired, and the disorder in my breast recurred ... But these symptoms gave me little disturbance in comparison with the ulcer on my forearm, which continued to spread until it occupied the whole space from about three inches above the wrist to the ball of the thumb so that I was entirely deprived of the use of my right hand, and the inflammation and pain daily increased. In the beginning of November, it was supposed to be cancerous. At that period I could not sleep without an opiate; my fever became continual; my appetite failed; and the rheumatism again invaded me from the neck to the heel. In a word, I despaired of ever seeing the end of winter, and every night when I went to bed, fervently wished that I might be dead before morning. In this situation, I consulted with Messrs Middleton and Sharp, the two most eminent surgeons in England ... I had my hand dressed before them, and proposed a course for the cure, which they approved ... My cure is looked upon as something supernatural; and I must own that I now find myself in better health and spirits than I have been at any time these seven years. Had I been as well in summer, I should have exquisitely enjoyed my expedition to Scotland, which was productive of nothing to me but misery and disgust. Between friends, I am now convinced that my brain was in some measure affected; for I had a kind of coma vigil upon me from April to November without intermission. In consideration of these circumstances, I know you will forgive all my peevishness and discontent; and tell Mrs Moore, to whom I present my most cordial respects, that with regard to me she has as yet seen nothing but the wrong side of the tapestry.

Gay Street: difficult, steep, slippery – and smoky

This last remark shows a good deal of self awareness, and puts some of Smollett's – and Matthew Bramble's – more vituperative outbursts in perspective.

Continuing up Gay Street, we come to the Circus, the foundation stone of which was laid in 1754, but which was not completed until 1766. Although designed by Smollett's hero, John Wood, he could not resist having Matthew Bramble describe it in less than flattering terms:

The Circus is a pretty bauble, contrived for shew, and looks like Vespasian's amphitheatre turned outside in. If we consider it in point of magnificence, the great number of small doors belonging to the separate houses, the

inconsiderable height of the different orders, the affected ornaments of the architrave, which are both childish and misplaced, and the areas projecting into the street, surrounded with iron rails, destroy a good part of its effect upon the eye; and, perhaps, we shall find it still more defective, if we view it in the light of convenience. The figure of each separate dwelling-house, being the segment of a circle, must spoil the symmetry of the rooms, by contracting them towards the street windows, and leaving a larger sweep in the space behind.

But, he continues, this architectural folly will soon be eclipsed:

The same artist who planned the Circus, has likewise projected a Crescent; when that is finished, we shall probably have a Star; and those who are living thirty years hence, may, perhaps, see all the signs of the Zodiac exhibited in architecture at Bath.

It is difficult, if not impossible, to see Bath as Smollett – or Matthew Bramble – saw it. Much of the Georgian city we see today has not changed, in its essentials, for two centuries or more. When it was being created, however, not only would large parts of it have resembled a building site, the buildings going up would have been at the cutting edge of urban design. The Circus was one of the most ground-breaking architectural projects of the age. Today's Bath, where conservation is the watchword and a timid neo-classicism many people's architecture of choice, is totally at odds with the spirit of innovation – combined with ruthless, reckless profiteering – that characterised its development in the eighteenth century. The Bath Smollett knew was constantly growing; every time he returned he would have seen major changes. It is unlikely to have occurred to him that one day the process of change would grind to a halt and the buildings thrown up so hastily be rebranded a World Heritage Site.

4

THE RUDEST MAN IN ENGLAND
An Introduction to Philip Thicknesse

Philip Thicknesse is not a name many people will be familiar with. This is hardly surprising. His literary talents were inconsiderable, as was his output. Insignificant though his published works undoubtedly are, he nevertheless deserves a place in this pantheon of literary giants. In a way few others have managed, he made his life a work of art, in which fiction was the key element. Fêted as the most vituperative man in England – a reputation he went to extraordinary lengths to cultivate – he nonetheless had many friends. This complex, contradictory character, who figured so largely in the social life of Bath in the latter half of the eighteenth century, is not only fascinating in his own right, but provides fresh insights into the milieu in which he operated. As with Smollett, we will begin with a survey of Thicknesse's life, before taking a walk around those parts of Bath associated with him.

He was born in 1719, the seventh son of John Thicknesse, rector of Farthinghoe in Northamptonshire, who died when Philip Thicknesse was six, obliging his widow to move to London to seek the protection of her family.

Philip was sent to Westminster School, from which, having distinguished himself chiefly in the arts of insolence and truancy, he was expelled. After a period as apprentice to an apothecary (terminated due to his partiality for the apothecary's choicest cordials), he resolved to shake the dust of England off his feet and emigrate to Georgia. The year was 1735; he was 16 years old.

Georgia was the newest of the American colonies; the first settlers had arrived there only three years earlier. Their leader was James Oglethorpe, MP for Haslemere, who had chosen the spot for Georgia's capital and named it Savannah.

In 1734, Oglethorpe returned to England, with a group of native Americans, whom he introduced to the king, and started advertising for more settlers. He set sail for Georgia once again on 20 October 1735, along with over 300 emigrants, including dispossessed Highlanders from Inverness, protestant refugees from Germany, debtors from Newgate and Philip Thicknesse. Also on board were John and Charles Wesley, whom Oglethorpe had recruited to tend to the spiritual welfare of the colony. The journey took 14 weeks, during which time Philip Thicknesse acquired a detestation of the Wesleys and their religious teachings that lasted him a lifetime.

Among the first things Thicknesse observed when he set foot on dry land were 20 alligators basking on a mud bank. He quickly fell out with most of the other settlers and decided to set up house about four miles from Savannah, building himself a log cabin on a patch of fertile ground on the banks of a creek which was cut off at high water. He recalled this period of his life in his *Memoirs*:

> My gun supplied me with squirrels, wild fowl, etc ... The Indians sometimes visited my island for a day or two ... This was a true Robinson Crusoe line of life, but it was such as even in those days suited my romantic turn. In this situation I wanted nothing but a female friend, and I had almost determined to take to wife one of Queen Cenauke's maids of honour.[1] I seriously paid my addresses to her and she in return honoured me with the appellation of 'Aucha' – friend. She had received a pair of Indian boots, some paint, a looking glass, a comb and a pair of scissors as token of my love, and one buffalo's skin, which gifts had certainly held us had not an extraordinary incident arose which determined me to return immediately to England, and this it was. Walking upon the margin of my creek and playing upon the flute, such was the effect of an affectionate and warm imagination, that I had a transient, but as perfect a sight of my mother as if she had actually been before me, *in propria persona*.

Back in London, now 18 years old, and finding, contrary to his fears, that his mother was alive and well, he took a job as a clerk in Oglethorpe's office. This was speedily terminated when he presented too frank an account of the fledgling colony to some prospective settlers. He next took a commission as a captain in the army and was sent to Jamaica. Jamaica had a problem: large numbers of maroons – runaway slaves who had established

---

1 Queen Cenauke was the wife of the local tribal leader.

settlements in the hills, from where they made frequent raids on the estates of their former masters. Thicknesse was put in charge of a company of 25 soldiers and instructed to go in search of them. He was told not to bring them in alive, but to kill them and cut off their ears. For every pair of ears he brought in he was promised a reward of £70. Despite this financial incentive, he was unhappy with the arrangement:

> I thank God in that business I was fortunate, for I never gathered a single pair, I thank God too that I very early in life had perception enough to learn that however honourable it may be deemed to invade, disturb or murther men of distant climes, it did not tally with my ideas of justice.

Despite these qualms, Thicknesse supported slavery throughout his life.

During one of these forays into the interior, Thicknesse's company was ambushed by a group of maroons, and it was alleged that he took flight, leaving his sergeant to fight off the attack. He vigorously denied the allegation and published his own account of the incident, in which he played an heroic role. Whatever the truth of the matter, Thicknesse soon fell out with his brother officers, and in 1740 asked for six month's leave in England.

He never returned to Jamaica, becoming instead a Captain of Marines in Southampton. It was not long before he received news that one of his Jamaican acquaintances, Lieutenant Briggs, was in Portsmouth, spreading malicious stories about him. When Thicknesse rode over to Portsmouth to confront him, he found him standing outside the King's Arms Inn,

> very elegantly dressed for the ball, and to do his person justice, he was a very elegant man. He had a sword on, and a cane in his hand, and as I had only a sword, and a small riding stick, I drew a more substantial one out of a bundle which stood to be sold at the next door, and without staying to pay the owner for it, I determined to pay Briggs with it. I believe he saw me draw it out, for before I got over to him, he was as white as the paper I am now writing upon. My word and my blow went in unison at his head and brought forth blood enough to spoil half a dozen brocade waistcoats. He did not draw his sword but struck at me with his cane. I then followed my blows till I had shivered my stick to pieces over him and then I took him, stick and all, and laid him at full length in the gutter of the High Street before the King's Arms door, gave him a blow or two with his own cane and told him he would find me at his service in Southampton.

Back in Southampton, Thicknesse heard that Briggs was likely to die and prepared to flee abroad. Briggs recovered, however, and both he and Thicknesse survived a subsequent duel.

It was at this time that the 23-year-old Thicknesse met and fell in love with Maria Lanove – or rather, with her fortune. The daughter of a rich

Huguenot refugee, she was heiress to a fortune of £40,000, a fact Thicknesse was careful to confirm by travelling up to London and examining her grandfather's will. Maria seems to have been in love with Thicknesse, and he noted in his journal that, 'I believe it is no great matter of difficulty to make a woman who loves a man believe anything he says.'

Her parents, not unnaturally, were opposed to their daughter's liaison with this penurious adventurer, and only allowed her out of the house escorted by a troop of soldiers. Nothing daunted, Thicknesse lay in wait for her, leaped out and announced to her escort that Maria was already his wife. In the subsequent confusion he managed to elope with her. Failing to find a compliant parson, he persuaded a fellow officer to dress as a vicar and perform a wedding ceremony. He then wrote to her parents, inviting them to call and try to persuade their daughter to return home, but added that, when they turned up, Maria and he would almost certainly 'be in bed together'.

Reluctantly, they accepted the situation and arranged for a proper wedding. As Thicknesse was all but penniless, they not only invited the newly-weds to come and live with them but also paid him an allowance of £50 a year. For a time, the arrangement worked tolerably enough (largely, one suspects, because Thicknesse had extended tours of duty in the Mediterranean) and Maria bore him three children. Inevitably, however, he eventually fell out with his in-laws and they cut off his allowance.

So it was that, in 1747, Thicknesse packed his bags and bundled his family off to Bath, where he soon discovered the delights of the EO tables at the Assembly Rooms. He grew so proficient at the game (according to his account) that he made enough to keep his family in the style to which they had become accustomed.

Two years after the Thicknesses arrived in Bath, the city was hit by an epidemic of diphtheria. Thicknesse's wife and children fell ill and he wrote to his mother-in-law asking her to come and nurse them. She refused, recommending that he hire nurses, but contributed nothing towards the cost. Within a matter of days, his wife and two of his children were dead. Fearing that he too was not long for this world, he sent his mother-in-law a valedictory letter:

> Madam, your daughter is dead, your grandchildren are dead, and I apprehend I am dying: but if I recover, the greatest consolation I can have is, that *now* I have no more to do with you.

Thicknesse recovered, but his father-in-law was inconsolable and died soon afterwards. After his death, 'his wife's mind, always cloudy, was so deranged, that she was seldom left alone'. One day, when she was left unattended, she threw herself out of a window, impaling herself on the railings in front of her house in Southampton High Street and dying in great agony. Thicknesse, however, instead of receiving the legacy of £40,000 he had expected, ended up with a mere £5,000. He was still trying to claim the outstanding amount almost 40 years later, when the House of Lords finally ruled against him.

He was soon on the lookout for another wife. Lord Chief Justice Willes, an old acquaintance, introduced him to a rich planter's widow and suggested that Thicknesse compromise her by visiting her in her lodgings on South Parade, going into her bedroom, putting on a nightcap and sticking his head out of the window 'when the walks are full of company'. This he duly did, but he soon lost interest in the rich widow when a more promising catch turned up. This was Lady Elizabeth Touchet, daughter of the sixth Earl of Castlehaven, whose principal attraction, as far as Thicknesse was concerned, was a £5,000 dowry.

Thicknesse was 30 when he married Lady Elizabeth on 10 November 1749, once again against her family's wishes. He used £1,200 of her dowry to buy the lieutenant-governorship of Landguard Fort in Suffolk. His tenure of the fort was predictably stormy, his most serious quarrel being with Colonel Vernon – later Lord Orwell – who was in charge of the Suffolk Militia. Petty disputes over the grazing of animals and the extent of each man's jurisdiction soon escalated, on Thicknesse's side at least, into all-out war. He even bought a printing press to publish attacks on Vernon when he stood as a parliamentary candidate.

Thicknesse and his new wife continued to spend much of their time in Bath. Among those who stayed with them was a remarkable woman called Ann Ford. By the age of 20, she had achieved fame as a virtuoso performer on the viola da gamba, guitar and glass harmonica, despite only performing in private houses. She was also rated, by those who heard her, as one of the top singers in the country. In 1758, for example, the Poet Laureate, William Whitehead, wrote from Bath that

> I have seen Miss Ford, nay almost lived with her ever since I have been here. She has a glorious voice and infinitely more affectation than any lady you know. You would be desperately in love with her in half an hour, and languish and die over her singing as much as she does in performance.

One of those who fell in love with Ann Ford was the Earl of Jersey. Despite being old and infirm – and married – the earl set his sights on her, offering her £800 a year to be his mistress, and promising to marry her when his wife (who was several years older than him and in even worse health) died. Many of Ann's acquaintances – although not the Thicknesses – urged her to accept the offer. Her father was also keen on the arrangement, promising her an extra £200 a year if she bowed to the earl's wishes. Although the earl was 'not disagreeable' to Ann, 'the idea of losing her fame and character shocked her to the soul.'

As news of the stand-off between Ann and the earl spread, Ann, 'fearful it might be interpreted in a manner detrimental to her character', decided to give her side of the story in a pamphlet entitled *A Letter from Miss Fxxd, addressed to a Person of Distinction*, which sold 500 copies within five days of its publication.

Her father, determined that she should become the earl's mistress, kept her under virtual house arrest in London, and forbade her to associate with any of her friends – including the Thicknesses – who took her side against the earl. Eventually she escaped, and, finding herself penniless, decided to give a series of public subscription concerts. She hired the Little Theatre in the Haymarket and engaged some of the finest musicians in London. The cheapest seats cost half a guinea, the best went for 20 guineas, but the concerts were a sell-out.

The first concert was fixed for 18 March 1760. Ann's nervousness at the prospect of performing before the cream of London society was not helped by her father ordering a group of constables to stop the performance and carry her away. The abduction was only thwarted when one of her supporters drummed up a band of soldiers to disperse the constables. Naturally, this only served to increase public interest in the concerts, and, after all expenses had been paid, she ended up with over £1,500.

Ann's business acumen and artistic triumph cut no ice with her father, who 'would rather have seen his daughter the mistress of a nobleman than she should have so dishonoured her family by exerting her talents to preserve her innocence'.

Now a woman of independent means, Ann Ford was the toast of society. She continued to give concerts and published a book of guitar lessons, as well as a manual – the first ever written – for the glass harmonica. It was her portrait that Thomas Gainsborough used as his calling card when he moved to Bath in 1759, on the advice – or so we are told – of Thicknesse.

While at Landguard Fort, Thicknesse had met Gainsborough in his Ipswich studio. He considered his paintings 'truly drawn, perfectly like, but stiffly painted, and worse coloured', and commissioned him to paint a picture of the fort, which was engraved and circulated among his acquaintances. Thicknesse later claimed that

that engraving made Mr Gainsborough's name known beyond the circle of his country residence, and he was soon after by me, and several of his friends, urged to remove to Bath, and try his hand at portrait painting, in that fluctuating city, at which time I had a house there and resided during the winters. After his arrival at Bath, I accompanied him in search of lodgings, where a good painting room as to light, a proper access, etc, could be had, and upon our return to my house, where his wife was impatiently waiting the event, he told her he had seen lodgings of £50 a year, in the church yard, which he thought would answer his purpose.

Above, the portrait of Ann Ford which Gainsborough displayed in his Bath studio; below, Roubilliac's statue of Handel

Gainsborough moved to Abbey Church Yard in June 1760. Among the paintings he displayed in his studio to attract potential customers was a portrait of Ann Ford holding a guitar with a viola da gamba in the background. The art critic, Michael Rosenthal, describes this as 'by far his most ambitious full-length work to date, a portrait of stunning virtuosity and colouristic bravura, in which the silver sheen of the dress is counterpointed by the saturated red of the curtain. It was a canvas calculated to exhibit its painter's exceptional abilities in an image that, although the epitome of refinement, presented the likeness of a woman whose exploits had earned her great notoriety.'

When Mrs Delany visited Gainsborough's studio on 23 October 1760, she described the portrait of Ann Ford as 'handsome and bold', but added that she 'should be very sorry to have anyone I loved set forth in such a manner'. Gainsborough portrayed Ann Ford with her legs crossed above the knee, something eighteenth-century manuals of etiquette advised women strongly against. It was, in fact, a distinctly masculine pose, echoing Roubilliac's famous statue of George Frederick Handel in Spring Gardens at Vauxhall. The allusion would not have been lost on those who saw the painting. The unfeminine nature of Ann Ford's pose is reinforced by a challenging turn of the head. Demure may be an apt word to describe many eighteenth-century female portraits; it is emphatically not appropriate here.

In 1762, Ann Ford went to Landguard Fort to look after Elizabeth Thicknesse, who was expecting her sixth child. Two months after the birth, Elizabeth contracted a liver complaint and died. Thicknesse engaged Ann to look after his children, and, less than six months later, married her. She was 25; he was 43. Despite the difference in their ages, there is little doubt that she was happy with the arrangement. After his death, she recorded that her husband had been 'as remarkable for his sense of penetration, as he was for every amiable quality that can do honour to a man'.

Nevertheless, the marriage did not get off to a good start, as Thicknesse soon found himself up on a charge of libelling a fellow officer. Thicknesse's campaign against Lord Orwell had been slowly escalating, and, when he chanced upon a piece of driftwood shaped like a cannon, he displayed it in Ipswich, with a label attached, accusing Orwell of cowardice. The Affair of the Wooden Gun, as it became known, led to Thicknesse's imprisonment for three months in the King's Bench Prison for libel – the same punishment that had been meted out to Tobias Smollett a couple of years earlier.

Although he was not deprived of the governorship of Landguard Fort, soon after his release from prison he gave it up and moved his family to Datchworth in Hertfordshire. Four years later, his wife received a legacy and, on the strength of this, he took his family on a tour of France, during which he deposited his 'ugliest daughter' in a convent, where she stayed for the rest of her life. On his return he published his *Observations on the Customs and Manners of the French Nation*, followed by *Useful Hints to those who make the Tour of France*. Having got a taste for authorship, his next work was *Sketches and Characters of the Most Eminent and Most Singular Persons Now Living*, published in 1770. In 1772 came *A Treatise on the Art of Decyphering and Writing in Cypher, with an Harmonic Alphabet*.

He also tried his hand at farming. His wife had inherited a farm in Monmouthshire, where they settled on their return from France. Thicknesse quickly developed a strong antipathy to the Welsh climate and the Welsh people and was soon at war with his only neighbour. So, on the strength of another inheritance, he sold up and moved back to Bath.

We do not know where Thicknesse lived in his early years in Bath.[1] In 1768, however, he bought a house in the most fashionable part of town, the

1 Edith Sitwell suggests 6 Walcot Terrace, but this was not built until much later.

Royal Crescent. John Wood the Younger had started building the crescent in 1767 and, although some of the houses at the east end were complete, much of it was still a building site. It was not finished until 1774, the year Thicknesse moved again, to a house called St Catherine's Hermitage on Lansdown.

In 1777, after another European tour, Thicknesse published *A Year's Journey through France and Part of Spain*, his most famous work, which attracted favourable comments from Dr Johnson. The following year, he published *The New Prose Bath Guide for the Year 1778*; two years later he followed this up with *The Valetudinarian's Bath Guide, or The Means of Obtaining Long Life and Health*. In both works Thicknesse went out of his way to court controversy. One of the most notorious sections in the 1780 *Guide* was a chapter 'on long life and health'. Here Thicknesse 'set before such of my readers who covet long life, the mode of obtaining that end ... by indulging themselves in one of the most pleasing gratifications that the human mind can enjoy'. His nostrum was simple. Long life, he declared, could be achieved by 'partaking of the breath of young virgins', adding that 'there is no place else in Britain where the prescription is so easily made up; to be so repeatedly had, nor where it may be so conveniently conveyed by the most lovely of the sex.'

Despite moving to the Hermitage, Thicknesse never gave up society, nor did his wife give up performing. On 29 November 1787, the *Bath Chronicle* announced that

> Mrs Thicknesse will sing Weldon's anthem and a hymn she set to music and accompany herself on the viola da gamba at Walcot Church. Doors open 11am, tickets five shillings. Proceeds to relief of casualties and surgical cases.

A couple of weeks later, it reported that

> it was the general opinion of the audience at St Margaret's Chapel yesterday that the singing of Mrs Thicknesse, in point of sweetness and expression, is not matched even by the first singer of the age.

In 1780, Ann Thicknesse published *Sketches of the Lives of the Ladies of France*; in 1800 she followed this up with *The School for Fashion*, a fascinating autobiographical novel which seems ripe for rediscovery.

Thicknesse is probably best remembered today for his celebrated falling out with Thomas Gainsborough. Thicknesse's side of the story can be found in *A Sketch of the Life and Paintings of Thomas Gainsborough, Esq*, which he published in 1788, a few weeks after Gainsborough's death. 'Mean-minded', 'petty', 'vindictive' are just a few of the adjectives that could quite justifiably be applied to this tedious work. Here is what the art historian Elbert Hubbard has to say about it:

> For books written for the double purpose of downing the subject and elevating the author, Philip Thicknesse's *Life of Gainsborough* must stand first. The book is so bad it is interesting, and so stupid that it will never die. Thicknesse had a quarrel with Gainsborough and three-quarters of the book is given over to a minute recital of 'says he' and 'says I'. It is really only an extended pamphlet written by an arch-bore with intent to get even with his man.

We get a fair idea of what is to come on the first page, when Thicknesse informs us that

> I was the first man who perceived, through clouds of bad colouring, what an accurate eye he possessed ... and who dragged him from the obscurity of a country town, at a time that all his neighbours were as ignorant of his great talents, as he was himself.

The grounds for their disagreement – according to Thicknesse – were as follows: Gainsborough, a keen amateur musician, was particularly taken by one of Ann Thicknesse's violas da gamba. Thicknesse presented it to him in return for an undertaking that he would paint a full-length portrait of him as a companion piece to the portrait of Ann Thicknesse. Gainsborough never got any further than washing in the background, however, and over a ten-year period made no less than 37 excuses for not completing the painting, all the time growing more disenchanted with Thicknesse's unpredictability and pomposity. Gainsborough's wife liked Thicknesse even less, on one occasion remarking that she would prefer to entertain Mephisto, because he at least had a sense of humour. But, even though they nicknamed him Thickhead, they could not shake him off. He treated Gainsborough's studio as though it was his own, telling visitors how he had discovered him and giving them the benefit of his views on art and artists. Eventually, Gainsborough decided that Bath was not big enough for both of them and packed himself and his family off to London. His subsequent success in the capital was, according to Thicknesse, also down to him, as he contacted Lord Bateman to provide Gainsborough with suitable introductions to fashionable society.

As if falling out with England's greatest living painter was not enough, Thicknesse also fell out with his own eldest son, who was the heir, through his late mother, to the baronetcy of Audley. When he was 21 he renounced the name Thicknesse and adopted his mother's maiden name. To say Thicknesse never forgave him is an understatement. He denounced him publicly in his *Queries to Lord Audley*, published in 1782. Six years later, in his *Memoirs*, he described himself on the title page as

PHILIP THICKNESSE
LATE
LIEUTENANT GOVERNOR
OF
LANDGUARD FORT
AND UNFORTUNATELY
FATHER TO GEORGE TOUCHET
BARON AUDLEY

He also made the following bequest in his will:

> I leave my right hand, to be cut off after death, to my son, Lord Audley, and I desire it may be sent to him, in hopes that such a sight may remind him of his duty to God, after having so long abandoned the duty he owed his father who once affectionately loved him.

Shortly after Thicknesse published his *Memoirs*, another work appeared – *Curious Facts and Anecdotes Not Contained in the Memoir of Philip Thicknesse, Esq, by Benjamin Goosequill and Peter Paragraph*. The author was one of Thicknesse's arch-enemies, Dr James Makittrick Adair. It included a poem, 'To Him Who Calls Himself the Unfortunate Father':

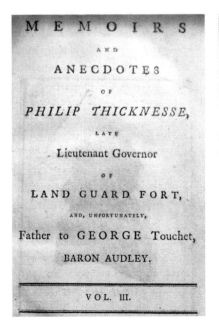
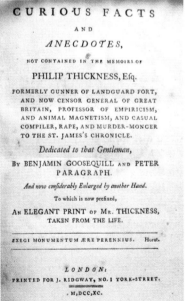

War of words: the title pages of Volume III of Thicknesse's *Memoirs*, with the notorious dedication to his son, and James Adair's pseudonymous response

Think what you please about your son,
But ne'er divulge your thoughts;
For nature says, you ought to hide,
And not expose his faults.

Suppose the wretch's conduct should
Our tend'rest feeling shock;
The world will only smile, and say
The chip is like the block.

Know then, and knowing, pray be still,
(Thou base malignant elf)
That he, who'd make his son a knave,
Must be a knave himself.

Adair had retired to Bath after managing a plantation in Antigua and seems to have been almost as irascible as Thicknesse himself. He described Thicknesse as a 'rape and murder monger'; Thicknesse replied by calling Adair a 'base defamer, vindictive libeller, a scurrilous indecent and vulgar scribbler'. This was very much a case of the pot calling the kettle black. Although Thicknesse seems to have made a reasonable living from writing, much of his income came from works which never saw the light of day. Without putting too fine a point on it, he wrote salacious gossip which people paid him not to publish. Lord Bute, for example, bought up the complete print run – one thousand copies – of some of Lady Wortley Montagu's letters which Thicknesse had seen fit to print. He was quite up front about his blackmailing activities. 'I know not what I should have done,' he wrote, 'to make both ends meet, in my old age, had it not been for the repeated kindnesses of my enemies ... I can at any time muster ten or a dozen knaves and fools, who will put a hundred pounds or two into my pocket, merely by holding them up to public scorn.'

Unlike the other writers featured in these literary walks, Thicknesse may seem like small beer, but, as Katherine Turner says, in her essay on him in the *Oxford Dictionary of National Biography*, 'Thicknesse's career crackles the veneer of politeness which has so influentially coloured our perceptions of the Enlightenment.' It was what he was rather than what he wrote that deserves to be remembered. Certainly, he is not a major literary figure, nor is he easy to read. His style is convoluted, possibly the result of spleen, or more likely the effect of gallstones, from which he suffered throughout his life, compounded by the heroic draughts of opium he took to ease the pain. He started taking opium when he was 23, calling it the 'first cordial in nature'. It was his firm opinion that a man who took up to 20 drops of opium a day would not only live longer and enjoy better health, but would suffer no impairment of his faculties. Unlike De Quincey, he seems never

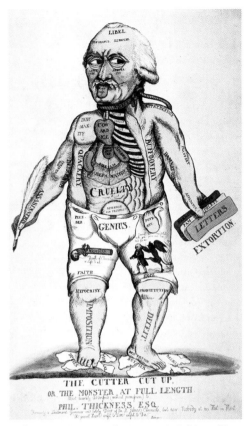

'The Cutter Cut Up or The Monster At Full Length' – a caricature of Thicknesse summing up what many thought of him

to have suffered nightmare visions or paranoia, but his bizarre behaviour makes far more sense when seen in the context of a lifetime of drug abuse.

Any account of Thicknesse must also acknowledge his three happy marriages, especially that to Ann Ford, one of the most celebrated and remarkable women of her age, who has left ample testimony of her regard for him. The epitaph she wrote for him – 'no man ever was his enemy whose friendship was worth coveting' – is echoed by her words at the end of *The School for Fashion*: 'we may venture to affirm, fearless of contradiction, that few men had less failings, but fewer still, possessed his eminent virtues.'

And we must also acknowledge that many of his most unpleasant actions were not reported by others, but by himself. He had a streak of almost transcendent honesty, admitting publicly to things most people would be afraid to admit to themselves. While visiting a hermitage in Spain, for example, the hermit left him alone for a moment. Thicknesse, seeing some chocolate on the table and feeling peckish, pocketed it and quickly left. Not a particularly admirable thing to do, but Thicknesse owned up to it in print without a qualm.

We should leave the last word to him, seated in his Hermitage on Lansdown, looking down on the city he had made his home, looking back too over an eventful life as it drew to its close, and recalling – with Georgia on his mind – the Indian maiden he had abandoned over half a century earlier:

Now that the turbulent scene of life, nay life itself, is nearly over, I would not have it thought that I consider myself so much an unfortunate, as an unlucky man; I set out in life, without any patrimony, and in struggling through it, I have obtained that which every man aims at, but few acquire, SOLITUDE and RETIREMENT, and have not only been in possession of it for some years, but have been sensible that it is the only line in the last stage of life, where, with a few friends, a man can find peace ...

Having lived 72 years on this little mite of the universe, after having lived, and often conversed intimately with men, deemed the greatest, the wisest, and best men of my native country, and with some of other nations; after having tasted moderately of the most

A silhouette of Thicknesse in 1789, when he was 70

exquisite sweets of life, and deeply of its bitters, both in body and mind; after having lived near a whole year in the society only of the native Indians of America, before they had heard a word of Christianity, or John Wesley; had that incomprehensible being who ordained animation to me, condescended to have consulted my spirit, among which race of mortal men I would have been clothed with flesh, I would have preferred the Indian cast of existence to any I have hitherto met with among civilised society.

And then, having listed instances of base behaviour among some of the most esteemed men of his age, he concludes:

I am sure a Creek or Chicasaw Indian could not have been found in America (I mean in the year 1736) who would have committed ... the crimes above recorded: but I will not pretend to say what they may, or may not do, since they have been a little civilised by Messrs Whitfield and Wesley ... So Little England adieu! adieu!

A WALK ROUND THICKNESSE'S BATH

Having made the acquaintance of Mr Thicknesse, it is now time to turn to his two guidebooks – published in 1778 and 1780 – and set off to see the city through his eyes. He leaves a great deal out and pays scant attention to attractions such as the Pump Room and the Royal Crescent. He does, however, include lengthy disquisitions on the health-giving properties and mineral content of the waters, which need not concern us here. He also includes numerous – and extremely tedious – anecdotes about many of his acquaintances, but, as you will probably have had quite enough of that sort of thing already, these too will, for the most part, be passed over.

The walk starts in the same place as the previous one, on **South Parade**, and, as the first part of it follows the same route as the Smollett walk, it is fascinating to see how Thicknesse's and Smollett's views of the city reflect or diverge from each other. It was on South Parade that Thicknesse stuck

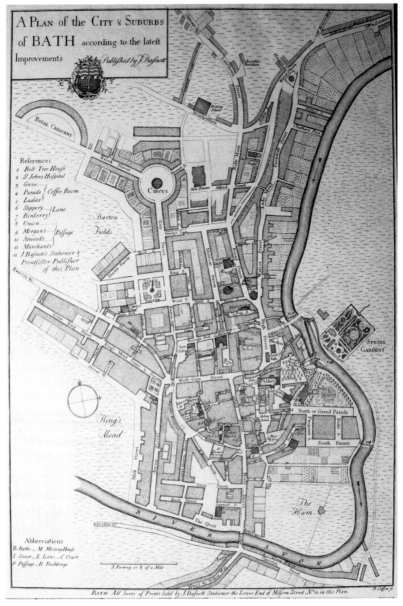

A map of Philip Thicknesse's Bath from around 1780

AN INTRODUCTION TO PHILIP THICKNESSE   81

his head out of the rich widow's bedroom window 'when the walks were full of company'.

In Thicknesses's day, Prior Park, built for Ralph Allen by John Wood, would have been clearly visible from here. Thicknesse's description of it – 'a noble seat, which sees all Bath, and which was built, probably, for all Bath to see' – serves as the prelude to a rapier-like assassination of Allen's character:

> The founder of this house and family was Ralph Allen, of low birth, but no mean intellect ... He was said to bear his great prosperity with humility, and to conduct all business with the utmost probity. That he affected a simplicity of manners and dress we can testify; but we can by no means allow that he was not a man deeply charged with pride, and without address enough to conceal it. His plain Quaker coloured suit of clothes, and shirt sleeves with only a chitterlin [frill] up the slit might, and did deceive the vulgar eye; but he could not bear to let Pope (who was often his visitor) call him what was true (low-born Allen) but made him substitute in its place, that which was false (humble Allen). He was not, however, mean, for we once ate a most magnificent dinner at his table, served to thirty persons, off Dresden china, and he seemed to take infinite pains to shew his munificence in every respect.

At the end of South Parade steps once ran down to a ferry across to Spring Gardens, which – fortunately for their proprietor – Thicknesse approved of:

> Considering their contiguity to so great a city, Spring Gardens, near the New Bridge [Pulteney Bridge], are very delightful, and afford, to all conditions of people, a very rational amusement. About the beginning of April, public breakfasts begin at these gardens on Mondays and Thursdays, which continue all the season; and during the time the company remain in the gardens they are entertained with a good band of music. Mr Purdie, the proprietor, is a good citizen, and spares no expense to render his gardens worthy of that encouragement they merit. Mr Purdie keeps also an excellent lodging and boarding house in Orange Court, the back apartments of which command a view of the gardens. The inhabitants of Bath, or strangers, who choose to walk in these gardens, have them always open by subscribing half a crown for the season.

Walk to the west end of South Parade, turn left along Manvers Street, cross at the pedestrian lights, turn right and then left along Henry Street, before turning right along Old Orchard Street to the old Theatre Royal. Thicknesse described the theatre as

> an elegant edifice, convenient, in every respect, for the audience, as well as the performers; and the performers are such as must be admired for their imitative powers. Mr Palmer has judgement to choose persons of merit, and spirit to reward them; and we will venture to assert that there is no place

in Britain (not excepting even London) where such as delight in the most rational of all amusements can be better entertained than at the theatre in this city ... The play nights are Tuesdays, Thursdays and Saturdays. It is almost needless to say, where so many good musicians dwell, that the playhouse is furnished with an excellent orchestra.

Carry on along Old Orchard Street, turn left into Pierrepont Street and left again along North Parade. The traffic island with the fountain marks the site of the Lower Assembly Rooms, which Thicknesse considered

much inferior [to the New Rooms] in point of magnificence. They have, however, all conveniences, and, from their situation, some advantages ... particularly, a good garden, and a retired walk on the margin of the river. The ballroom is 90 feet long and 36 feet wide.

Carry on to the left of the Huntsman pub to find Sally Lunn's tearoom. Virtually all the historical persiflage on the walls of this building is wrong, and has been known to be so for some time. It is not the oldest house in Bath, nor does it date from 1482. It can, in fact, be dated fairly accurately to around 1622. The earliest known reference to Sally Lunn buns appears in Thicknesse's 1780 *Guide*. One of Thicknesse's older brothers, Ralph, was a master at Eton College before joining the army. He was also a talented violinist and composer, and was performing one of his own works at a concert in Bath on 11 October 1742 when he suffered a stroke and dropped dead. Thicknesse, writing 38 years later, was in no doubt as to the cause of his death:

An early twentieth-century view of Sally Lunn's. The first reference to the iconic comestibles sold here was made by Philip Thicknesse in his 1780 *Guide* – and came with a strong health warning.

I had the misfortune to lose a beloved brother in the prime of life, who dropt down dead as he was playing on the fiddle at Sir Robert Throgmorton's, after drinking a large quantity of Bath waters, and eating a hearty breakfast of spungy hot rolls, or Sally Luns ...

As it is very evident that without health and good spirits, life is a burthen, and these two first of all blessings, cannot be obtained but by exercise and abstinence; it is astonishing that men, especially after the heigh-day of their youth is over, will go on loading their bodies with distemper, pain, and sorrow, till life is not worth accepting, and then repair to Bath, as if the aid of these fountains, without their own, were capable of working miracles, and yet I daily see people who professedly come to Bath for these purposes, first drink three pints or a quart of the Bath waters, and then sit down to a meal of Sally Luns or hot spungy rolls, rendered high by burnt butter! Such a meal, few young men in full health can eat without feeling much inconvenience, and I have known and seen it produce almost instantaneous death to valetudinarians.

Carry on to the end of North Parade Passage (originally known as Lilliput Alley), **turn right and walk along to Kingston Parade.** This is the site of the Duke of Kingston's Baths, of which Thicknesse had this to say:

The Roman Baths, which were discovered in the year 1765 when the Abbey House was pulled down, were laid open for a considerable time, and the great number of years they had been frequented, appeared manifest, by the steps which descended into them, being worn into deep hollows by the foot steps of the bathers; of these Roman baths, sufficient remains are left to show, that they were not only convenient, but sumptuous, they lie about twelve feet, below the present soil, and stood just opposite the south side of the Abbey church. It appears that when the gothic building, called the Abbey House, was pulled down, that it had been built over the remains of the Roman baths, but unknown to be so, to the builders, for between the baths and the foundations of the house, were found to be a great number of large rough hewn stone coffins, in which were the remains of human bodies, as well as a great number of Saxon coins ... The baths, having been first cleared of the rubbish, and a free egress of the waters obtained, the Duke of Kingston caused them to be perfected, and they are now the only place where persons of condition, or delicacy, can bathe decently. Each person pays five shillings each time for bathing in the Duke's Bath.

Regarding the Abbey, Thicknesse was no more impressed than Smollett:

It is very doubtful whether the Abbey Church is not, on many accounts, a very improper place (except to people in full health) to attend Divine Service at. The vast number of bodies buried within the church and near the surface, and the frequency of the ground being opened, before the effect of the putrefaction is over, the doors and windows not being sufficiently, or constantly kept open, renders the confined air perceptibly disagreeable at first entering the church; and, we are told, there is an opening, or ventilator, in the roof, over which if any one place their nose, they will meet, at all times, a stench scarce to be imagined. The malignant sore throat is not very uncommon in Bath, and who can say from what source of corruption it arises? The churches of St James, St Michael, the Octagon or St Margaret's Chapel near the crescent are ... certainly preferable to the Abbey.

It had one redeeming feature, however:

In speaking of the Abbey Church, we are sorry to have pointed out its defects, without giving due praise to a most excellent organ; as we are informed, and believe, there are few church organs in Europe superior to it. Mr Tyley, the organist, a very, decent, civil man, who lives near the New Rooms, furnishes ladies, who make but a short stay at Bath, with very good harpsichords, forte pianos, etc, by the week, or month; and sells all sorts of musical instruments, and music.

The Abbey was associated with another form of music, however, which Thicknesse could not abide:

One of the principal grievances of this city is the bells, which are continually ringing either for joy, sorrow, or for the amusement of a parcel of idle fellows. But the magistrates ought to consider, that in a city where so many miserable, low-spirited sick, and dying people, are disturbed by such peals of noise, it ought not to be suffered ... What can be more dreadful to a poor, worn-out, exhausted wretch, in his last hours, than to be warned of his approaching dissolution, by the great bell that is to announce it? ... The etiquette is, that whoever enters Bath with a set of horses, their arrival must be announced by the clappers of four and twenty bells, while two hundred miserable sick are to be tortured by them. Let the ringers, in God's name, have their fee, when they attend for it; but only when they deserve it, by their silence.

As you **walk through into the Abbey Church Yard**, the building on the corner – now the entrance to the Roman Baths Museum – stands on the site of the house Gainsborough took in 1760, and where Ann

The Abbey, with Gainsborough's house – pulled down in the 1890s – on the right

Ford's portrait was displayed to potential customers. Three years later, Gainsborough moved from this 'house in the smoake' to a more salubrious location on Lansdown Road, but kept the 'painting room and best parlour to shew pictures in'. Four years later, he moved again, to the Circus, but kept his studio here until he left Bath in 1774. It was pulled down and replaced by the present building in the 1890s. All that survives – stowed away in a vault below the Roman Baths Museum – is the pediment that once graced its façade.

Another artist who had – according to Thicknesse – 'a just claim to the notice of every encourager of arts' – was Patience Wright. She was an American who made wax models of the great and the good and had a studio in the Abbey Church Yard. Thicknesse was impressed less by her models than by the 'simplicity of her manners, her strong, natural sense, her vivacity, and the open and honest manner in which she indiscriminately discloses her political sentiments, to persons of whatever rank, condition, or party'. She was, unbeknown to him or indeed to any of those – such as William Pitt and George III – she immortalised in wax, an American spy, who sent information to the colonists inside her wax figures.

If you **go into the Pump Room**[1] **on the south side of the Abbey Church Yard**, you will see, from a viewing platform near the Stall Street exit, the King's Bath, which occasioned some of Thicknesse's most memorable observations:

> Neither sex can come out of the King's Bath without being stripped quite naked by an old woman, who takes off the wet and puts on dry apparel. For our part, we think being thus stripped by an old hag, alive, is little better than being served the same sauce when dead in the field of battle. Or whether it is contrasting the matter, by considering the difference of being stripped by an old woman, or stripping oneself, to meet a young one, we cannot say; but it is somehow a painful operation; and it is worthy the consideration of the corporation, whether the slips where the bathers dress and undress might not be made more commodious? ...
>
> There is indeed a singular amusement in bathing, which none but those who have experienced the effect can well conceive, and which is only to be perceived in certain parts of the bath: spots, well known to the guides, and which they seldom omit leading their bathers into. Thirty years since being in the King's Bath, and near a goodly looking country woman, she was either led, or accidentally stept over
>
> '*Where the bubbling fountain flows*'
>
> Which she had no sooner done, than she called out most lustily, so as to alarm me, and every one near her! And upon asking her the cause, she again

---

1 The present Pump Room is not the one Thicknesse would have known, but as he pays it scant attention, we can pass quickly through.

called out, and in agitation, exclaimed, 'I have been mother of ten children!' Not understanding what she meant, I desired to change places with her, and then I recollected I too, had been father of as great a number. Those who wish to be further informed I must refer to an experienced Prose Guide ... If the author should be charged, with treating a serious subject wantonly, let it be remembered that he did it with a virtuous intention, and to show, how indecent it is, for men and women to bathe promiscuously. The man who can look on a fair woman in loose attire, whose beauty is heightened by the glowing warmth of the bath, with an eye of indifference, must be one of the male sex, I fortunately, have never yet met with, and if the good countrywoman, who with the most perfect simplicity of manners, could be suddenly alarmed, who can say that the most chaste virgin who ever dabbled in warm water, may not, by making a false step over these fountains, be alarmed also. Is this the place then, where the sexes are to meet, in a manner half naked? Nay often join hands, as in the dance, to conduct each other from recess to recess? Surely not.

Head into Stall Street (either through the Stall Street exit or, for a step-free alternative, via the Abbey Church Yard). Stall Street was once lined with coaching inns, most of which disappeared in the late eighteenth or early nineteenth centuries when the street was widened. Thicknesse would undoubtedly have approved of them being cleared away:

> Who would lodge, or even put up for a night or two, in such a dark, narrow, dirty, noisy place, as Stall Street, when they can find better accommodations, a pure air, clean streets, and little noise, within a few hundred yards of it?

Head west along Bath Street, turning left at the end to find the Hot Bath, built by John Wood the Younger and opened in 1778, as Thicknesse was preparing the first of his *Guides* for publication:

> Since the sheets in which we have mentioned the Duke of Kingston's Baths were printed off, we have been (by favour) admitted to see the New Baths, now almost finished, near what is called the Cross Bath. The building over this hot spring has been erected at a very great expense, and with every degree of convenience and elegance which the most delicate person of either sex can conceive or desire. There are four private apartments, which have fireplaces, water closets, etc, contiguous to the baths, which, by water gates, are made as private as a bathing tub in a dressing room. Into these private baths the bathers descend by an easy flight of steps, which accommodate them to the depth most suitable to their height, or ease. Contiguous to these baths are two sudatories; a steam bath; dry pump; and, in short, every mode of using these excellent waters, either for health or pleasure, which can be desired. Over the baths and dressing rooms, large reservoirs are fixed, to retain the hot water to feed the baths for those who use them at different hours, as well as reservoirs for rain water or cold bath water, to lower the degree of heat (for this is the hottest of all the springs) for such who find it too violent.

Upon the whole, we may say, no part of Europe can boast of baths, in all respects, so well contrived, nor more completely finished, than these new baths. This building has been raised under the direction of Mr Wood; nor has he, or his father, among all the various buildings they have been employed in erecting about this city, raised a single edifice, which has, in our opinion, been so perfectly complete in all its parts ... Here, I am told, the corporation have very wisely determined, that each bather shall pay only one shilling each time, which, even with chair hire, guide, etc, will not shut out patients of moderate fortune; while those who bathe at the Duke's Bath had need possess a little of her Grace (the Duchess's) fortune.

Today the Hot Bath has been incorporated into the Bath Spa complex.

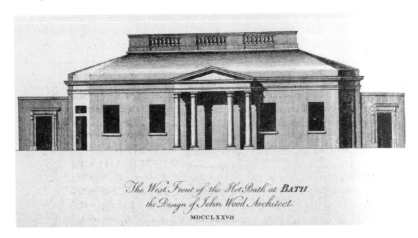

The West Front of the Hot Bath at BATH
the Design of John Wood Architect
MDCCLXXVII

Walk down Hetling Court (beside the old Hetling Pump Room). Here was the studio of Robert Edge Pine, whom Thicknesse described as 'one of our best portrait painters [and] the best historical painter in England ... The portrait of Mr Garrick, and several well-known persons of distinction ... may be seen at his house.' We will be meeting Pine, who was a fervent republican and supported American independence, in the sixth walk.

Carry on along Hetling Court and turn right into Westgate Buildings. At 2 Westgate Buildings – on the other side of the road on a site now occupied by Pizza Hut – was the studio of Thomas Beach. Thicknesse wrote of him that 'we do not know a portrait painter who is more happy in giving a strong likeness, nor a more worthy, good-natured, honest man.'

Carry on up to the Sawclose and the Theatre Royal. The Garrick's Head, to the left of the theatre, occupies a house built for Beau Nash around 1720. Thicknesse, writing 50 years later, had this to say about it:

In St John's Court, now a dirty and unfashionable area of Bath, stands empty the house in which Mr Nash lived and died, and which was almost the first house built in Bath which attracted notice by its external ornaments; within, indeed, it was furnished with the beauties of the age, painted in crayons, chiefly by the ingenious Mr Hoare; and the palace of the King of Bath, was then, both within and without, a first sight for strangers. But, alas! How perishable is all human greatness.

To see where William Hoare lived, **walk up to Queen Square.** Hoare's first house, when he came to Bath in 1738, was on the east side of Queen Square at No 4. By the time Thicknesse was writing, however, he had moved to a more fashionable address. **Carry on up the east side of Queen Square, continue up the east side of Gay Street, turn right into George Street, carry on across the top of Milsom Street and cross at the pelican crossing.** According to Thicknesse, by 1778, Hoare was living in Princes Buildings – the block to your right. However, this seems to have been a mistake, as records show that he lived at 4 Edgar Buildings, along to the left and now occupied by a cocktail bar called Sub 13. Thicknesse considered that 'it is almost needless to mention Mr Hoare, whose long residence at Bath has made his genius for painting in crayons, and oil, universally known.' Hoare was born in Suffolk and

Edgar Buildings, with a circus parade passing, around 1900

studied in London and Italy before settling in Bath around 1740. He was one of the co-founders of the Royal Academy; one of his greatest works, *The Pool of Bethesda*, painted for the Octagon Chapel in Bath, can be seen in the old Theatre Royal in Old Orchard Street.

On the other side of George Street, the Royal York – now a Travelodge – was originally the York House Hotel, built by John Wood the Younger and opened in 1769. Thicknesse regarded it as 'an excellent hotel and inn … It stands in an airy and central situation, the host is a gentleman, and the traveller will of course be politely and properly entertained.'

Carry on to the end of Edgar Buildings and turn right by the Porter pub along Miles's Buildings, bearing right at the end and then left up to Alfred Street. Thicknesse singled out 14 Alfred Street for special mention:

> We must not overlook Alfred House, the residence of that great historian Mrs Catharine Macaulay, and the greatest of all patriots, the Rev Dr Thomas Wilson. This house is, at present, particularly marked, by having the bust of King Alfred over the door. But as all things animate, as well as inanimate, are perishable, we think pointing out the very spot to future generations, where two such extraordinary personages dwelt, ought not to be omitted.

This paean, which appeared in the 1778 *Guide*, is – if you haven't already guessed – ironic, as Thicknesse, along with many who did not share her republican sentiments, regarded Mrs Macaulay as a figure of fun. He devotes several pages to a detailed description of her birthday celebrations a year earlier, but, as we will be encountering her again in the sixth walk, we will turn our attention to Thicknesse's description of the Assembly Rooms, across the street from Alfred House:

> We will hazard pronouncing them to be the first of the kind in Europe. But, while we confess our admiration of the whole, both within, and without, we lament, that the upper town inhabitants seem to have (like the American Congress) a strong tendency to withdraw themselves from the parent state ... It must also be confessed, that, on a ball night, in a full season, when all the benches are filled with ladies in full dress, the rooms magnificently lighted by wax, the splendour of the lustres, girandoles, and the superlative charms of so many lovely women, whose natural beauties being awakened by the variety of amusements which, on all sides, surround them – renders it one of the most pleasing sights that the imagination of man can conceive; and what, we are convinced, no other part of Europe can boast of ... It is always remarked by foreigners, that the English nation, of both sexes, look as grave when they are dancing, as if they were attending the solemnity of a funeral ... We are aware that the ladies think gravity of countenance a necessary attendance on modesty and sentiment; but, till they can prove that a cheerful pleasing smile is incompatible with virtue, prudence, or discretion, we must beg leave ... to

LITERARY WALKS IN BATH

assure them, that they cannot bestow, on mortal man, a more pleasing nor a more innocent mark of their public favour, than by showing their features, under the advantage of a smile.

Despite his criticism of the residents of the upper town, he shared their prejudice against the lower part of the city:

> There cannot remain a doubt, but that the new buildings, from their more elevated situations, the width of the streets, the free circulation of fresh air, as well as the clean manner in which they are kept, must have a purer air than the lower parts of the city, where we have observed, for a long time together, near the old town hall, such dunghills of fish offals, of flesh, and refuse of garden stuff, which were sufficient to breed the plague. Perhaps the putrid sore throats, observed above to be no uncommon disorder in Bath, may have arose from that shameful neglect in the police of the city ... We very much doubt, whether the lower part of Bath would not be a very unwholesome residence, were it not that the air is constantly ventulated by the steams which the influx of the hot waters occasion ... They have lately given us, in this city, a noble instance of their desire to embellish it, by erecting so handsome a structure as the new town hall; and we hope they will consider, that unless the markets and environs are particularly attended to in the matter of cleanliness, all their magnificence will be disregarded. The lower part of Bath stands upon a hard rock, all conveniences are above ground; and whatever is thrown upon the surface, remains there, till it has evaporated.

Elsewhere in the 1778 *Guide*, he remarks on the contribution of 'butchers' stinking meat, concealed till it can be conveyed privately into the river', to the putrid atmosphere of Bath. 'The butchers,' he explains in a footnote, 'rather than sell to the poor at an under price, have often large quantities of stinking meat, which they privately convey to the river. If a sin of so deep a dye is punishable, or can be prevented by the magistrates of this city, it is hoped they will attend to it. The corruption of the water by stinking fish and flesh thrown into the river, in dry seasons, certainly is punishable; and we hope the butchers, fishmongers, etc, will remember, that, if they can escape the punishment of man for such enormous crimes, that they cannot conceal it, nor, we fear, atone for it to God.' This accusation led to Thicknesse being attacked by the mob – an incident which is dealt with on pages 96-7.

Head past the Assembly Rooms, turn left along Bennett Street and right into the Circus, where you will find Gainsborough's house at No 17. Gainsborough was the first occupant of the house and one of the carvings reflects his love of music.

Head west out of the Circus along Brock Street. The archway between Nos 20 and 21 is on the site of the entrance to the chapel where in 1787 Ann Thicknesse sang and played on the viola da gamba to such acclaim.

Carry on to the Royal Crescent, which Thicknesse moved to in 1768. He is believed to have lived at No 8. Five years later, writing to a friend, he described his daily routine:

> Here I can go to the coffee house and spend two hours from seven to nine; I can look round me and see seven or eight men – all of general knowledge, and some skilful in some particulars, and then suit my present mood to the conversation I feel most inclined to partake of – age and youth, fun and gravity. The manager of the theatre has given me the run of his house, so I sometimes take a bit of our friend Shakespeare's wit, add to this, for five shillings each subscription (three in the year) there is a good library, well furnished with books and well warmed with fires, where you may always find men of sense, clothed either in woollen or calf-skin. I might add the balls, the concerts, etc; but I seldom go to either, but have often music at home.

For a man seeking peace and quiet, the Royal Crescent was not a wise choice. Not only was it a building site for much of the time Thicknesse was there; it quickly became the most fashionable spot in town for promenading. On one sunny January morning in 1780, for example, Edmund Rack (another of Thicknesse's adversaries) saw between 3,000 and 4,000 people promenading in front of the Crescent, making it 'quite full from point to point'.

Thicknesse was already tiring of the social whirl – or so he claimed. But, instead of moving to some remote spot, he simply moved a little way up the hill. In 1774, after living in the Royal Crescent for six years, he sold up for £2,000 and moved to a newly-built house called St Catherine's Hermitage set in its own grounds. Largely due to Thicknesse's reputation – and his eccentric ideas of garden design – it soon became one of the city's top tourist attractions. He even published a guidebook to the garden.

Although the house where Thicknesse lived is no longer there, the garden has survived, although without most of the ornaments he added to it. It is in private hands and only a very limited view can be gained of it, but for those wishing to get some idea of Thicknesse's last residence in Bath, **head north** along Upper Church Street (to the east of the Royal Crescent), turn left along Crescent Lane and cross Julian Road at the zebra crossing. Turn left and then right along St James's Street to St James's Square. Head to the far corner of the square and walk up Park Street. At the top, carry on up a footpath and continue up All Saint's Road to Lansdown Place West, to the left of which you will see a high wall. The grounds of Thicknesse's Hermitage lie behind that wall, although, when he owned it, not only was there no wall, there were no buildings on either side. With the exception of his house and garden this was open country, with uninterrupted views across the valley. You may be able to glimpse the garden over the wall; otherwise, you can walk a little way up Somerset Lane to see the gateposts to the Hermitage, or a little way up Upper Lansdown Mews (under the archway linking Lansdown Place West and Lansdown Crescent), where a turning to the left provides another view over the garden.

We will conclude with some extracts from Thicknesse's Guide to the Hermitage:

> It commands a south-west prospect, and hangs on the side of Lansdown hills, and so close under a high tump to the north, that we are perfectly sheltered from the severe winds of that quarter, and in a great measure from the east winds also.

S.t CATHERINE'S HERMITAGE near BATH

From my little study window, however, I look down upon Bath with that indifference, which age, and a long knowledge of its contents, or rather discontents, have furnished me, and with infinite pleasure on a mile and a half of the gentle Avon gliding down the vale, and now and then, seeing the swelling bosom of deep-laden barks freighted with merchandise; which I consider as returning messengers, whom I have sent forth to fetch me tea from Asia, sugar from America, wine from France, and fruit from Portugal.

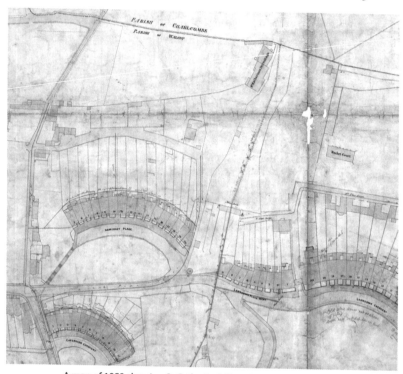

A map of 1852 showing St Catherine's Hermitage set back behind Somerset Place and Lansdown Crescent

No little spot of ground can be more beautifully irregular, broken, and divided, than this dingle; and no wonder; for it is as God formed it, and as He willed the stately trees to grow, which shade it, and who causes the whole surface annually to be covered with the primrose, violet, and all the elder sisters of the spring ... The inclosed drawing [reproduced on page 93] is sketched from a point, in which only a bit of the house is seen, peeping through the trees. You will see however, the hermit's hut, built on the side of the dingle, at which we chiefly reside in the summer.

Three stone coffins have been dug up, two Saxon and one Roman; the latter had the body in it, quite perfect, and some of the flesh on the skull. It had been covered with a pickle ... Near a rude arch, on all sides embraced with the twisted eglantine, is a perforated rock-stone, from which constantly runs a small stream of the purest water imaginable, that falls into a Saxon coffin dug up hard by; from the length and narrowness of which I have disposed myself to believe the body which I found in it to be that of a beautiful Saxon virgin; so that instead of being hurt with the idea of its original use, it is become only a memento of what we must all come to. And who knows but 'some kindred spirit' may, a thousand years hence, make the same use of my departed daughter's coffin; which, alas! lies hard by, and in close contact with the old Roman knight's mentioned above, which is to receive what remains of myself .

Some years since I had scooped out a cave on the side of the dingle, under the spreading root of an ash tree, and turned a rude arch in front of it; and there placed, cut in relief, the head of that wonderful genius Thomas Chatterton, with the following lines beneath it:

Sacred to the Memory of
THOMAS CHATTERTON.
Unfortunate Boy!
Short and Evil were thy Days,
But the Vigour of thy Genius shall immortalize Thee.
Unfortunate Boy!
Poorly wast Thou accommodated,
During thy Short Sojourning among us.
Thou livedst unnoticed,
But thy Fame shall never die.

Thicknesse's plan to be buried in this Arcadian grove of departed spirits was frustrated when he succumbed to the grim reaper while on holiday in France and was buried there.

We cannot leave Thicknesse without mentioning the extraordinary account in his *Memoirs* of 'An Attack by the Mob ... at the Author's House at Bath-Hampton'. Having upset Bath's butchers by the accusations levelled at them in his 1778 *Guide*, he further inflamed their wrath by tricking one of his servants into accompanying him to Bristol where he arranged for him to be seized by a press gang and forced on board ship. He did this after one of his maids had persuaded him to employ the young man, who then got her in the family way and broke off the relationship. Thicknesse was so incensed by this that he decided to teach him a lesson he would never forget. He takes up the story:

Soon after I had finished the *Prose Bath Guide*, in which I had told some tales out of school, that proved offensive to some butchers and dishonest tradesmen, the mob ... assembled to the amount of some hundreds, in order to beset my house, or destroy me, under the pretence that I had caused my man to be treacherously impressed at Bristol ... Soon after my return, being, at Bath, a mile and a half from my house at Bath Hampton, I was informed that a mob, consisting of some hundreds, were gone to pull my house down.

I immediately ordered a chaise from York House, to fetch my wife and two daughters to town, and followed the empty chaise on horseback, previously putting pistols into my saddle. I found men, women and children sitting upon the road side, and asking them what occasion brought them thither, they informed me, 'I should soon know,' and as I passed a mow, two men on top of it struck their forks down at me with such force, that had either of them hit me or my horse it might have destroyed us. When I came within a mile of Bath Hampton, I heard the shouting of voices, rattling of tins, sounding of horns, etc, and upon a hundred yards nearer approach, I saw a grimalkin hanging in a tree, which I supposed to be a representation of the offender. Upon entering the town neither I nor the chaise could hardly approach my house, for the numbers which surrounded it; I said nothing, however, till I had put my family in it, and seen them drove off towards Bath ... Upon such occasions as these, in spite of whatever apprehensions may lurk in the bosom, the safest way is, to pretend at least, not to be apprehensive of personal danger; I therefore stood my ground, till all the mobility had gathered around me, and then with the appearance of good temper, asked them the cause of their assembling, and whether they had anything to charge me with, from which I could not defend and justify myself. They said I had, in a most treacherous manner, taken my servant with me to Bristol, and sent him out to buy lemons, in order to throw him into the hands of a press gang, who had confined him on board a tender. As all things under the sun are governed by women, and as many of my assembly were of that sex, I considered it safest (for I did not think myself safe) to appeal to them. I observed that many of them knew our Betty, that she was a handsome, and I will add, said I, a virtuous girl, that John had, under the most solemn promises of marriage, seduced and ruined her, and now refused to fulfil his engagements, that I had rendered him services, and now wished to do so by the woman he had so highly injured. And as we were in sight of the tree where my effigy was suspended by a rope, I took occasion to observe, that by the laws of this country, no man ought either to be condemned, or executed without a trial, and a jury of his countrymen; but as they had hanged me first, I begged that they would try me afterwards, and instantly declared my willingness to have a jury of twelve women impannelled upon the spot, and that I would submit to a trial, and to the sentence of that female jury.

Thicknesse was acquitted with honour, on condition that he arranged for his servant to be released. His effigy was cut down, and the next day he placed a barrel of beer upon the spot 'and I and my neighbours became better friends than ever'.

What is curious about this account is that Thicknesse tells us he was living at Bathampton after the publication of his 1778 *Guide* – four years after he had moved to the Hermitage on Lansdown. We know he was still at the Hermitage when he published his *Memoirs* in 1788, so what was he doing at Bathampton? Was he living there temporarily while work was being carried out at the Hermitage? Did he have two houses? We can only speculate. The confusion can be laid squarely at the door of Thicknesse and his failure to explain what he was doing at Bathampton – yet another enigma in the life of this paradoxical and problematic man.

The most remarkable thing about this incident, however, is that it took place at all. This was not the wild west or some god-forsaken moorland fastness – this was the Bath that George Austen had got married in over 20 years earlier, the city his daughter was to immortalise in *Northanger Abbey* a decade later – the most wealthy, fashionable and elegant place in the country outside London. Smollett showed us how often the veneer of refinement masked behaviour of appalling vulgarity; Thicknesse just gives us the vulgarity – condemning himself, as much as others, in the process. Jaundiced, splenetic and more than a little bonkers his take on eighteenth-century Bath society may have been, but it is a healthy antidote to the frilled and furbelowed version so often inflicted on us.

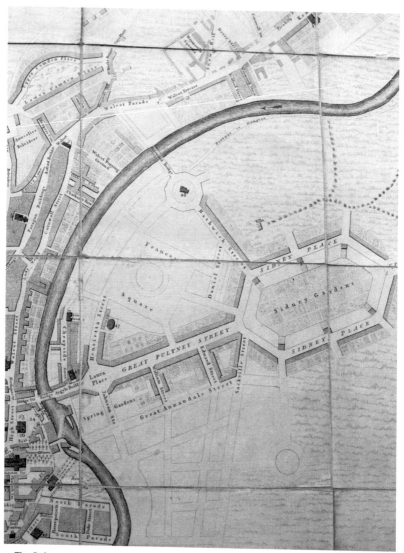

The Pulteney Estate in 1793, with intended streets, crescents and squares on either side of Great Pulteney Street, Sydney Gardens ringed by projected buildings, and the old church of Bathwick in the centre of a circus. None of this ever came to pass. Bathwick Villa, visited by Fanny Burney in 1780, before the development of the Pulteney Estate got under way, can be seen in the fields north of Sydney Gardens. South Parade, where Fanny Burney stayed with the Thrales, can be seen at bottom left.

5

PLEASURE, PAIN AND GRIEF
Fanny Burney in Bath

Fanny Burney is still remembered today – there is even a Burney Society – but her name is certainly not as well known as that of Jane Austen, whose books have captured the public imagination when translated to film or television. Yet in her day, Fanny was far better known, and her first book, *Evelina*, was a sensation which brought her instant fame.

Fanny Burney, after a portrait by her cousin Edward Francisco Burney

In many ways, Fanny Burney was a mass of contradictions. She is seen as a feminist writer leading the way for female novelists but was under the thumb of her father and his friend Samuel Crisp, whom she called 'Daddy' and had a curious, quasi-flirtatious relationship with. Despite being shy and nervous, she relished her fame. She was an acute observer of human nature, but there was frequently a spiteful touch to her comments, which makes her diaries fascinating reading. She trembled when King George III, in one of his periods of mental disturbance caused by porphyria, ran after her calling her name and demanding to speak to her[1], but coolly underwent a mastectomy without the benefit of anaesthetics when in her forties.

In an age when most genteel ladies such as Jane Austen lived lives confined to their social circle, Fanny found herself caught up in adventures which varied from the occasionally nerve-wracking but often tedious life at court to the excitement of Napoleon's return to France and ensuing defeat at Waterloo. At a time when unmarried women were considered to be on the shelf by their late twenties, as Ann Elliot is in Jane Austen's *Persuasion*,

---

1 However, as TH White acutely noted in *The Age of Scandal*, her fear seems to have been mingled with a certain flirtatious excitement at having captured the king's attention.

Fanny Burney married her beloved Count D'Arblay when she was 41 and gave birth to her only child Alexander a year later.

Throughout this remarkable life she made frequent visits to Bath, and was resident here for three years. Here she rejoined the other members of her family who had made Bath their home. Here, too, she met many old acquaintances and made new ones, whom she described with a shrewd and sometimes cynical eye. It was not always a happy time. As Fanny herself wrote to her son after the first visit of Queen Charlotte in 1817:

> We have here spent nearly a week in a manner the most extraordinary, beginning with hope and pleasure, proceeding to fear and pain, and ending in disappointment and grief.

That could almost be a summary of her life.

She was the fourth child and second daughter of Charles Burney and his wife Esther. He was a talented musician who was apprenticed to the composer Thomas Arne. It was not a happy relationship, Arne being reluctant to teach Burney, whom he saw as a potential rival. However, he allowed him to spend time with Fulke Greville, a rich and well-connected gentleman who adored music.

In 1747 Greville brought Burney to Bath, where Burney played in the Assembly Rooms and was well received. Here he met other musicians who were making a name for themselves, such as Thomas Chilcot, the Abbey organist, who would later promote Handel's music in Bath, and his apprentice, the 14-year-old Thomas Linley, who would go on to father an extraordinarily musical family. Despite this, Burney claimed that the only music he heard at the Assembly Rooms was minuets and country dances. Here Burney watched fascinated as the rich and famous gambled huge sums of money at the EO tables[1], and entertained the aristocracy by playing Scarlatti to them on an old harpsichord hired from Chilcot. The two young men clearly enjoyed themselves, and each other's company.

Keen to have Burney as his permanent companion, Greville negotiated with a reluctant Arne to free Burney from his apprenticeship. Shortly after returning to London, Greville eloped with the beautiful Frances Macartney. He had no need to do so – both families approved – but Greville thought it would add spice to the marriage, and Burney, not her father, gave the bride away.

Greville was not the only one in love. Burney had met Esther Sleepe, the daughter of another musician and a talented harpsichordist herself. When Greville told Burney he and his wife were going abroad, and asked him to go with them, Burney told him he wished to stay at home, and marry

---

1 EO had been made illegal in 1745, but the law was openly flouted.

Esther, showing Greville her portrait. The susceptible Greville, charmed by her beauty, readily gave his blessing, but when he attended the wedding as witness, on 25 June 1749, he found it was also a christening of the Burneys' daughter Esther (always known as Hetty), who had been born in January of that year.

Burney, now without an income, took on a variety of jobs, as a music teacher, *répétiteur* for Handel, organist at a fashionable City of London church and finally composer and musician at Drury Lane theatre. He was making important connections, but after the birth of two further children and the death of one, he was taken ill in 1751, possibly as a result of overwork. For his health the family moved out of London, and eventually settled in King's Lynn, in Norfolk – or Lynn Regis, as it was then known. It was here that the Burneys' second daughter was born, on 13 June 1752. She was christened Frances, after her godmother, Mrs Frances Greville. Although it is the custom in America to refer to her as Frances Burney – which is the name you will find her under in Wikipedia – she was never known by this name, but always as Fanny.

In 1760, the Burneys moved back to London with five children in tow. Although her elder sister, Hetty, had already performed in public on the harpsichord, Fanny was not only unmusical but a late developer. Even her younger sister Susan was able to read before Fanny could. She was also shy – not helped by extreme short-sightedness and lack of height – but enjoyed participating in the joyful games played by the family, and used the secret terms invented by her brothers and sisters. She had too a remarkable memory, committing to heart extracts from books and poems. However, the happy family was soon to suffer a tragic loss when, shortly after giving birth to another girl, Charlotte, Mrs Burney's health began to deteriorate rapidly, and she died in 1761. Fanny was grief-stricken.

Charles Burney, left with six children ranging in age from twelve years to ten months, muddled along for some years, aided generously by his and Esther's families. Fanny particularly enjoyed the company of her maternal grandmother. She also began to write – not just short pieces but an entire novel. But all these juvenile writings would soon be destroyed by fire. Unknown to the family, Charles began courting a family friend from King's Lynn, the widowed Mrs Elizabeth Allen. Relations between Fanny and Mrs Allen, who soon became her stepmother, were never good. Mrs Allen made it plain to Fanny that she disapproved of girls writing, and on her fifteenth birthday, Fanny consigned all her manuscripts to a bonfire, vowing never to write again. Was this an attempt to ingratiate herself with Mrs Allen or a fit of pique at the criticism? Probably the former – in her memoirs of her father, Fanny indicates that the girls were anxious to do everything in their power to please their new stepmother.

Mrs Allen's acceptance of Burney's proposal of marriage led to Fanny's first visit to Bath in 1767. Burney had to go to Bristol, to persuade Mrs Allen's brother that he was a suitable husband for her, and he took Fanny with him. On their way back, they stayed for three days in Bath, but as Fanny was still sticking to her vow never to write again – a vow that fortunately would soon be broken – we have no record of this visit. Nine months later, Fanny had renounced her vow and begun the journal that she would keep, on and off, for the rest of her life.

It is thanks to this journal that we know so much about Fanny's second visit in 1780, by which time she was a celebrity. Despite her stepmother's disapproval, and encouraged by 'Daddy' Crisp, she had quietly written a book mainly for her sister Susan's amusement, called *Evelina or a Young Lady's Entrance into the World*. She decided it should be published, but wrote it out in a disguised hand for fear her own should be recognised, as she had acted as her father's secretary for some time. Then her brother Charles, heavily disguised, took it to a publisher, and it appeared anonymously in 1778. It immediately received highly favourable notices, and trying to guess the author's identity became the topic of the day in fashionable society. Fanny steeled herself to show it to her father. Far from being angry, he was enchanted as, perhaps surprisingly, was her stepmother. Burney was so proud of his daughter, he began to tell his friends. Among them were Mr Thrale, an MP and brewer from Streatham, and his wife, Hetty. Mrs Thrale, who had gathered round her a coterie of artists and writers, including Dr Johnson, insisted on meeting Burney's talented daughter.

The impulsive Hetty Thrale and the rather shy Fanny Burney became friends. No one could be stiff with Hetty Thrale for long. Fanny also found that, unlike almost everybody else who met him, she was completely at ease with Dr Johnson, while he was charmed by her. Fanny stayed with the Thrales frequently, and when Mr Thrale was told to go to Bath for his health in 1780, following a stroke, Fanny was invited to go with them. When the party arrived in Bath, they put up at the York House Hotel, which

Philip Thicknesse was so complimentary about. Fanny described what happened next:

> Mrs Thrale sent immediately to Sir Philip Jennings Clerke, who spent the Easter holidays here. He came instantly, with his usual alacrity to oblige, and told us of lodgings upon the South Parade, whither in the afternoon we all hied, and Mr Thrale immediately hired a house at the left corner. It was most deliciously situated; we have meadows, hills, Prior Park, 'the soft-flowing Avon' – whatever Nature has to offer, I think, always in our view. My room commands all these; and more luxury for the eye I cannot form a notion of.

It is here, at No 14 South Parade, overlooking the river, that our walk starts. In Fanny's enthusiasm for her room with a view, she seems to have forgotten Evelina's lukewarm response to the Parades:

> The Parades, I own, rather disappointed me; one of them is scarce preferable to some of the best paved streets in London; and the other, though it affords a beautiful prospect, a charming view of Prior Park and of the Avon, yet wanted something in itself of more striking elegance than a mere broad pavement, to satisfy the ideas I had formed of it.

Fanny's accounts of their stay and the visits they made sound ominously like the sort of private party that Jane Austen found so tedious, but Fanny seems to have enjoyed it. However, one outing, taken at the behest of the Bishop of Peterborough, would certainly have amused Jane. It involved a bizarre visit to the home of the disgraced but unabashed Alderman James Ferry. Fanny and the Thrales would have probably have set off with the bishop down the steps at the end of South Parade, before taking a ferry across the river. The steps have gone and the ferry no longer runs, so to follow them we need to **head along Duke Street, turn right over North Parade Bridge** (not built until 1835)**, cross the road and take the spiral** steps down to the river bank.[1] Although we will be heading north towards Pulteney Bridge, first make a diversion under the bridge to look across at South Parade.

The grotto below North Parade – now on the patio of a meze bar – is Delia's grotto, where Richard Sheridan and Elizabeth Linley hid love letters for each other. Fanny knew both of them, and Sheridan encouraged her to write a play called *The Witlings*. It was never produced, although Sheridan did stage a play she wrote later, called *Edwy and Elgiva*. It was a disastrous flop.

Now head up towards Pulteney Bridge along the towpath, which has changed somewhat since Fanny came this way in 1780:

> The three Thrales, the bishop and I, pursued our scheme, crossed the Avon, had a sweet walk through the meadows, and drank tea at Spring Gardens, where the bishop did the honours with a spirit, a gaiety, and an activity that jovialised us all, and really we were prodigiously lively.

Spring Gardens (shown on the map on page 81) was a pleasure garden with a long room where public breakfasts and teas were served. From here the party walked to Mr Ferry's along a track through fields which in a few years would become a building site. Pulteney Bridge had already been built, but work had not yet begun on the streets on this side of the river.

Carry on along the road under Great Pulteney Street, then right up to Argyle Street and left across Laura Place and along Great Pulteney Street. At the end, bear left along Sydney Place, stopping outside No 4, where Jane Austen lived between 1801 and 1804. There is no record of Fanny Burney ever mentioning Jane Austen, although she would have known about her; her half-sister Sarah had read *Pride and Prejudice* and *Emma*, and Fanny was on friendly terms with Jane's godfather. It is claimed that Jane was a great admirer of Fanny; she was certainly listed as a subscriber when *Camilla* was published and several of her novels include complimentary references to Fanny's novels. At times, however, it seems as though Jane, who could never resist a parody, is subtly sending them up. Even if others did not – and still do not – notice, the ultra-sensitive Fanny would have realised what she was up to. Fanny must also have been aware that Jane was the greater writer, and would have been jealous of her success – especially as she had paved the way for an acceptance of female novelists.

Carry on to **the corner of Bathwick Street and look across the road to the Crown Inn.** The area behind it was known as Villa Fields, in which stood Bathwick Villa, the home of Alderman Ferry, a former silk-mercer. Built in the Strawberry Hill Gothick style, it was already heavily mortgaged, and,

---

1 To avoid the steps, turn left along North Parade, cross to the right at the lights, head north along Grand Parade and turn right over Pulteney Bridge.

shortly after Fanny's visit, Ferry would suffer the indignity of being dismissed as city chamberlain. It was here that the Bishop of Peterborough led Fanny and the Thrales. Let Fanny tell the story in her own words:

> They kept us half an hour in the garden, while they were preparing for our reception in the house, where after parading through four or five little vulgarly showy closets, not rooms, we were conducted into a very gaudy little apartment, where the master of the house sat reclining on his arm, as if in contemplation, though everything conspired to show that the house and its inhabitants were carefully arranged for our reception. The bishop had sent in his name by way of gaining admission.
>
> The bishop, with a gravity of demeanour difficult to himself to sustain, apologised for our intrusion, and returned thanks for seeing the house and garden. Mr Ferry started from his pensive attitude, and begged us to be seated, and then a curtain was drawn, and we perceived through a glass a perspective view of ships, boats, and water. This raree-show over, the maid who officiated as show-woman had a hint given her and presently a trap-door opened, and up jumped a covered table, ornamented with various devices. When we had

> expressed our delight at this long enough to satisfy Mr Ferry, another hint was given, and presently down dropped an eagle from the ceiling whose talons were put into a certain hook in the top of the covering of the table, and when the admiration at this
>
> was over, up again flew the eagle, conveying in his talons the cover, and leaving under it a repast of cakes, sweetmeats, oranges, and jellies.
>
> When our raptures upon this feat subsided, the maid received another signal, and then seated herself in an armchair, which presently sank down underground, and up in its room came a barber's block, with a vast quantity of black wool on it, and a high head-dress.
>
> This, you may be sure, was more applauded than all the rest; we were *en extase*, and having properly expressed our gratitude, were soon after suffered to decamp.

She added that that they laughed all the way back though the meadows.[1] Before we retrace our steps, however, we will **cross the road and enter Sydney Gardens** to meet another of Fanny's friends. Sydney Gardens opened in 1795 and, like Bathwick Villa, had a touch of the Gothick about

---

1 The house was later demolished, although some of its more elaborate carvings were saved and incorporated into houses built on the site. These can be seen on the north side of Forester Road.

them. Not only was there a crumbling, ivy-covered sham castle, there were grottoes, a hermit's cottage, trysting places for lovers, and a mysterious labyrinth, at the centre of which was a Merlin swing. This was one of the mysterious inventions of an 'ingenious mechanic' called JJ Merlin, who was well-known to Fanny. Born in Belgium, he had come to England to work for a clock-maker called Cox. A clock in the Castle Museum at York by

John Joseph Merlin by Gainsborough

Cox bears all the Merlin hallmarks, as does one at Waddesdon Manor, while the Bowes Museum has a Cox automaton, the Silver Swan, with a mechanism designed by Merlin. He also 'improved' musical instruments and was an accomplished musician, which is how he came into the Burney circle. He also invented the in-line roller skate and – the most enduring of his inventions – the self-propelling invalid chair.

The Thrales and the Burneys loved his company. In one letter to Fanny, her sister Charlotte wrote:

Merlin has taken to visiting us again, to my delight. If ever I am at all my own mistress, I'll certainly always have my doors open to Merlin.

He had an often bizarre sense of mischief. On one occasion he announced that he had invented a mill to grind old ladies young. He had his own London showrooms in Hanover Square, where he cashed in on his name and the vogue for all things Druid by dressing up as the magician to welcome visitors. But what was the Merlin Swing? It has been suggested that it was a Ferris wheel or a swing-boat style plank which swung to and fro, but neither suggestion seems likely. For a start, there was another Merlin swing in Grosvenor pleasure gardens, across the river, which was advertised as a chair swing; secondly, he made portable ones which you could have in your own home. It is more likely that it was the type of swing-boat where you sit inside and pull ropes – but that too is a conjecture.

We now head back along Great Pulteney Street to Laura Place and the Bath Fanny knew on her later visits to the city. Her first visit ended abruptly in June 1780. Unbeknown to the jovial party as they made their way back to South Parade, trouble was brewing in the capital. Lord George Gordon, outraged at plans to extend toleration to Roman

Catholics, whipped up the mob into an orgy of destruction, which soon spread to other cities, most notably Bath.[1] The Thrales and their entourage decamped for Salisbury. Fanny would not return for another eleven years, during which time her life took a strange and unexpected turn.

In 1783, Fanny met the celebrated bluestocking, Mrs Delany. 1783 and 1784 were unhappy years for Fanny. 'Daddy' Crisp and Dr Johnson both died and Hetty Thrale, by now widowed, remarried someone of whom Fanny disapproved – Gabriel Piozzi, her daughters' music teacher. Perhaps to compensate for these losses, Fanny attached herself to Mrs Delany, who was a friend of Queen Charlotte. In 1785, Fanny was presented to the King and Queen and was invited to be second keeper of the robes. She had serious qualms about accepting this post, but, as she was 34 and unmarried, and it seemed to offer status, she accepted.

For five unhappy years, she held the post, during which time she was constantly bullied by the Keeper of the Robes, Mrs Schwellenberg, and had to watch the King's first descent into what was then thought of as madness but is now known to have been porphyria. Eventually ill-health, brought on by stress, allowed her to retire, although she retained the goodwill of the royal family. To help restore her health and spirits, a family friend, Anna Ord, took her on a tour of England's spas. In 1791, she returned to Bath, where she was astonished at the changes that had taken place. She wrote in her diary:

Bath is extremely altered since I last visited it. Its circumference is perhaps trebled but its buildings are so unfinished, so spread, so everywhere beginning and nowhere ending, that it looks rather like a space of ground lately fixed upon for erecting a town, than a town itself, of so many years' duration. It is beautiful and wonderful throughout. The hills are built up and down, and the vales so stocked with streets and houses, that, in some places, from the ground-floor on one side a street, you cross over to the attic of your opposite neighbour.

Despite finding it 'beautiful and wonderful', she soon became disenchanted with all the building work and wrote to her sister Hetty:

This city is so filled with workman, dust and lime that you really want two pairs of eyes to walk about in it – one for being put out and the other to see with afterwards.

The grand development planned for Bathwick was about to run out of impetus, and would never be completed. Streets that were meant to lead to squares and crescents lead nowhere, and this was already evident when Fanny returned in 1791. The letter to her sister continued:

1 The Gordon Riots are dealt with at greater length in the next walk.

One street, leading out of Laura Place, of a noble width and with broad handsome pavement, pompously labelled at the corner JOHNSON STREET, has in it – only one house: – nor can another be added, for it opens to Spring Gardens, and even its vis-à-vis is occupied by a dead wall belonging to a house in Laura Place.

Johnstone Street, as it should properly be called, runs south from Laura Place and has a few more houses than that now, but the crescent to which it should lead was never built.

Cross Pulteney Bridge, turn left along Grand Parade, cross two sets of pedestrian lights to reach Terrace Walk and look across to North Parade. On 20 August 1791, Fanny confided to her journal that:

> I went to look (and sigh at the sight) at the house on the North Parade where we dwelt, and almost every old place brings to my mind some scene in which we were engaged.

It was, of course, South Parade where she had stayed – whether this was a slip of the pen or a lapse of memory we cannot know, although the former seems more likely.

On 21 December 1820, Bath's original Assembly Rooms, which stood where the traffic island is today, was destroyed by fire. A few months earlier, in January 1820, Hetty Thrale, widowed for the second time and somewhat impoverished – but like Don Maquis' Mehitabel the Cat, *toujours gai* – held her eightieth birthday party there. In *The Autobiography, Letters and Literary Remains of Mrs Piozzi*, published in 1861, the event is described thus:

The original Assembly Rooms on Terrace Walk

LITERARY WALKS IN BATH

One of the most characteristic feats or freaks of this extraordinary woman was the celebration of her eightieth birthday by a concert, ball, and supper, to between six and seven hundred people, at the Kingston Rooms, Bath, on the 27th January 1820. At the conclusion of the supper, her health was proposed by Admiral Sir James Sausmarez, and drunk with three times three. The dancing began at two, when she led off with her adopted son, Sir John Salusbury, dancing ... 'with astonishing elasticity, and with all the true air of dignity which might have been expected of one of the best bred females in society'. When fears were expressed that she had done too much, she replied: – 'No: this sort of thing is greatly in the mind; and I am almost tempted to say the same of growing old at all, especially as it regards those of the usual concomitants of age, viz, laziness, defective sight, and ill-temper.'

Though she was widely regarded at the time as something of a laughing stock – on hearing of this ball, the *Morning Post* churlishly commented, 'Lord! will this Mrs Piozzi never have done singing and dancing?' – one has to admire her indomitable spirit. She had alleviated her poverty by holding a grand sale at Streatham, only to lavish much of her new-found wealth on this entertainment. She died just over a year later.

On their earlier visit, Mrs Thrale had got into something of a scrape at these Rooms by mistaking Alicia Macartney for Catherine Macartney – both sisters of Mrs Frances Greville. Catherine was of impeccable character but Alicia was notorious as a blackmailer, usurer and political manipulator. Even in her sixties, her sexual adventures – and drunkenness – were notorious. Nevertheless, she had established herself as a society hostess in Bath, and gave elegant parties at her house in the Royal Crescent. Fanny was horrified when she saw Mrs Thrale chatting happily

to her, and, when the matter was explained, Mrs Thrale was in a quandary over what to do about an invitation she had accepted from Alicia Macartney, who was known to seek revenge against those who snubbed her. In the end, after a determined pursuit of their company, Mrs Macartney was fobbed off by Mrs Thrale explaining that she had mistaken her for her sister, with whom she was very well acquainted. It says something about the social mores of the time that this explanation was accepted.

Hetty Thrale

Head west along York Street, turn right into Kingston Parade and head to the left of the Abbey into Abbey Church Yard. If you feel inclined, you may wish to go into the Abbey to find the tombs of four of Fanny's acquaintances. The first two are Jane Gomm and Maria Goldsworthy, whose memorials are on the wall of the north aisle, together with that of Jane's niece, Sophia Louisa. Nothing quite catches the snobbery of the era – the sort of snobbery that Jane Austen satirised – as do these monuments. Both Jane Gomm and Maria Goldsworthy had been in the service of the royal family, as sub-governesses – this nice distinction is made clear on the memorial. Although professing to be friends, and living together after their retirement from court, Fanny said in 1791 that each humiliated, disliked and distrusted the other. It was an odd sort of relationship.

Also in the north aisle is a monument to Henry Harrington. Fanny met him while staying with the Thrales. He was a noted amateur musician and member of a glee club which Fanny was distinctly underwhelmed by.

Finally, in the sanctuary may be seen the elaborate monument to Lady Miller of Batheaston. She held soirées at her house, where poems would be placed in an urn, then drawn out and read one by one, with the best awarded a prize. The standard of poetry was not high, and Fanny, like many others, could not resist the temptation of poking fun at Lady Miller:

> Lady Miller is a round, plump, coarse looking dame of about forty, and while all her aim is to appear an elegant woman of fashion, all her success is to seem an ordinary woman in very common life, with fine clothes on. Her manners are bustling, her air is mock-important, and her manners very inelegant.

Walk over to the Pump Room on the south side of the Abbey Church Yard. The pump room Fanny knew on her first visit was replaced by the present one in the 1790s. In 1793, Fanny married Count D'Arblay, an impoverished French émigré, in the face of opposition from her father. Despite various adventures, during which Fanny found herself trapped in France after war broke out between France and Britain, the two remained devoted to each other. Their love and regard for each other never wavered in the face of calamities which, had Fanny stayed safely in the bosom of her family, she would never have been exposed to. Eventually, they were reunited in England in 1815, and lived in Bath until D'Arblay's death in 1818. It was in the present Pump Room that D'Arblay was presented to Fanny's old mistress, Queen Charlotte, in 1817.

During Fanny's visit in 1791, changes were already in the air, and she commented unfavourably upon them to her sister:

> Even the streets round the Pump Room are pulling down for new edifices, and you can only drink from their choice stream, by wading through their

chosen mud ... I should advise you not to see this place these two years, at least, for pleasure; as the avenues to the Pump Rooms will not sooner be finished, and walking here in winter must be next to impracticable.

It was outside the old Pump Room that Fanny had a meeting with a new friend she had made during her second stay in Bath. Fanny noticed a lady in a sedan chair kissing her hand to her, but as she was so short-sighted, she could not see who it was. At last, as the chair came nearer and the lady put her face to the glass, calling out 'How d'y'do? How d'y'do?' she recognised her – Georgiana, Duchess of Devonshire. As a member of the circle around the King, Fanny was naturally opposed to the Whigs and supporters of the Prince of Wales, and especially one like the duchess who carried a whiff of scandal around with her. Yet, as we shall see, the Spencer family set out to woo her with all their charm, and succeeded in winning her over.

Above: The entrance to the King's Bath under construction in 1789 by SH Grimm

Below: Georgiana, Duchess of Devonshire by Gainsborough

In *Evelina*, the party visit the old Pump Room and gaze down at the bathers in the King's Bath. The heroine says:

At the pump-room, I was amazed at the public exhibition of the ladies in the bath; it is true, their heads are covered with bonnets; but the very idea of being seen, in such a situation, by whoever pleases to look, is indelicate.

Public Bathing at Bath, or Stewing Alive

The King's Bath in 1825 by Robert Cruikshank

Pass through the colonnade, and cross to Bath Street. This was part of the rebuilding which caused Fanny so much distress. **Walk along Bath Street, go to the left of the Cross Bath and along the alleyway to the right of the old Hetling Pump Room, before turning right up to the Sawclose and on up to Queen Square.**

This is where Fanny stayed with Mrs Ord in lodgings. She was here one day – quite alone, as she tells us – when Lady Spencer, the mother of the Duchess of Devonshire, came to call. Fanny had already met her at Mrs Delany's but she was a little surprised and more than somewhat dismayed to be singled out for attention. Lady Spencer had brought her other daughter, Lady Duncannon, to Bath for her health after an alleged miscarriage, although rumour had it that she had actually had an abortion or attempted suicide. Her marriage was an unhappy one, and she had earlier had an affair with another of Fanny's circle, Richard Sheridan. She eventually took a chill, and the family decamped to Clifton, leaving the Duchess of Devonshire's son in his own lodgings, where his mother visited him daily.

Lady Spencer took Fanny under her wing, taking her to the Abbey to see the Sunday School of which she was patroness, and on other charitable outings. This impressed Fanny, and she was won over, but Mrs Ord remained disapproving of the group which included Lady Elizabeth Foster, the duke's mistress as well as the duchess's bosom friend.

Fanny noted how well the Duchess of Devonshire looked – commenting on her vivacity and blooming looks. However, she also felt that the duchess was troubled in some way. What she did not know was that the blooming looks and air of faint anxiety were the result of pregnancy – although the child was not her husband's. The duchess was having an affair with Charles Grey, meeting him while they were in Bath, and a daughter would be born of this liaison in February 1792. Her husband, who had installed his mistress as part of the household, was outraged and contemplated divorce. She was forced to give the child away to Grey's parents, who brought her up. Thus the family was never as happy again as they were when Fanny met them. Georgiana died in 1806 aged 48, her beauty gone.

Walk along the south side of Queen Square and continue along Chapel Row. Carry on across Monmouth Street at the lights, continue down Charles Street to a set of pedestrian lights and cross to New King Street. The houses in New King Street were less grand and much cheaper than those in the upper part of town, as Lady Nelson wrote and told her husband in 1797. She had rented No 17 because, as she said, 'the higher you go the dearer'. Thus it became a refuge for genteel families on small incomes. It was here that the former Hetty Thrale lived after the death of her second husband, until her fortunes were restored by the grand sale at Streatham. In January 1817, shortly after she left, she wrote that friends of hers had 'congratulated me on my removal from New King Street, and well they might. Those streets and part of the Bristol Road are under water. Such a flood, however, tho' a partial evil is of infinite benefit to Bath: cleaning our river from all the foulnesses thrown into it by the market folks.' A few weeks later she wrote that 'one more winter in that New King Street would have killed me.' The Herschel family lived at No 19 in the 1770s, and Fanny's sister Esther occupied the same house in 1826. Fanny and her husband, however, managed to afford something a little grander.

Continue on along New King Street into Great Stanhope Street. When Fanny and her husband came to Bath in 1815, they were persuaded by her nieces to take lodgings in Rivers Street, but could not afford to stay there. However, Fanny had set her heart on Bath. Neither of the D'Arblays was in good health. Fanny, having given birth at the age of 41, had, while living in France, had a mastectomy. Had she still been in England, she would probably have died, but the French surgeons were noted for their competence. Still, it was done without the benefit of anaesthetic – the shock to the system does not bear thinking about[1]. Her husband, meanwhile,

---

1 In 1812, nine months after the operation, Fanny finally felt able to write a full description of it to her older sister Esther. It makes horrific reading, and not only proves how invaluable anaesthetics have been in improving health, but also demonstrates the courage of this indomitable if not entirely lovable woman.

had suffered septicaemia after being kicked by a horse. Fanny was convinced that Bath's waters were the answer.

She took lodgings on the first and second floors of 23 Great Stanhope Street. She enjoyed being near what she described as 'a delicious winter's walk called the Norfolk Crescent'. When they were first married, Alexandre D'Arblay had augmented their income by growing vegetables, and he was not ashamed to do so again, renting a plot of land nearby. They lived happily in Great Stanhope Street for the rest of their time together. Esther had already moved to Bath, living at Larkhall, which was still semi-rural. The two nieces who had taken the lodgings for her in Rivers Street lived just off Lansdown Road. Fanny visited Hetty Piozzi while she was living in New King Street, but it was not a happy occasion, as Hetty Piozzi was still feeling very bitter about the way she had been treated by Fanny – with considerable justification.

In 1817, her sister Charlotte arrived, with her son Dolph, and stayed in lodgings at 17 Great Stanhope Street. Dolph had always

23 Great Stanhope Street

A map from 1810 – with north oriented to the right – showing Great Stanhope Street and New King Street on the left, and Rivers Street to the right of the Circus

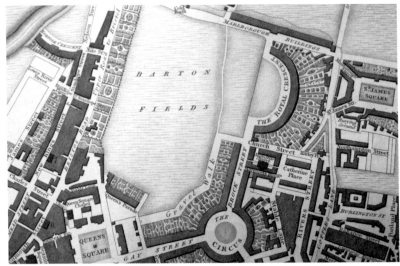

LITERARY WALKS IN BATH

been frail, and the journey was too much for him. He died four days after they arrived. 1817 also saw the arrival of Queen Charlotte in Bath. On 6 November, a great banquet in her honour at the Guildhall was cut short when news arrived of the death of her grand-daughter Princess Charlotte in childbirth. However, the queen returned to Bath a month later, and Fanny made several visits to her lodgings at New Sydney Place. Thus it was that Alexandre was presented to the Queen at a reception in the Pump Room. By now, he was so ill that he could hardly walk, and Fanny recalled that

> the queen no sooner ceased to address him, than the pains he had suppressed became intolerable, and he retreated back from the circle and sunk upon a form next the wall!

Six months later, in May 1818, Alexandre D'Arblay was dead. In September, Fanny left Bath for the last time, to be with her son, Alexander.

Turn right up Nile Street and left along the Upper Bristol Road. Cross the pedestrian crossing, carry on and turn right up Marlborough Lane. Go past Royal Avenue and turn right in front of the Royal Crescent.

Fanny loved the Crescent – she called it 'demi-divine' and in *Evelina* mentioned the prospect – now lost thanks to trees planted from the 1830s on. Several of her friends lived here, including Mrs Montagu – the Queen of the Bluestockings as she was known, whom Fanny gently parodied in her play *The Witlings*. The Crescent was also for a time home to the Linley family. Fanny did not like the father,

Thomas, calling him 'a musician of Bath, a very sour, ill-bred, severe, and selfish man', yet enthused over his daughter Elizabeth:

> Had I been for my sins born of the male race, I should have certainly added one more to Miss Linley's train. She is really beautiful; her complexion a clear lovely animated brown, with a blooming colour on her cheeks; her nose that most elegant of shapes Grecian; fine, luxurious, easy-sitting hair, a charming forehead, pretty mouth and most bewitching eyes. With all this her carriage is modest and unassuming and her countenance indicates diffidence and a strong desire of pleasing, a desire in which she can never be disappointed.

Other Crescent residents included Christopher Anstey, author of *The New Bath Guide*, and the Rev Whalley, whom Fanny met during her visit with Mrs Thrale. It was another Crescent resident, though, who precipitated the Thrale's hasty retreat from Bath. John Butler, footman to the city architect Thomas Baldwin, was alleged to have inflamed the mob when the Gordon Riots spread to Bath. Mr Thrale had been warned that, as he had Roman Catholic friends, he might be at risk, and his house at Streatham was guarded by the militia. Fanny had heard rumours that the chapel might be burned but refused to believe them. She wrote to her father:

> Wagers have been laid that the popish chapel here will be pulled or burnt down in a few days; but I believe not a word of the matter, nor do I find that anybody is at all alarmed.

She soon had to add a postscript:

> The above I writ this morning, before I re-collected this was not post-day, and all is altered here since. The threats I despised were but too well grounded, for, to our utter amazement and consternation, the new Roman Catholic chapel in this town was set on fire at about nine o'clock. It is now burning with a fury that is dreadful, and the house of the priest belonging to it is in flames also. The poor persecuted man himself has I believe escaped with life, though pelted, followed, and very ill used.

Subsequently, Butler was, with others, tried for his part in the riots. Although the rest of the accused were acquitted, Butler was found guilty and hanged – but by then the Thrales and Fanny had long gone. They fled Bath two days after the firing of the chapel and did not stop till they got to the relative safety of Salisbury.

On a happier note, below the park there are still allotments, and it was here that Alexandre found a more satisfactory plot for growing vegetables than his original one near Great Stanhope Street, which was too near the river. Over to the west are **Marlborough Buildings**. It was here that the Duke and Duchess of Devonshire took lodgings in 1791. Their son, the

Marquis of Hartington, was considered frail, and they took a separate house for him, to which entrance was restricted, to prevent him catching smallpox.

Continue to the end of the Crescent and carry on along Brock Street to the Circus. Fanny liked the Circus – in *Evelina* she talked of its 'elegant symmetry' and referred on another occasion to 'all the excellence of architecture that adorns the Circus'. In 1780, Mrs Montagu lodged at No 23, although she did not share Fanny's enthusiasm, saying that, although the Circus appeared a good stone edifice on the outside, inside it was a nest of boxes, 'in which I should be stifled, if the masonry were not so bad as to admit winds at many places'. She much preferred the Crescent, which she moved to later. Some other friends of Fanny's, whom she knew through her father, were Maria and Sarah Matilda Parry, who lived at No 27.

Bear right and walk to the top of Gay Street, where Lady Spencer was staying when she met Fanny in 1791. Lady Duncannon was also at her house, and due to her poor health, was using one of the self-propelling invalid chairs invented by Fanny's lively friend JJ Merlin. Hetty Piozzi also lived in Gay Street for a time after the sale at Streatham – she described moving back to the more fashionable part of Bath as 'returning to the living world again'.

Carry on round the Circus, turn right into Bennet Street and second left up Russel Street to Rivers Street. It was in this elegant street that Fanny's nieces took lodgings for their aunt and her husband at No 23, but, as Fanny explained, they were obviously deceived by his rank into thinking he was wealthy – sadly this was not the case, and they only lived here for a month.

Turn and walk eastwards along Julian Road until you come to Lansdown Road. A little way up on the other side on the road, to the right of the entrance to Hedgemead Park, is Hartley House, named after David Hartley and his sister Mary, who lived here and were friends of Fanny. David was a polymath – philosopher, politician and inventor – and Mary was noted for her accomplishments in literature and the fine arts. She was a correspondent of Mrs Montagu and Fanny Burney, as well as of Elizabeth Carter, a friend of Mrs Montagu's whom Fanny found quite intimidating.

Cross over and walk down Guinea Lane. At the bottom, look across to No. 33, which was once the home of Sarah Siddons. As recounted in the second walk, at a time when many actresses were regarded as little better than prostitutes, Sarah Siddons always had a reputation for respectability. Fanny first met her at a friend's house in London in 1782, and recalled:

> We found Mrs Siddons, the actress, there. She is a woman of excellent
> character, and therefore I am very glad she is thus patronised, since Mrs

Abington, and so many frail fair ones, have been thus noticed by the great. She behaved with great propriety; very calm, modest, quiet, and unaffected – She has a very fine countenance, and her eyes look both intelligent and soft. She has, however, a steadiness in her manner and deportment by no means engaging. Mrs Thrale, who was there, said: – 'Why, this is a leaden goddess we are all worshipping! However, we shall soon gild it.'

33 The Paragon

When Richard Sheridan was accused of having an affair with her, he replied that he would as soon have an affair with the Archbishop of Canterbury. It was perhaps this air of respectability that encouraged Fanny to have Sarah Siddons and her brother, John Kemble, take the leading parts in her tragedy *Edwy and Elgiva*. The production was a complete flop – Mrs Thrale reported that the audience hooted, and everybody ended up pointing a finger of accusation at everybody else. Fanny had not written it properly, the actors did not know their lines – the prompter could be heard throughout the performance – and it lacked dramatic effects. Only Sarah Siddons came out of the debacle with any dignity, for Fanny saw that she had made every effort to create the character. To be fair to Fanny, she was heavily pregnant at the time, giving birth to Alex a month later. Although some critics admired the writing, Fanny had had enough – it was never produced again in her lifetime, and only now is receiving attention.

Turn left, cross at the pedestrian crossing and look through the railings to the left of the church to see the gravestone of George Austen, moved here from the crypt when the Austen family achieved posthumous celebrity status. As a result, he now lies in an unmarked grave, a distinction he shares with Fanny Burney and her husband. Having eschewed scandal all their lives, in death they have been subjected to an undignified shuffling of tombs and memorial stones. Beyond George Austen's gravestone lies a large block, and this is the monument which once stood over Fanny's grave. It was moved here in 1955, with the intention of moving the coffin as well, but this was never done. Only this stone, weighing about three tons, was dragged up here from the burial ground. Not only that, but two wall monuments inside the church, commemorating Fanny and her sister Sarah Harriet were removed when an organ was installed. They should have been placed elsewhere but were mislaid. The only surviving wall monument relating to Fanny is that to her husband, Alexandre D'Arblay.

St Swithin's Church, Walcot in the 1880s. The buildings on the right were in the process of being demolished following a series of landslips.

Walk down the steps to the left of the gravestones, cross Walcot Street, turn right and then left down Walcot Gate to Walcot Mortuary Chapel, built in 1842. If you are fortunate, there may be an exhibition on in the chapel, which means you will be able to enter the graveyard – otherwise you will have to peer through the railings.

The first of the D'Arblay family to be buried here was Alexandre. The intention was that Fanny would eventually lie near him. He had requested a plain black marble headstone as his only memorial. This has been lost and it is not known where he lies. Then, in 1837, Fanny's son Alex died suddenly at the age of 42. His body was brought to Bath and buried near that of his father. Then, in 1840, Fanny herself died. In her will she had written:

> I desire that wheresoever I may die, my corpse may be conveyed to Bath, there to be interred in a like manner with my beloved son's, and as near as possible to my dear and honoured husband's.

We can assume that her name was added to her son's gravestone, or perhaps there was a new stone commemorating both of them. The wall tablet in the church – now lost – recorded that she had been buried in the same vault as her son. However, in 1905 a local journalist, JF Meehan, reported that the inscription on the stone was almost obliterated and the grave was surrounded by weeds. A year later, the Burney family were persuaded to replace the simple gravestone with the slab you saw earlier. But where was the grave? Meehan says it was '26½ feet from the south wall and about 17 feet from the mortuary chapel'. We know that it was on the west side of the chapel as a sketch by the Bath artist Samuel Poole, probably dating from the 1920s, shows it in situ, although with no sign of a black marble stone nearby. In 1951, Professor Joyce Hembury, the Burney scholar, photographed it. Yet all sign of where it might be is lost. However, in July 2005, the Burney Society erected a commemorative plaque near the spot.

Fanny had lived in a fast-changing world. Scientific discoveries, revolution and political turmoil had all combined to turn the world of her childhood upside down. Even styles in writing had changed. Jane Austen, with her pacy, conversational style, is far more modern than Fanny. By the time Fanny died, Charles Dickens was writing in a very different style again. But nothing shows the changes in her lifetime better than an incident at her funeral, to which many of the family came. One of them, her niece Charlotte Barrett, was persuaded to 'take the railroad'. Although she could only get as far as Twyford, this still cut travelling time considerably. A year later, the completion of the Great Western Railway would allow travellers to make an uninterrupted journey between London and Bath in three hours, thirty-five minutes. The engineer was Isambard Kingdom Brunel. How much more this son of a French émigré and an Englishwoman would achieve than Fanny's rather ineffectual son! And perhaps that too illustrates the difference between the old world and the new order. Alexander D'Arblay had been brought up as a Georgian gentleman's son – cultured, polite and destined for the church, like Henry Tilney or Edmund Bertram. But time had moved on. Isambard Kingdom Brunel was the classic Victorian achiever, who worked his way up by skill and daring – a modern hero.

Despite being so shy and retiring, Fanny had led a quite extraordinary life, and met many of the people who are familiar to us through eighteenth century accounts. She had travelled far from the Norfolk town where she was born. But of all the places she visited, despite the terrifying experience which abruptly ended her first stay, it was Bath which remained in her heart.

6

REBELS AND ROMANTICS
Catharine Macaulay, Samuel Taylor Coleridge, Mary Shelley & Percy Bysshe Shelley

On 2 April 1777 the bells of Bath Abbey rang out to celebrate the 46th birthday of one of its most celebrated residents, the historian Catharine Macaulay. Although she is almost totally forgotten today, at the time she was one of the most famous people in the country. Portraits of her were

A porcelain figurine of
Catherine Macaulay

on every print-seller's counter and Derby porcelain figurines of her were prized collectors' items. In 1772, a life-size wax model of her was exhibited alongside models of Lord Chatham and Lord Lyttelton. The *London Magazine* said that, of the three figures, hers was the 'most familiar'. She was represented on the London stage in at least two plays. Thomas Gray said that she had written 'the most sensible, unaffected and best history of England we have had yet', Horace Walpole said that she 'exerted manly strength with the gravity of a philosopher', and Pitt the Elder delivered a panegyric on her in the House of Commons. Even those who disagreed with her had to admit that she was a formidable opponent. Edmund Burke, who dubbed her a 'republican virago', acknowledged that 'none of that set' could do better, adding that 'the Amazon is the greatest champion among them'.

Her 46th birthday was the occasion for an extravaganza the like of which few us will ever have the misfortune to endure. The celebrations received full coverage in the *Bath Chronicle*:

At the opening of the entertainment, Mrs Macaulay was placed, elegantly dressed, and seated in a conspicuous elevated situation, in the front of the company, when six excellent poems, replete with acknowledgements of her exalted merit, and which had been composed and presented on this joyful occasion, were read by six gentlemen selected out of the company, with great propriety and expression, and were honoured with her approbation; comparisons would be illiberal and invidious, but it would be both unjust and insensible not to take notice, that one poem was delivered with a grace and elocution that would do honour to Garrick, and another with an energy and action not unworthy of Demosthenes. At the close of these poetic offerings, that honour to the church and to human nature, the pious, learned, and patriotic Dr Wilson, advanced, and presented to Mrs Macaulay, a large curious gold medal, struck in the reign of Queen Anne (and presented by her majesty to one of the plenipotentiaries at the Peace of Utrecht) which he accompanied with a speech, strongly expressive of her merit, and of his friendship and veneration. Next advanced Dr Graham, to whom the world is much indebted for restoring health to the guardian of our liberties, and enabling her to compleat her inimitable history; he, with great modesty and diffidence, presented to her a copy of his works, containing his surprising discoveries and cures, in which, he observes, that the world might for ever have been deprived of these inestimable blessings, had he not providentially and seasonably forsook the beaten track of the faculty. At the conclusion of these solemnities, wine was served round to commemorate the day; then the company dispersed into different and most elegantly furnished apartments, and entertained themselves with cards, dancing, and conversation, till ten o'clock, when the doors of another apartment were thrown open, where sideboards were ranged round, and covered in a most sumptuous manner with all kinds of creams, ices, wines, cakes, dry and fresh fruits, particularly grapes and pineapples. The company broke up about two, and concluded with the utmost appearance of satisfaction, a day, which will be remembered with pleasure, both on account of the exalted personage to whose honour it was dedicated, and also on account of her worthy and generous benefactor.

The odes specially composed for the occasion were published a few weeks later. One brief extract will suffice to indicate their style:

> Ye Gods! who guard our sacred isle
> On fair Macaulay deign to smile!
> Whose worth ten thousand tongues proclaim,
> Who glory adds to England's fame;
> Strike, strike, the chorded shell,
> Let melodious numbers swell.
> 'Tis she, 'tis she, 'tis she!
> The child of liberty!
> To whom Britannia gave the prize,
> Oh! sound her triumph through the skies!

It all sounds in the worst possible taste, but there was a serious point to it. The American Declaration of Independence had been signed less than nine months earlier. Catharine Macaulay's writings had been a major influence on George Washington and other Americans, who saw their struggle against the British government in terms of the English parliament's struggle against the crown over a century earlier. She not only provided them with a historical precedent for their actions but also declared her support for them in print. In 1775, she wrote a pamphlet warning the government against pushing the Americans into a corner where they would have no option but to take up arms. She also made it clear that she considered they would have natural justice on their side.

All of this naturally made her even more unpopular among her enemies when the American colonists did eventually rebel. Some even saw her as an enemy of the state. So the party held in her honour was not just a vote of confidence in her, but also an implicit declaration of sympathy for the rebels. And, given the tensions in the country, it was a pretty courageous act. So, while Catharine Macaulay's 46th birthday party may seem, on the face of it, a rather embarrassing affair, it had an unmistakable political subtext.

Catharine Macaulay would have been a remarkable woman in any age, but in the eighteenth century, when women were excluded from political life and not expected to have strong opinions, she was especially so. Why then has she been so totally forgotten?

Catharine Macaulay was born – as Catharine Sawbridge – in Kent in 1731. Her father was one of the directors of the South Sea Company, while her brother, who became Lord Mayor of London, counted among his friends many prominent Whigs, including John Wilkes and Alderman Beckford, William Beckford's father. Although Catharine had free rein to read the books in her father's library, her education was, like that of most eighteenth-century women, rudimentary, and she was largely self-taught. In 1760, at the age of 29, she married a rich London physician called Dr George Macaulay, who, like her father, encouraged her literary and historical interests.

Her aim in writing a history of seventeenth-century England was 'to do justice ... to the memory of our illustrious ancestors'. Her contemporaries, she believed, had forgotten that the privileges they enjoyed had been fought for by 'men that, with the hazard and even the loss of their lives, attacked the formidable pretensions of the Stewart family, and set up the banners of liberty against a tyranny which had been established for ... more than 150 years'. When the first volume of her history appeared in 1763, it caused a sensation. It was not just her point of view that caught the public's attention; she was the first historian to make extensive use of primary sources. This meant that her opinions were always supported by documentary evidence, so that her opponents, although they might disagree with her, could not discredit her. Her reliance on primary sources was due, at least in part, to an awareness that, if she made statements without backing them up, her enemies would dismiss them as the misguided fantasies of a scatterbrained woman. This defensive strategy was a fortuitous one, making her not only a trail-blazer for female historians but also a pioneer of historical research.

One of her opponents was Dr Johnson, whose well-known put-down of her is obtuse even by his standards:

> Sir (said he to Boswell), there is one Mrs Macaulay in this town, a great republican. One day when I was at her house, I put on a very grave countenance, and said to her, 'Madam, I am now become a convert to your way of thinking. I am convinced that all mankind are on an equal footing, and to give you an unquestionable proof that I am in earnest, here is a very sensible, civil, well-behaved fellow citizen, your footman. I desire that he may be allowed to sit down and dine with us.' I thus showed her the absurdity of the levelling doctrine. Sir, your levellers wish to level *down* as far as themselves, but they cannot bear levelling *up* to themselves.

This famous encounter is all many people know about Catharine Macaulay, which is a great pity, because Dr Johnson clearly missed the point of her writings. Far from being a leveller, her ideal form of government was timocracy – rule by men of property – and her ideal ruler was King Alfred, whom she called 'a prince of the most exalted merit that ever graced the English throne'. Alfred, she believed, had established a rule of law based on natural liberties, which had been crushed by the Norman yoke. For Catharine Macaulay, history was the story of the struggle to reclaim those rights. She declared that, since the reign of Henry VIII, England 'had preserved a steady course towards slavery and public ruin', only briefly interrupted in the seventeenth century by the Commonwealth, when 'the English after the expence of a ten-years civil war, had totally subdued the despotic family of the Stewarts, and overturned the tyranny settled by the Norman invader'. She also believed that the so-called Glorious Revolution of 1688 had ushered in a system with the vices of 'all the monarchical, oligarchical, and aristocratical tyrannies in the world'.

The English Civil War, in which a king who had broken his covenant with the people was deposed, was justified because it re-established the rule of law laid down by King Alfred. The Commonwealth was 'the brightest age that ever adorned the page of history ... Never did the annals of humanity furnish the example of a government, so newly established, so formidable to foreign states as was at this period the English Commonwealth.'

The revolution had been betrayed, however, by Cromwell, the 'vainglorious usurper' who had seized power for himself. Although Catharine Macaulay held most English monarchs in low esteem, the historical figure for whom she reserved the greatest contempt was Cromwell. He was, she declared, an 'individual, no ways exalted above his brethren in any of those private endowments which constitute the true greatness of character, or excelling in any quality, but in the measure of a vain and wicked ambition'. He was 'more diabolically wicked than it was possible for the generality of the honest part of mankind to conceive', and motivated by 'the most sordid principles of self-interest, with their concomitant vices, envy, hatred, and malice'.

Catharine Macaulay suffered from ill health, possibly stress-related, for most of her life, and came to Bath several times to seek a cure. Her husband died in 1766, and several years later she decided to abandon London and settle in Bath, where she could receive constant medical attention. She arrived in 1774 and took lodgings in St James's Parade. built in the late 1760s by Thomas Jelly as a genteel enclave with no access for wheeled traffic. For a brief period it was one of the most fashionable places in Bath. Like John Wood's Parades, St James's Parade was built on the flood plain of the River Avon. Unlike John Wood's Parades, however, it was not raised high enough to keep it clear of the floods that regularly inundated the area. When a great flood hit Bath in March 1774, the residents of St James's Parade found their houses several feet under water. That was the end of its brief spell in the limelight. It was abandoned by fashionable society and went rapidly downhill.

Whether or not it was flooding that drove Catharine Macaulay out of her lodgings, she was not in St James's Parade very long before Dr Wilson, a friend of hers, invited her to come and live with him at the house he had had built in Alfred Street. The Reverend Dr Thomas Wilson was the wealthy absentee vicar of St Stephen's, Walbrook, who not only shared Catharine Macaulay's view of King Alfred but had called his house Alfred House and placed a bust of Alfred over the door. He may even, when he put the money down for John Wood the Younger to build

him a house in an as yet unnamed street, persuaded him to name the street after Alfred as well.

Dr Wilson was in his seventies when Mrs Macaulay moved in with him. She was in her mid-forties and had been widowed for almost ten years. He was also a widower, but there was never any suggestion of impropriety in their relationship. Nevertheless, as we will see, he seems to have read more into the relationship than she did. He comm-

Catharine Macaulay by Robert Edge Pine

issioned a statue of her 'in the character of history', which he erected in his church in London, over what was clearly intended as her future tomb. Many of the congregation were outraged. It was said to be 'the scandal of the devout, the astonishment of the learned and the disgust of the royalists among the congregation'. The churchwardens threatened to take him to court to get him to remove it. If it was a strange idea to build someone a tomb before they were dead, the inscription underneath it was even stranger:

> You speak of Mrs Macaulay;
> She is a kind of prodigy.
> I revere her abilities;
> I cannot bear to hear her voice sarcastically mentioned;
> I would have her taste the exalted pleasure of universal applause;
> I would have statues erected to her memory;
> And once in every age I could wish such a woman to appear
> As a proof that genius is not confined to sex;
> But at the same time – you will pardon me –
> We want no more than
> One Mrs Macaulay

It seems inconceivable that Dr Wilson meant this to be funny, but it is almost as inconceivable that he did not realize it was hilarious. It may, however, have simply been an early indication of the creeping dementia which a couple of years later manifested itself in spectacular style.

With Catharine Macaulay ensconced in Alfred House it rapidly became the most exclusive literary and political salon in Bath. Dr Wilson described it as 'our little Tusculum which is honoured with the visits of all the literary persons who frequent this place; and foreigners particularly, for she is known and admired abroad more than at home'. The birthday celebrations of 1777 were its apogee. As we have already seen, one of the celebrants was a Scotsman called Dr James Graham. Today Dr Graham is generally regarded as a quack, but there is no doubt that many of his contemporaries took him very seriously. Notices of his miraculous cures appeared regularly in the *Bath Chronicle*. He was a pioneer of the curative properties of mud – something that many spas still feature today. So keen was Dr Graham on mud, however, that he delivered lectures buried up to his neck in it. He was also a keen proponent of electricity and administered electric shocks to his patients while they were immersed in mud.

He also claimed to have developed a cure for impotence, in the form of a celestial bed which cost £50 for a night's hire. Quite what the treatment consisted of is unclear, although it involved electricity, aromatic oils, wind music, magnets, a large mirror positioned above the bed, and the services of several scantily-clad young ladies. One of these young ladies was Emma Lyon, who later married Sir William Hamilton, and later still became the mistress of Horatio Nelson.

Dr Graham's approach to medicine was alternative in more ways than one, but it clearly worked for Mrs Macaulay. Quite what he did for her – and whether the treatment included a stint on the celestial bed – is unknown, but its consequences were dramatic, for in 1778, to the surprise of her contemporaries and the intense fury of Dr Wilson, she married Dr Graham's brother.

It was, of course, acceptable, even *de rigueur*, for widows to remarry in the eighteenth century. Had Catharine Macaulay married Dr Wilson – even though he was almost 30 years older than her – nobody would have batted an eyelid, even though John Wilkes declared him so decrepit that 'it would scarce be a sin to bury him as he is'.

Dr Graham's brother, however, was only 21; Catharine Macaulay was 47. Dr Wilson was incandescent. He tore down the statue of her in his church and declared his house an exclusion zone. He referred to her as a 'modern Messalina' and promised to publish 'an authentic narrative of the conduct and behaviour of Mrs Macaulay (now Mrs Macaulay Graham) during her residence at Alfred House, Bath; containing a succinct and faithful history of the extraordinary means made use of by that lady to obtain such a profusion of expensive gifts from her benevolent patron the Rev Dr Wilson ... with all the original letters, notes and anecdotes'. He added that certain passages in her letters 'too gross for the public eye' would be omitted, but that he would include a 'dissertation on swindling'. However, Richard Cruttwell, Dr Wilson's – and Catharine Macaulay's – publisher, dissuaded him from publication and the promised book never appeared.

It was not only Dr Wilson who was scandalised by Catharine Macaulay's remarriage. A farce about it called *A Widow – No Widow* appeared on the London stage. Richard Polwhele, one of those who had composed an ode for her 46th birthday, wrote that, 'she is irrecoverably fallen. Frailty, thy name is woman. Her passions ... were too strong for her reason; and she has taken to bed a stout brawny Scotsman of 21. For shame!' With her erstwhile friends and admirers turning against her, it was the perfect opportunity for her enemies to stick the knife in, which they did with a vengeance. Her reputation in England never recovered. She went to live with her new husband in Leicestershire and her connection with Bath came to an end.

Two years after her marriage, England suffered the worst civil disturbance in its history. The Gordon Riots were sparked off by Government plans to extend religious toleration to Roman Catholics. It was less than a century since James II had been deposed because of his Catholic leanings and there were still fears that Catholics on the continent were plotting to take over England. Amongst the most fervent anti-Catholics were those on the political left, including Catharine Macaulay, who believed that Catholicism was inextricably linked with political absolutism and tyranny. Until the French Revolution swept away the *ancien régime*, there was a persistent fear of a universal Catholic plot against England. Catharine Macaulay spoke of Catholics' 'never-ceasing attempts by every kind of means, to bring all things again to subjection to the Church of Rome. Their religious principles,' she declared, were 'calculated for the support of despotic power, and inconsistent with the genius of a free constitution.' In 1775, she wrote an *Address to the People of England on the Present Important Crisis of Affairs*, urging a change of government policy towards the American colonists before it was too late. She warned that, if war broke out, England would 'become an easy prey to the courts of France and Spain, who ... will fall upon you as soon as they see you fairly engaged'.

Although the Gordon Riots are hardly remembered today, they were probably the closest England ever came to a full-blooded revolution. More damage was done in London during one week of mob rule than in Paris during the whole of the French Revolution. Hundreds of properties were destroyed and 290 people killed. The riots were sparked by a demonstration against the Catholic Relief Act, led by the rabble-rousing Lord George Gordon, on 2 June 1780. This quickly spiralled out of control as the mob took it as an excuse to kick up, not just about the alleged threat of Catholic domination, but about a system they saw as iniquitous and corrupt, where they were always hungry, always one step away from the gallows or a convict ship, while others lived a life of ease. As so often before and since, however, they vented their anger on a minority group. It is a story with a sickeningly contemporary ring to it. Catholic immigrants from Ireland and Holland had settled in the East End of London, competing for jobs in the tanning and weaving industries, just at the time those jobs were disappearing due to the introduction of new technology and an influx of cheap imports from the East Indies. But, although they bore the initial brunt of alcohol-fuelled mob violence, it soon escalated into a general orgy of destruction.

For the best part of week, London was to all intents and purposes under mob rule. Anyone appearing in the streets without a blue ribbon to show their allegiance to the Protestant cause and a ready 'No Popery' on their lips was likely to be beaten up or lynched. Stagecoaches from London arrived in Bath with 'No Popery' daubed on their sides. Protection money was extorted from householders to stop their houses being burnt down. Newgate, King's Bench and Fleet Prisons were stormed and their prisoners liberated. Not until 9 June, when troops began to arrive in the city in large enough numbers to reimpose some sort of order, did the tumult start to die down. At which point, the tocsin of rebellion rang in Bath. The *Bath Chronicle* takes up the story:

> Friday evening a most alarming riot happened here, which was begun by a footman and some boys breaking the windows of a house where the Roman Catholic priest resided, adjoining to a new chapel, newly built for persons of that religion. In a very short time, as night came on, they were joined by a great number of people, most of them strangers, and armed with carpenter's tools, who broke open the chapel doors immediately and began gutting it and throwing the materials out of the window. The magistrates and other peace officers assembled as quick as possible, but ere they could exert themselves the mob had increased to such a multitude that every effort to disperse them was ineffectual. The riot act was read and some persons seized, but instantly rescued. The magistrates and many respectable citizens used every possible exertion to prevail on the mob to disperse, but without effect.

Major Molesworth with a few of the City Volunteers hastily collected went into the chapel, to the imminent hazard of their lives, and so far prevailed with the rioters as to be suffered to put out the fire several times, which they repeatedly kindled for its destruction. About 20 more of the Volunteers were soon after got together, and Captain Duperre, at the request of the mayor, headed them and led them into the chapel, with their pieces not loaded. The instant they entered the building the mob rushed in upon them on all sides, and a pistol was fired at Captain Duperre, which fortunately missed, and as fortunately destroyed an old rioter who had been once before wounded at an insurrection at Trowbridge – but it so incensed the mob, who supposed him shot by one of the Volunteers, that they immediately fired the chapel, and the corps having received a few wounds and finding it utterly impossible to resist so large a body, made a slow and good retreat. The chapel and about six or seven houses that surrounded it were entirely burnt by about four in the morning, when this desperate rabble, by the repeated and laudable exertions of the magistrates and citizens, were prevailed upon to disperse, without carrying the remainder of their diabolical plan into execution, they having declared their determination to fire the old chapel and the houses of several Roman Catholics residing here.

As soon as the mayor and corporation saw the impossibility of so numerous and desperate a mob being quelled by the civil power, amounting to some thousands, they sent expresses to Wells, Devizes, etc, and to the commanding officers of the troops there to come to their assistance ... It is impossible to say too much in commendation of all the officers both horse and foot for their uncommon expedition on this occasion. They understood from the messengers that the town was fired in several places, and how desperate and large a body they were to encounter, which the flames they saw from the neighbouring hills seemed to confirm – yet the danger only served to hasten them to our relief. Most of the corporation stayed up all night to watch the city and receive the officers at their arrival, whom they very properly invited to an elegant dinner. By the disposition of the troops and peace officers everything here now is perfectly quiet. It is universally agreed that the leaders in the riot were persons sent from London, the gutting and firing the chapel was executed with amazing haste and regularity, and not a single person in the city was insulted except those who attempted to seize them.

It seems that the villains who have chiefly headed the riots in London have a list of every Roman Catholic chapel and school throughout the kingdom, particularly of every new one, and have dispatched their emissaries to go from town to town and destroy them. It is therefore necessary for the magistrates of every city, from the unhappy example of this, to be most strictly on their guard, and desire the inn and lodging house keepers to give notice of every suspicious person that comes there – particularly as the suddenness of this disaster was such that the utmost prudence could neither foresee or prevent.

Among those who fled the city in the aftermath of the riots was, as you saw in the previous walk, Fanny Burney.

Fortunately, Bath was the only place outside London that experienced widespread civil unrest. Nevertheless, the Gordon Riots were a watershed and, more than any other single factor, ensured that the French Revolution did not spread across the Channel. The middle classes had seen what could happen when the mob went wild. The Gordon Riots effectively undermined the assumptions upon which Catharine Macaulay's philosophy was based. Her belief that progress could be achieved by revolutions whose course was guided by enlightened individuals was called into question. It was apparent that, while a revolution could start out with high ideals, it was not always possible to control it once it had gathered momentum.

The French Revolution was a case in point. It started off as a middle-class movement, led by friends of Catharine Macaulay such as the Comte de Mirabeau and Jacques Brissot, but soon descended into an anarchy from which it was only rescued by the Cromwellian figure of Napoleon. Catharine Macaulay did not live to see the failure of the French Revolution, but she did live to see what she regarded as the vindication of her ideas in the American Revolution. Although her reputation in England was largely destroyed by her second marriage, in America it remained untarnished. In 1781, at the age of 50, she embarked on a year-long trip to the United States, during which she spent ten days at Mount Vernon with George Washington, who wrote of his pleasure in meeting 'a lady ... whose principles are so much and so justly admired by the friends of liberty and mankind'. Five years later, she visited France on the eve of the Revolution, to find the country 'all America mad ... All the enlightened French [want] a large empire established on a republican basis to keep the monarchies of the world in order.'

Several of the American colonists were inspired by Catharine Macaulay's historical justification for republicanism. And, in turn, it was the American Declaration of Independence which stirred latent republican ideas in France into life. When Catharine Macaulay wrote to George Washington in 1789 congratulating him on becoming the first president of the United States, and sending him news of the French Revolution, she added that 'all the friends of Liberty on this side of the Atlantic are now rejoicing for an event which in all probability had been accelerated by the American Revolution.' The French, she continued, 'had set an example ... unique in all the histories of human society' by overthrowing despotism through 'the firmness of their union, the universality of their sentiments and the energy of their actions', and the revolution was 'an event, the most important to the dearest interests of mankind, the most singular in its nature, the most astonishing in its means'.

When Catharine Macaulay died in 1791, her obituary in the *Annual Register* noted tersely that she 'had the misfortune ... in a great degree to outlive the respect of the public'. Among those who still revered her name, however, was Mary Wollstonecraft, the author of the *Vindication of the Rights of Woman* – and the mother of Mary Shelley – who declared her to be 'the woman of the greatest abilities, undoubtedly, that this country' had ever produced.

Although Catharine Macaulay was hugely influential in her day, and played a major role in crystallising the ideas that led to the American and French Revolutions, her philosophy was based on the belief that a perfect society was not only possible, but could be created and led by enlightened individuals. Although this seemed to work in America, the experience of France convinced many of her contemporaries that her view was fundamentally flawed. Instead of dreaming of a perfect society, the generation which succeeded Catharine Macaulay, seeing the chaos which had followed on from an attempt to create a political utopia in France, turned their attention inwards and concentrated on how individuals could achieve perfection. Thus was Romanticism, with its stress on individual experience, born, and this brings us onto the second of our rebels and romantics, Samuel Taylor Coleridge. As we shall see, his experience of Bath, was, if anything, even less happy than that of Catharine Macaulay.

Born in 1772, the son of the vicar of Ottery St Mary in Devon, Coleridge was inspired by the French Revolution while a student at Cambridge and wrote a poem in praise of the fall of the Bastille. He quickly became disenchanted with what was happening on the other side of the channel, however. In June 1794, he met an undergraduate from Oxford called Robert Southey (who had been brought up in Bath). Between them they decided to set up a utopian commune in America, which was still seen as embodying many of the ideals Catharine Macaulay had espoused. Coleridge and his band of pioneers were not aiming to work towards creating a perfect society, however; they planned to retreat from society and create a private utopia. 'What I dared not expect from constitutions

Samuel Taylor Coleridge

of government and whole nations,' Coleridge later wrote, 'I hoped from religion and a small company of chosen individuals, and formed a plan, as harmless as it was extravagant, of trying the experiment of human perfectibility on the banks of the Susquehanna.'[1]

Much of the planning for the commune took place in Bristol. Southey and another prospective emigrant, Robert Lovell, were already married to two sisters – Mary and Edith Fricker. There was a third, unmarried, sister called Sara, and as Coleridge was on the rebound from a failed relationship, he decided to propose to her. He did so in August 1794 at 8 Westgate Buildings in Bath, where she was staying with Southey's mother. This was the first of the three things that Coleridge had reason to hate Bath for; his marriage was a dismal failure, and for most of his life he and his wife lived apart.

To raise money, Coleridge wrote articles and gave lectures. Among the places he lectured at in Bristol were Castle Green, the Corn Market and the Assembly Coffee House. All his lectures were anti-government and anti-war, and after one of them the hall was surrounded by a small crowd complaining of the 'damned Jacobin … jawing away'. After receiving death threats he gave up public speaking for a while. 'Mobs and mayors,' he wrote, 'blockheads and brickbats, placards and press gangs have leagued in horrible conspiracy against me – the democrats are as sturdy in their support of me – but their number is comparatively small.'

In November 1795, he attended an anti-war rally in Bristol Guildhall to petition the King 'for a speedy termination of the present war' against France. Despite having few illusions about the horrors which were unfolding in France, he still honoured the libertarian impulse which had led to the French Revolution. 'The vine of liberty,' he declared, 'shall not be blasphemed by us, because the Noahs of the revolutionary deluge, who first planted it, were made drunk by its untried fruits.'

Coleridge eventually abandoned the idea of an American commune. He came to the conclusion that even trying to achieve a perfect society among a small, select band was an unrealistic dream and turned to Unitarianism. The Unitarian community in England, which traced its origins back to 1673, boasted several distinguished members, including Sir Isaac Newton and Joseph Priestley, yet was regarded with deep suspicion by the establishment. Some of its members had even been imprisoned for sedition. Coleridge, with his radical background, was so taken with its doctrines that he considered becoming a minister and was invited to Bath

---

1 Although a communal rather than a solitary settlement was planned, Coleridge's utopian dream is uncannily reminiscent of Philip Thicknesse's Robinson Crusoe-like existence on the banks of the Savannah almost 50 years earlier.

by Mr Jardine, the minister of the Unitarian chapel in Frog Lane, to preach a sermon one Sunday morning. Coleridge's friend and publisher Joseph Cottle takes up the story:

> The moment for announcing the text arrived. Our curiosity was excited. With little less than famine in the land, our hearts were appalled at hearing the words: 'When they shall be hungry, they shall fret themselves, and curse their king, and their God, and look upward' (Isaiah viii. 21). Mr. Winterbotham, a little before, had been thrown into prison for the freedom of his political remarks in a sermon at Plymouth, and we were half fearful whether in his impetuous current of feeling, some stray expressions might not subject our friend to a like visitation. Our fears were groundless. Strange as it may appear in Mr Coleridge's vigorous mind, the whole discourse consisted of little more than a lecture on the Corn Laws! which some time before he had delivered in Bristol, at the Assembly Room.

> Returning from our edifying discourse to a tavern dinner, we were privileged with more luminous remarks on this inexhaustible subject: but something better (or worse, as the reader's taste may be) is still in reserve. After dinner Mr Coleridge remarked he should have no objection to preach another sermon that afternoon ...

> He rang the bell, and on the waiter appearing, he was sent, with Mr Coleridge's compliments, to the Rev Mr Jardine to say, 'if agreeable, Mr C would give his congregation another sermon, this afternoon, on the Hair Powder Tax!' On the departure of the waiter, I was fully assured that Mr Jardine would smile, and send a civil excuse, satisfied that he had had quite enough of political economy ... in the morning; but to my great surprise, the waiter returned with Mr Jardine's compliments, saying, 'he should be happy to hear Mr Coleridge!'

> Now all was hurry lest the concourse should be kept waiting. What surprise will the reader feel, on understanding that, independently of ourselves and Mr Jardine, there were but 17 persons present, including men, women, and children. We had, as expected, a recapitulation of the old lecture, with the exception of its humorous appendages, in reprobation of the Hair Powder Tax; and the twice-told tale, even to the ear of friendship, in truth sounded rather dull!

> Two or three times Mr C looked significantly toward our seat, when fearful of being thrown off my guard into a smile, I held down my head, from which position I was aroused when the sermon was about half over, by some gentleman throwing back the door of his pew, and walking out of the chapel. In a few minutes after, a second individual did the same; and soon after a third door flew open, and the listener escaped! At this moment affairs looked so very ominous, that we were almost afraid Mr Jardine himself would fly, and that none but ourselves would fairly sit it out ...

> We all returned to Bristol with the feeling of disappointment; Mr C from the little personal attention paid to him by Mr Jardine; and we, from a dissatisfying sense of a Sunday desecrated.

Coleridge made a few more attempts at becoming a Unitarian minister, with varying success, but these came to an end when Thomas and Josiah Wedgwood, wealthy fellow Unitarians, granted him an allowance of £150 a year so that he could concentrate on writing. He settled at Nether Stowey in Somerset and shortly afterwards persuaded William Wordsworth, whom he had recently met, to rent a house nearby. A few months later, he wrote 'The Rime of the Ancient Mariner'. It is perhaps churlish to point out that, although this is one of the best-known maritime poems in English, Coleridge's only experience of sea travel when he wrote it had been the Chepstow ferry.

Coleridge's gradual descent into opium addiction in the years that followed makes a sorry tale. He left his wife and spent much of his time living, cuckoo-like, as the guest of various friends who could tolerate the effects of his addiction. One set of benefactors were the Morgans, who lived at Clifton and invited Coleridge to dinner one night in 1807. One of the side-effects of opium is severe and prolonged constipation. Unfortunately, prolonged constipation often leads to explosive consequences. So it was on the night Coleridge visited the Morgans. He ended up lying prostrate on their sofa, suffering from sickness and diarrhoea, for the next four weeks.

At the end of four weeks, the Morgans invited him to stay on, and he eventually moved with them to London. In 1813, John Morgan went bankrupt and fled to Ireland, leaving Coleridge to look after his wife, Mary, and her sister Charlotte. He rose to the occasion, giving a series of lectures to raise money to clear John Morgan's debts. He also resurrected a play called *Osorio* he had written 16 years earlier and managed to get it produced at Drury Lane. It was a surprise hit, and was performed in Bath on 27 March 1813, just two months after its first London performance. However, he received no royalties, as performing rights would not be introduced for another half century.

After his series of lectures ended in London, he made plans to repeat it in Bristol and rented a cottage at Ashley, near Box, where he settled with Mary and Charlotte. But the effort of rescuing John Morgan, plus the sexual chemistry of living alone in a small, isolated cottage with two women, was too much for him. Things came to a head on the evening of Sunday, 5 December 1813. We do not know exactly what happened, but the result was that Coleridge swallowed a massive dose of laudanum and stormed out of the cottage, taking only a small satchel of books with him. The last stagecoach to Bath had left and Coleridge had no choice but to trudge along the dark, muddy road in the pouring rain. By the time he reached Bath, the effects of the drug were only too apparent. He dragged himself along the London Road and down Walcot Street, until he came to Northgate Street and the Greyhound Inn, on the corner of Upper Borough Walls.

He somehow managed, in his delirious, dishevelled state, to convince the innkeeper to take him in. He was, after all, a famous writer who had had a play staged at the Theatre Royal a few months earlier. Even so, he was consigned to a small garret room, where he collapsed 'into a nightmare of hallucinations, sweating, agonizing muscular pains, and a burning fever that left him unable to sleep, eat or talk coherently'. The innkeeper, William May, thought he was dying and called a doctor. By a stroke of luck, it was Dr Caleb Parry, the father of an old friend, who turned up.

On 19 December he wrote to Mary Morgan:

> Yesterday was the first day, Mary! that I could leave my bed, except in a blanket to have it made – even from the day I quitted you – the terrors of the Almighty have been around and against me – and tho' driven up and down for seven dreadful days by restless pain, like a leopard in a den, yet the anguish and remorse of mind was worse than the pain of the whole body. – Oh, I have had a new world opened to me, in the infinity of my own spirit! Woe be to me, if this last warning be not taken. Amidst all my anguish you and Charlotte were present to me – and formed a part of it. Dr Parry, who was called in by accident (for I was too wild with suffering to direct anything myself) attended me day after day, and often twice a day, with parental kindness. – Mrs May says, he did what she never knew him do – stay with me two and three hours at a time – and to him under God's mercy I owe that I am at present alive. For seven days consecutively I never swallowed a morsel – Dr Parry said daily, 'so much the better – why should you take what you cannot digest?' I shall put myself into a post chaise this afternoon, please God! and proceed to Bristol – from thence I will write you immediately. Feeble as I am, and so depressed in spirit, I dare not come over to you – lest I should not be able to get away: and Dr Parry says it is quite necessary that I should be in company and drawn away from my own thoughts.

In Bristol, he stayed at the house of Josiah Wade in Queen's Square until September 1814, when he returned to Ashley. An interesting footnote, for anyone interested in Bath's industrial history, is that he sent a box containing his books and clothes ahead of him down the canal from Bristol to Bath. At Ashley, he was joined by John Morgan, whom he had helped to save from debtors' prison. 'I am now joint tenant with Mr Morgan,' he wrote, 'of a sweet little cottage at Ashley, half a mile from Box, on the Bath Road. I breakfast every morning before nine – work till one – and walk or read till three – thence till teatime, chat or read some lounge book – or correct what I have written – from 6 to 8, work again – from 8 to bedtime play whist or the little mock billiard called Bagatelle and then sup and go to bed.'

So much for Coleridge's association with Bath. He later moved with the Morgans to Calne, and, among other things, enjoyed boating on the lake at Bowood House. But to continue our story, and to provide a link with the third of our rebels and romantics, we must go forward a couple of years to 1816, when Coleridge, seeking a backer to publish some of his poems, contacted Lord Byron, who had achieved enormous fame – and wealth – with the first part of *Childe Harold's Pilgrimage*. The two men met only once, but it was a fateful meeting. Coleridge read to Byron an unfinished poem called 'Christabel', which he had written at Nether Stowey over 15 years earlier. When he asked Byron for suggestions as to how he should complete it, Byron told him to publish it as it stood. Byron also managed to charm out of Coleridge the story of how he had begun another poem at around the same time, but was less than 60 lines into it when he was rudely interrupted, and had never managed to get any further. Byron eventually persuaded Coleridge to read this 'psychological curiosity' and was so impressed that he urged him to publish it at once. When Coleridge demurred, Byron pointed out that, if he was going to help him get his poems into print, he had some say as to what appeared. If Byron had not insisted, who knows if Coleridge's 'psychological curiosity' would ever have seen the light of day. And, in case you are wondering, its opening lines were

> In Xanadu did Kubla Khan
> A stately pleasure dome decree ...

It is not 'Kubla Khan' but 'Christabel' that concerns us here, however. A couple of months after it was published in May 1816, Byron was staying in the Villa Diodati on Lake Geneva with Percy Bysshe Shelley, Shelley's partner, Mary Wollstonecraft Godwin, their six-month-old son William, Mary's half sister, Claire Claremont (with whom Byron was having an affair), and Dr William Polidori.

The night they spent at the villa on 18 July 1816 was, by any standards, an extraordinary one, as Dr Polidori recalled:

> Twelve o'clock, really began to talk ghostly. Lord Byron repeated some verses of Coleridge's 'Christabel', of the witch's breast; when silence ensued, and Shelley suddenly shrieking and putting his hands to his head, ran out of the room with a candle.

Shelley later told Dr Polidori that the poem had conjured up an image of a woman whose breasts had eyes instead of nipples. It is hardly surprising that, when she eventually went to bed, Mary had bad dreams. She later described what happened:

When I placed my head on my pillow I did not sleep, nor could I be said to think. My imagination, unbidden, possessed and guided me, gifting the successive images that arose in my mind with a vividness far beyond the usual bounds of reverie. I saw – with shut eyes, but acute mental vision – I saw the pale student of unhallowed arts kneeling beside the thing he had put together. I saw the hideous phantasm of a man stretched out, and then, on the working of some powerful engine show signs of life and stir with an uneasy, half-vital motion … His success would terrify the artist; he would rush away from his odious handiwork, horror-stricken. He would hope that, left to itself, the slight spark of life which he had communicated would fade, that this thing which had received such imperfect animation, would subside into dead matter … He sleeps; but he is awakened; he opens his eyes; behold, the horrid thing stands at his bedside, opening his curtains and looking on him with yellow, watery, but speculative eyes.

I opened mine in terror. The idea so possessed my mind that a thrill of fear ran through me, and I wished to exchange the ghastly image of my fancy for the realities around. I see them still: the very room, the dark parquet, the closed shutters with the moonlight struggling through, and the sense I had that the glassy lake and white high Alps were beyond. I could not so easily get rid of my hideous phantom; still it haunted me. I must try to think of something else, I recurred to my ghost story – my tiresome, unlucky ghost story! Oh! If I could only contrive one which would frighten my reader as I myself had been frightened that night!

Swift as light and as cheering was the idea that broke in upon me. 'I have found it! What terrified me will terrify others; and I need only describe the spectre that haunted my midnight pillow.' On the morrow I announced that I had *thought of a story*. I began that day with the words, 'It was on a dreary night of November,' making only a transcript of the grim terrors of my waking dream.

Frankenstein was still little more than a rough draft when the party broke up a month later and Mary set off for England with Shelley, their son William and her half-sister Claire, who was now several months pregnant. They crossed from Le Havre to Portsmouth on 8 September 1816, and, in view of Claire's condition, decided against returning to London and a load of awkward questions. Instead they headed to Bath, where they planned to stay until a more permanent home could be found.

They arrived on 10 September and took rooms at 5 Abbey Church Yard, above a circulating library run by William Meyler, a well-known local poet and the editor of the *Bath Herald*. Here Mary continued to work on *Frankenstein*, as well as studying Latin, reading John Locke and taking drawing lessons twice a week with a drawing master called John West at 2 North Parade. She also attended scientific lectures by Dr Wilkinson at the Kingston Lecture Room. Dr Wilkinson was

The Abbey Church Yard in the late nineteenth century. Mary wrote part of *Frankenstein* above the Grand Pump Room Library & Reading Room on the right

a debunker of quackery and conducted experiments to show that Dr Graham's claims for the efficacy of electricity were bunkum. Despite this he was a firm believer in the possibility of electricity being used to animate or reanimate lifeless matter. He was keen not only to bring science to the masses, but, unusually for the time, was happy for young ladies to attend his lectures. How different would *Frankenstein* have been had Mary been excluded from Dr Wilkinson's lectures. The detailed description of the laboratories in which the monster was created would, at the very least, have been far less convincing.

It is no exaggeration to say that *Frankenstein* is the most famous book written in Bath. Mary did not start it in Bath, and it was not finished by the time she left, but even so the claim stands. Its portrayal of a creature who is innately good, but who learns about evil by studying the ways of mankind and is driven to revenge by the treatment meted out to him because of his hideous appearance, shows how much sensibilities had changed since Catharine Macaulay had written about the perfectibility of society 40 years earlier. In *Frankenstein*, not only is society irredeemable; it corrupts a being who is innately good and makes him evil as well. The implication seems to be that, even if man is capable of achieving perfection, society will subvert his attempts to do so at every turn.

The immediate inspiration for *Frankenstein* may have been the ghostly atmosphere of Coleridge's 'Christabel', but a more profound influence was his 'Rime of the Ancient Mariner'. This not only provided the setting for the book's opening section, as well as couple of lengthy quotations, but also its theme of evil being brought into the world by the actions of men.

And if you think the idea of Count Frankenstein cobbling together his monster out of human body parts is far-fetched, it would not have seemed so to Mary's contemporaries. Grave-robbing was a very real problem. In 1826, ten years after Mary's brief stay in Bath, William Clark, who lived in a house overlooking Walcot graveyard, confessed to having removed 45 newly-buried bodies from the graveyard over a five month period and sending them to London by stagecoach (suitably boxed) for anatomical study.[1] It was a lucrative business, netting up to ten guineas a corpse.

Mary had more than her share of evil and human misery to contemplate during her short stay in Bath. Shortly after their arrival, Shelley went up to London to sort out various matters, including an attempt to get custody of his two children by his estranged wife Harriet. While in London, he met Fanny, Mary's half sister, who had lost her teaching job as a result of the scandal caused by Mary running off with Shelley.[2] Most biographers seem to agree that Fanny was in love with Shelley, but, if she was, this would only have been one of her problems. Without a job, and aware that she was a financial burden to her step-father, William Godwin, she was in a more desperate state of mind than Shelley, or anyone, realised.

On 9 October, Shelley was back in Bath with Mary, when a letter arrived from Fanny at Bristol. She had travelled down from London, and, although her coach had stopped at Bath, she had chosen not to visit Shelley and Mary. He immediately took a coach to Bristol to find her. He was too late. She had already left, and, with no clue as to where she had gone, he returned to Bath, arriving at two in the morning. By then Fanny was already dead, having taken an overdose of laudanum in a garret room of the Mackworth Arms, Swansea's main coaching inn. She was 22. Her suicide note read:

> I have long determined that the best thing I could do was to put an end to the existence of a being whose birth was unfortunate, and whose life has only been a series of pain to those persons who have hurt their health in endeavouring to promote her welfare. Perhaps to hear of my death will give you pain, but you will soon have the blessing of forgetting that such a creature ever existed as …

1 This provides a somewhat gruesome link to the previous walk, for Alexandre d'Arblay, Fanny Burney's husband, was buried in Walcot graveyard in 1818.
2 This is where things start to get complicated, so you may find it helpful to refer to the simplified family tree on the opposite page.

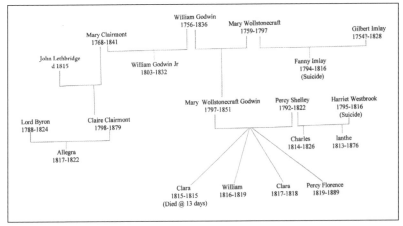

A simplified family tree indicating the complex relationships of the Shelleys and their circle

And there the note ended, her name torn off on the instructions of her stepfather, William Godwin, who wanted to ensure that her identity did not appear in the local papers. He also forbade any of the family, including Mary, to attend the funeral, and Fanny was buried in an unmarked grave.

Shelley and Mary were still reeling from this tragedy when news arrived, on 15 December, of another suicide. Shelley's estranged wife, Harriet, had walked into the Serpentine with stones in her pockets, and drowned herself. She was heavily pregnant, although by whom was never established. Shelley travelled up to London once again to try to gain custody of the children. He wrote to Mary from London on 16 December:

> It is through you that I can entertain without despair the recollection of the horrors of unutterable villainy that led to this dark, dreadful death. I am to hear from Desse [his father-in-law's attorney] whether or no I am to engage in a contest for the children[1] … Everything tends to prove, however, that beyond the shock of so hideous a catastrophe having fallen on a human being so nearly connected with me, there would in any case have been little to regret.

A few days later Mary joined him in London, and on 30 December they were married at St Mildred's Church, Bread Street. Later that day, Shelley wrote to Claire, who was in the final weeks of her pregnancy and had moved out of the house in the Abbey Church Yard to 12 New Bond Street, where she was being looked after by a Mrs Gilbert:

> We cannot come tomorrow, there being no inside place in any of the coaches, or in either of the mails. I have secured a place for Wednesday, so you will infallibly see us on that evening.

---

1 The Court of Chancery eventually decided that neither Shelley nor Harriet's family should have custody, sending the children to foster parents instead.

Mary Shelley in 1841

On 12 January Claire gave birth to a girl whom she initially called Alba, but later renamed Allegra at Byron's request.

This period of Shelley's life saw a quickening of his political consciousness. This is generally attributed to his growing awareness of the unrest and hardship in the country, together with the influence of Leigh Hunt, the editor of a journal called the *Examiner*. There was, however, something much more immediate, something that occurred while he was staying in Bath.

The winter of 1816-17 was particularly grim. 1816 was 'the year without a summer', after the eruption of Mount Tambora blotted out the sun, temperatures plummeted and crop failures led to food shortages throughout the northern hemisphere. Many people were seized by the conviction that the end of the world was nigh. The *London Chronicle* tried to allay their fears:

> The large spots which may now be seen upon the sun's disk have given rise to ridiculous apprehensions and absurd predictions. These spots are said to be the cause of the remarkable and wet weather we have had this summer; and the increase of these spots is represented to announce a general removal of heat from the globe, the extinction of nature, and the end of the world.

On 18 July – the same day that the party at the Villa Diodati sat up telling each other ghost stories – an Italian scientist announced that the world was about to end, triggering millennial panic across Europe. A few days later, it was reported that 'a Bath girl woke her aunt and shouted at her that the world was ending, and the woman promptly plunged into a coma.' On the shores of Lake Geneva, meanwhile, Byron penned his extraordinary poem, 'Darkness':

> I had a dream, which was not all a dream.
> The bright sun was extinguish'd, and the stars
> Did wander darkling in the eternal space,
> Rayless, and pathless, and the icy earth
> Swung blind and blackening in the moonless air ...

Clearly this atmosphere of millennial anxiety must have influenced Mary as she contemplated her ghostly tale. For many, though, the problems of hunger and starvation were more immediate, and in England, as elsewhere, adverse natural phenomena were compounded by an iniquitous and unjust social system. Britain had emerged victorious from a long and costly war that many had bitterly opposed. Yet peace had not brought not plenty but penury. The old order, which many had hoped to see swept away in the wake of the French Revolution, was more firmly entrenched than ever. And Bath was one of its bastions. The scandal of rotten boroughs like Old Sarum, where only a handful of voters elected members of parliament, is well known. Bath, although a thriving, populous city, was an even more glaring example of a rotten borough, with its members of parliament elected by the city corporation, an unelected, self-perpetuating oligarchy consisting of between 27 and 31 members.[1] In 1812, a local businessman called John Allen had challenged their power by organising an alternative election, which led to rioting and the smashing of the windows in the Guildhall.

Five years later, on the day after Shelley arrived back in Bath with his new wife, a rally organized by the radical orator, Henry Hunt, and calling for electoral reform, was held in the city. Although 37 years had passed since the Gordon Riots, the authorities were still twitchy about large-scale gatherings. This is how the *Bath Chronicle* reported the event:

> On Thursday last Mr Hunt, of political notoriety, presented a requisition to the mayor, requesting him to call a meeting of the inhabitants, to consider 'the propriety of petitioning Parliament for the *immediate* abolition of all sinecure grants, pensions, and emoluments, not merited by public services, as a *temporary measure*; and a reform in the Commons or People's House of Parliament, as a *permanent means* of relief for the unexampled and complicated distress and misery of the country'. The mayor having declined complying with the request, Mr Hunt and 29 other persons appointed a meeting of the inhabitants, for the aforesaid purpose; and on Monday the meeting took place at twelve o'clock, at Mr Hunt's Yard. It was shortly after adjourned to the Grove, where a temporary hustings being erected, next the Abbey Church, Mr Hunt was called to preside. The meeting was then severally addressed by Messrs Hickman, C Young, Crisp, Carpenter and Williams (of Bristol) and the result was the adoption of certain resolutions, attributing the distress of the country to the 'unjust' wars in which we have been engaged, and in which we were 'involved owing to the corrupt system of representation'; insisting, therefore, upon the necessity of a reform in parliament, and of altering the form of election to that 'by ballot, in order to prevent the influence of the rich powerful'; and urging the abolition of unmerited pensions and sinecure places, particularly noting Marquis Camden's

---

1 The Freemen of Bath had on at least three occasions, in 1705, 1715 and 1728, petitioned parliament for the franchise to be extended, without success.

enormous sinecure as teller of the exchequer. A petition embracing these topics (to be presented by Lord Cochrane, supported by Sir F Burdett) was agreed to; and the proceedings were concluded by a vote of thanks to the promoters of the meeting and its objects. Mr Carpenter, indeed, proposed a vote of thanks to the editor of *The Independent Whig*; but after being twice put by the chairman, it was negatived, with the exception of one hand held up in its favour. The number of persons assembled might have been 500.

So far so good – but the report ended with a chilling codicil:

Precautionary measures had been judiciously taken by the magistrates, to prevent any breach of the public peace; a great number of the respectable inhabitants came forward, and were sworn as special constables; masters of families, tradesmen, etc were requested to keep their servants, workmen, etc *at home* on the day of the meeting; and the publicans were desired to prevent tippling in their houses. Two troops of the 23rd Dragoons, under Major Grove, the Bath, Frome, Shepton, and Batcombe troops of the North Somerset Yeomanry, commanded by Colonel Horner, and the Bath Rifle Corps were also assembled in aid of the civil power, had occasion required; but the day and evening passed off without any occurrence worthy of particular notice.

Such an imposing military turnout seems a trifle excessive for a gathering of 500 people. Except, of course, that it wasn't a gathering of 500 people. Newspapers in 1817 were even less reliable than they are today when it comes to reporting demonstrations. The *Bath Chronicle* in its role of publishing nothing that might deter potential visitors was guilty of a slight understatement. When Henry Hunt wrote his *Memoirs* three years later, he said that he was followed from his yard in Walcot Street to the Orange Grove by an 'immense multitude of from twelve to fifteen thousand people'. He may have been exaggerating, but, in the absence of an impartial observer, we can only point to the number of signatures Hunt collected on a petition calling for reform in Bath – 20,000. With that level of support, it seems unlikely that only around 500 people turned up to hear him speak.

Shelley in 1819

We do not know whether Shelley attended the rally, but he was certainly in Bath, and, living in Abbey Church Yard, he could hardly have been unaware of such a crowd less than 100 yards away. It seems no coincidence that, a couple of weeks later, he wrote a pamphlet entitled *A Proposal for Putting Reform to the Vote throughout the Kingdom* and gave £100 to help set up an action fund.

Two years later, when Henry Hunt addressed a similar meeting at St Peter's Fields in Manchester, 80,000 people turned up. Despite, once again, there being no threat of civil unrest, the magistrates ordered the meeting to be broken up, and mounted soldiers charged into the crowd, killing at least eleven people and wounding about 400. The massacre was christened Peterloo, an ironic echo of the British victory at Waterloo four years earlier. Bathonians can be thankful that the authorities in the Orange Grove on that January day managed, unlike their counterparts in Manchester, to keep their heads. Shelley, who was abroad when the massacre took place, must have reflected on what could so easily have happened in Bath as he picked up his pen and wrote his most famous anti-government poem, *The Mask of Anarchy*:

> As I lay asleep in Italy
> There came a voice from over the Sea,
> And with great power it forth led me
> To walk in visions of Poesy.
> I met Murder on the way –
> He had a mask like Castlereagh –
> Very smooth he looked, yet grim;
> Seven bloodhounds followed him.

Shelley left Bath with Mary late in February 1817, after a stay of less than six months, to go and live at Marlow in Buckinghamshire. Given the two suicides, it was probably the worst six months of their short time together. The only good thing to come out of it was Claire's daughter, Allegra, but sadly she died five years later, in 1822. 1822 also saw Shelley's death in a boating accident off Livorno – where Smollett had died 51 years earlier. He was a few weeks short of his thirtieth birthday.

Mary was only 19 when she left Bath with the half-completed manuscript of *Frankenstein*. The suicides of Fanny and Harriet had introduced her to feelings of horror, guilt and despair which found a release in her writing. *Frankenstein* was written at white-heat, out of intense, undigested, and only partly comprehended personal experience. It started out, on the shores of Lake Geneva, as a Gothic ghost story. In Bath, it was transformed into one of the most intensely felt, most disturbing, and most enduring tales ever written.

Almost 30 years later, in 1846, Mary, by now in ill health, returned to Bath, staying this time at 14 Queen Square. The reforms which Henry Hunt and Shelley had called for had been, at least partially, realised. Mary was a literary celebrity and her dead husband was a Romantic icon for a new generation of poets. Victorian Bath, no longer the haunt of rebels and romantics, was a very different place to the city where she had written *Frankenstein*.

A REBELLIOUS WALK ROUND BATH

Start at Alfred House in Alfred Street, where Catharine Macaulay lived between 1774 and 1778, and where her 46th birthday was celebrated in grand style in 1777.

Walk along to Wood's restaurant and turn right down Bartlett Street. When you reach George Street, cross at the pedestrian lights, turn right and then left down Milsom Street. At the bottom, carry on round to the left into New Bond Street. No 12, on the south side, was where Claire Clairmont lived during the final weeks of her pregnancy and where she gave birth to Byron's daughter on 16 January 1817.

New Bond Street was built in 1806, replacing a narrow thoroughfare called Frog Lane. About halfway along on the north side of Frog Lane was Bath's first Unitarian Chapel, where Coleridge preached in 1796.

Turn right down New Bond Street Place, on the south side of New Bond Street, and then left along Upper Borough Walls. The large archway leading to a service yard on the south side of the street is on the site of the entrance to the yard of the Greyhound Inn, whose front entrance was round the corner in the High Street. It closed in the 1860s, after the opening of the railway took much of its trade away, and what was left of the building was demolished in the 1960s. It was here that Coleridge came on the night of 5 December 1813, having walked from Ashley in the pouring rain.

Carry on to the end of Upper Borough Walls and turn right along the High Street. The figure of Justice above the Guildhall was designed in 1777 by Robert Edge Pine, the site of whose studio in Hetling Court was visited in the fourth walk. 1777 was, of course, the year of Catharine Macaulay's birthday celebrations. A couple of years earlier, Pine had painted the portrait of Catharine Macaulay which appears on page

126 and bears a striking resemblance to the figure on the Guildhall. Like Macaulay, Pine was a republican who supported the American Revolution – so much so that in 1784 he left England for Philadelphia, where he painted portraits of many of the founding fathers of the United States. All of which seems to indicate that Pine modelled the figure

of Justice on Catharine Macaulay. If that is indeed the case, it seems ironic that, for over two centuries, Bath's corporation has conducted its business beneath the statue of an eighteenth-century republican.

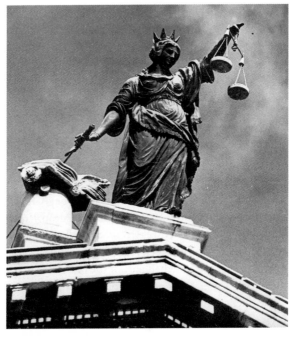

Carry on along the High Street and turn left into the Orange Grove. This area has changed enormously since Henry Hunt held a rally here in January 1817.[1] Only the Abbey and the row of shops on the south side still survive. There were buildings to the east, which have all gone, and a row of inns and pubs along the north side, which were replaced by the present buildings in the late nineteenth century. It was into this confined space that twelve to fifteen thousand people (or 500, if you believe the *Bath Chronicle*) crammed to hear Henry Hunt press for reform as the militia looked on.

Walk along the south side of the Orange Grove and turn right into Terrace Walk. No 2 North Parade, where Mary Shelley took art lessons from John West, now forms part of the Abbey Hotel, which you can see ahead.

Turn right along York Street to Kingston Parade. The buildings that once stood here included the Kingston Lecture Room, where Mary Shelley heard Dr Wilkinson's theories on electricity.

---

1 You will see the yard from where the rally started in the next walk.

Head to the left of the Abbey into Abbey Church Yard. On the south side, to the left of the entrance to the Pump Room, stood the building where the Shelleys lived between September 1816 and February 1817. In Peter Lovesey's 1999 detective novel *The Vault*, a severed hand is discovered in a vault that once formed part of the building, but the police investigation soon runs into complications when an American academic on the trail of Mary Shelley turns up.

Head through the colonnade into Stall Street, turn left and then second right into Beau Street. Turn left into Bilbury Lane, cross Lower

Borough Walls, take the footpath to the right of the open space ahead, and turn left along St James's Parade. This is where Catharine Macaulay took lodgings in 1774 before moving to Alfred Street. Although we do not know where she stayed, if you walk along to No 33 you will see a bust of Minerva over the door. As you saw in Alfred Street, she had a penchant for busts over doors; she also had her portrait painted as Minerva, which suggests that this is where she stayed.

Head back to the open space on Lower Borough Walls, where the building on the west side – now a pet shop but originally a Quaker meeting house – stands on the site of the Catholic chapel burned down in the Gordon Riots in 1780. Despite the enormous damage done by the rioters, only one person was hanged for taking part in them. This was John Butler, footman to the city architect, Thomas Baldwin, who lived in the Royal Crescent. Although he was not implicated in the destruction of the chapel, he was found guilty of spurring on the mob and chasing the Catholic priest through the streets.

Three days after his trial, a gallows was erected on a plot of waste land near the site of the chapel. **Turn left and walk to the end of Lower Borough Walls**, where a pub now stands on the site of the gallows. John Butler left the prison in Grove Street at noon on Monday 28 August 1780, accompanied in the cart by his two brothers, 'each supporting by turns his drooping head upon the fraternal bosom, manifesting the truest affection and the acutest sorrow'. At the Guildhall, 400 special constables, sworn in on the day after the riot, joined the procession. Trouble was clearly anticipated, and the authorities were taking no chances. The Bath Volunteer Regiment and the Scots Greys were in Queen Square, ready to swing into action if the call came. The bells of the city tolled as the cart carrying John Butler on his final journey trundled through the streets. When he reached the place of execution, a vicar climbed into the cart and prayed with him 'with great devotion' for full half an hour, before reading out a letter in which John Butler protested his innocence. Then, 'taking the last farewell of his brothers, he was turned off, surrounded by many thousands of weeping spectators. After hanging about half an hour, his body was taken down, put into a coffin, and carried away in a hearse to be interred in his native parish near Wells. He was about 26 years old.'

Compared with the other rebels and romantics whose footsteps we have followed, John Butler hardly gets a mention in any of the books on the period. But his story was just as much a part of those troubled times, and perhaps the saddest one of all.

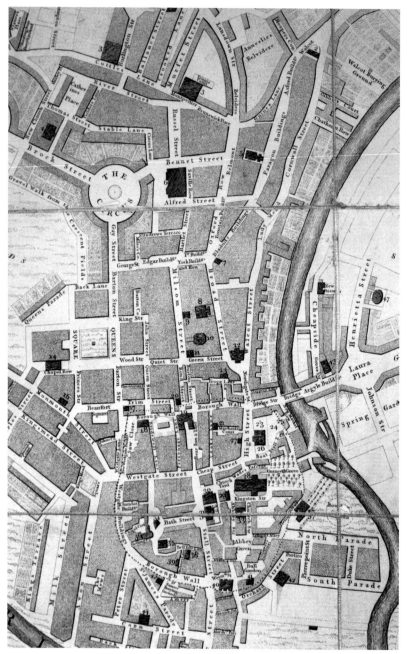

Bath in 1793

7
'THE RHYTHM OF TOM PAINE'S BONES'
Radicalism and Repression in Pitt's 'Reign of Terror'

This walk, which complements the previous one, differs from all the others by celebrating not the impact Bath had on a particular writer or group of writers, but the impact a book had on the city. If ever proof were needed that the pen is mightier than the sword, then Tom Paine's *Rights of Man*, published in two parts in 1791 and 1792, provides it.

We **start in Orange Grove**. In 1817, as described in the previous walk, Henry Hunt addressed between twelve and twenty thousand people here – or 500 if you believe the *Bath Chronicle* – calling for universal suffrage, under the watchful eye of the military. Two years later, when he addressed a similar meeting at St Peter's Fields in Manchester, mounted soldiers charged into the crowd, killing at least eleven people and injuring hundreds more.

In 1839 Henry Vincent, the Chartist leader, addressed another mass rally here, again calling for universal suffrage. A few months later, he was imprisoned after the Chartist march on Newport ended with soldiers firing on the demonstrators and killing at least ten of them.

So, although blood was not shed in Bath, it very easily could have been. The fight for parliamentary representation was not an easy one. And that representation would not have been gained without thousands of ordinary people having the courage to put their lives on the line and stand up to authority.

Had you stood here sometime in the late 1790s leafing through a copy of Tom Paine's *Rights of Man*, you would have risked being arrested, thrown into prison, losing your livelihood, and possibly having your house torn down by a drunken mob. At the very least, you would have been regarded with intense suspicion, tailed by council informants, and had your letters opened. It was inadvisable to talk too freely of rights in what was to all intents a police state, as Pitt's government inaugurated its 'reign of terror'.

Although Tom Paine is one of the most influential writers of all time, most people know little about him – and the official view seems to be that he was a revolutionary firebrand and an apologist for the worst excesses of the French Revolution. Nothing could be further from the truth. His prose style is lucid, witty and dazzlingly rational. He was a product of the Age of Reason, and it was his very reasonableness and sense of humour – always happy to prick the bubble of pomposity – that made the authorities so alarmed.

Tom Paine was born in Thetford in Norfolk in 1737, the son of a Quaker stay maker. At 15 he ran away to sea, enlisting on the privateer Dr Death, but soon saw the error of his ways and became an apprentice stay maker himself. There followed a number of jobs – including a spell as an excise man and a teacher – but all the time he was engaging in debate with fellow artisans in clubs and societies, and starting to write. Along the way, he met Benjamin Franklin, who suggested he went to America. When he got there, a friend of Franklin's gave him a job on a newspaper. In 1776,

he published an anonymous pamphlet called *Commonsense* which made the case for American independence so convincingly that it was decisive in stiffening the resolve of the colonists to make the break with Britain. It also influenced the wording of the Declaration of Independence.

At a key point in the War of Independence, two days before Christmas 1776, he wrote the following words, which George Washington ordered to be read to the troops:

> Let it be told to the future world … that in the depth of winter, when nothing but hope and virtue could survive … that the city and the country, alarmed at one common danger, came forth to meet it … These are the times that try men's souls – tyranny, like hell, is not easily conquered, yet the harder the conflict the more glorious the triumph.

Stirring stuff. But, although Paine was the hero of the hour and rewarded with the post of secretary of state for foreign affairs, he had too much integrity to settle down and enjoy the fruits of his labours. For a start he had a problem with George Washington, along with many of the other founding fathers, keeping slaves, something they managed to square with their notions of equality. He also spoke up on behalf of the native people and called for the rich to be taxed to pay for the army. All of which soon made him very unpopular and he was sacked.

Returning to England, he turned his hand to the design of iron bridges, a project that occupied him for several years, with some success. Had things gone differently, we might remember Paine today as a key player in the industrial revolution, along with Telford, Stephenson and Brunel. But things did not quite work out like that, for in 1789, a revolution, inspired by and initially modelled on the revolution in America, broke out in France.

At first, most people in Britain – most people of a liberal persuasion at any rate – were in favour of the revolution and saw the fall of the Bastille as a good thing. But, when Versailles was stormed and the royal family forced to flee to Paris, many started to revise their opinions. Attitudes quickly became polarised. A Unitarian minister, Dr Richard Price, preached a sermon celebrating the storming of Versailles. This prompted Edmund Burke, who had initially been in favour of the revolution, to publish, in November 1790, his *Reflections on the Revolution in France*, which was to become one of the seminal texts of Conservativism.[1] His scathing attack on the folly of those who had overturned the status quo in France stemmed from a conviction that the notion of the Rights of Man, which lay at the heart of their revolutionary manifesto, was a dangerous chimera:

> They first destroyed all the balances and counterpoises which serve to fix the state and to give it a steady direction, and which furnish sure correctives to any violent spirit which may prevail in any of the orders. These balances existed in their oldest constitution, and in the constitution of this country, and in the constitution of all the countries in Europe. These they rashly destroyed, and then they melted down the whole into one incongruous, ill-connected mass. When they had done this, they instantly, and with the most atrocious perfidy and breach of all faith among men, laid the axe to the root of all property, and consequently of all national prosperity, by the principles they established and the example they set, in confiscating all the possessions of the Church. They made and recorded a sort of institute and digest of anarchy, called the Rights of Man, in such a pedantic abuse of elementary principles as would have disgraced boys at school: but this declaration of rights was worse than trifling and pedantic in them; as by their name and authority they systematically destroyed every hold of authority by opinion, religious or civil, on the minds of the people. By this mad declaration they subverted the state, and brought on such calamities as no country, without a long war, has ever been known to suffer, and which may in the end produce such a war, and perhaps many such.

1 Burke, who was MP for Bristol from 1774 to 1780, also had a connection with Bath. In 1757 he married Mary Nugent, the daughter of a doctor who lived in the Circus, and in 1797, by which time he was in poor health, he lived at 11 North Parade, where there is a plaque to his memory.

This was the cue for Tom Paine to step forward and demolish Burke's arguments. Paine had been a friend of Burke – had even gone hunting with him – and Burke had supported the American Revolution. The split between them can be seen as marking the point at which, starting from the same principles, modern Conservatism and modern radicalism veered off in different directions to take up opposed and mutually exclusive positions.

The first part of *The Rights of Man* was a detailed refutation of Burke, and in particular of the hereditary principle and the idea that the settlement after the Glorious Revolution of 1688 should stand for all time. 'The idea of hereditary legislators,' Paine declared, 'is as inconsistent as that of hereditary judges or hereditary juries; and as absurd as an hereditary mathematician, or an hereditary wise man; and as ridiculous as an hereditary poet-laureate.' In the second part, Paine made detailed proposals for social and political reform – and it was these that made the government act against him. Reading his proposals today it is difficult to see what all the fuss was about. Give or take a few exceptions, *The Rights of Man* seems like a straightforward manifesto for universal suffrage and a welfare state – redistribution of wealth, old age pensions, state education, child allowances, unemployment relief. However, Paine also advocated something still to be introduced and far more radical – a land tax and the abolition of inherited land.

Pitt House in Johnstone Street

The Rights of Man articulated what many people felt and was an instant best seller. It sold 300,000 copies in six months – a staggering figure considering that the population was around ten million, at least 40% of whom could not read.

Walk along Grand Parade, over Pulteney Bridge, carry on along Argyle Street to Laura Place and turn right into Johnstone Street, where a plaque on No 15 commemorates Wiliam Pitt the Younger's residency. Pitt, who was prime minister from 1783 to 1801 and again from 1804 until his death in 1806, declared war on France after the execution of

Louis XVI. His government also passed acts suspending Habeas Corpus and imposing draconian punishments on anyone circulating seditious writings or holding seditious meetings. Pitt lived here in 1802 while he was out of office.

Walk down the south side of Great Pulteney Street to No 76 where a plaque commemorates Hannah More's residency. Tom Paine was one of the

Hannah More

great pamphleteers of the 1790s; Hannah More was the other. They both claimed to be friends of the working class, but their views were diametrically opposed. Just as Paine was spurred into print by Burke, so Hannah More was spurred into print by Paine.

Hannah More has been described with some justification as the sort of friend the working class could have done without. She was an evangelical Christian who set up village schools to inculcate Christian values in the poor. Education in the broader sense of the word was strictly taboo, however. 'I am extremely limited in my ideas of instructing the poor,' Hannah More declared, 'I would confine it entirely to the Bible. To teach them to read without giving them principles seems dangerous; and I do not teach them to write, even in my weekly schools.'

At first, Hannah More welcomed the French Revolution. 'What English heart did not exult at the demolition of the Bastille?' she later wrote, 'What lover of his species did not triumph in the warm hope that one of the finest countries in the world would soon be one of the most free?' Like Burke, events soon made her revise her opinions.

Hannah More did not like Bath, and was opposed to its extravagance and moral depravity. But, although she regarded the system as rotten, that did not give the working classes the right to overthrow it. Hannah More was against political action as a way of redressing grievances. She believed that injustice should be dealt with on an individual level. If God allowed misery in the world, she believed, it was so that good men could have the opportunity of lessening it. The reformation and redemption of the individual – whether rich or poor – was the only legitimate course of action. Even if the country's rulers were unworthy, it was necessary for the ruled to submit – not only was this the will of God, but it also ensured that civil order would be maintained.

One of the reasons she was against teaching the working classes to read was that popular literature sold by chapmen and hawkers – which she described as 'vulgar and indecent penny books' – was a bad influence on them. *The Rights of Man*, however, was far worse. 'This pernicious pamphlet,' she wrote, 'is in every cottage, highway, mine and coal pit.' Her friends pressed her to reply to Paine's irreligious 'poison':

> As soon as I came to Bath, our dear Bishop of London came to me with a dismal countenance, and told me that I should repent it on my death-bed, if I, who knew so much of the habits and sentiments of the lower orders of people, did not write some little thing tending to open their eyes, under their present wild impressions of liberty and equality. It must be something level to their apprehensions, or it would be of no use. In an evil hour I consented, against my will and my judgment: on one sick day I scribbled a little pamphlet, called *Village Politics*, by Will Chip; and the very next morning sent it off to Rivington, changing my bookseller the more surely to escape detection. It is as vulgar as heart can wish, but it is only designed for the most vulgar class of readers. I heartily hope I shall not be discovered, as it is a sort of writing repugnant to my taste, though indeed it is rather a question of peace than of politics.

Village Politics was a dialogue between Jack Anvil, the village blacksmith, and Tom Hood, the village mason. Hood is an advocate of *The Rights of Man*, but Anvil defends the status quo, arguing that Paine's ideas will make men poorer and not richer. He goes on to point out that equality is an illusion because some people are stronger and cleverer than others – a common argument on the political right, but in this case, as so often, refuting something Paine never said. He concludes by stating his conviction that, if the principles expressed in *The Rights of Man* are put into practice, 'battle, murder and sudden death' will inevitably follow.

Hannah More went on to write many more such tracts, printed by Samuel Hazard in Cheap Street in Bath as well as in London. Millions were printed, often being bought in bulk by the gentry to distribute to the poor, and remained popular for many years. To be fair to Hannah More, her tracts did not always reflect her true beliefs: in her popular writings she urged the poor to trust their leaders, but in private correspondence she often questioned whether their trust was misplaced. Whether you think this was hypocrisy or worthwhile because it preserved civil order is a matter of opinion.

If you look (or walk) along Great Pulteney Street, you will see, near the end on the other side, No 36, where William Wilberforce stayed in 1802 and again in 1805. In 1797, Wilberforce married Barbara Spooner in Walcot Church. Her parents lived in the Royal Crescent and he stayed there in the winter of 1798. He also stayed at 9 North Parade in 1831. It is on 36 Great Pulteney Street, however, that the plaque commemorating his connection with the city has been placed.

Wilberforce, who was a friend of Hannah More, is best remembered today for his opposition to slavery. Like More, he was an evangelical Christian and, like her, his views were often deeply conservative. He advocated change in society through the inculcation of Christian principles and was opposed to radical changes to what he saw as a God-given political and social order. Wilberforce supported the suspension of Habeas Corpus and voted for Pitt's 'Gagging Bills', which banned meetings of more than 50 people and imposed harsh penalties on anyone suspected of seditious beliefs. In 1799, when he spoke in favour of the Combination Act outlawing union activity, he called trade unions 'a general disease in our society'. He also opposed an enquiry into the Peterloo Massacre because, he claimed, it would give encouragement to 'bad men who wished to produce anarchy and confusion'. William Cobbett was among those who attacked what they saw as Wilberforce's hypocrisy in campaigning for the emancipation of slaves while refusing to support campaigns to improve the lot of the working classes at home. 'Never have you done one single act, in favour of the labourers of this country,' he declared angrily, while William Hazlitt condemned Wilberforce as one 'who preaches vital Christianity to untutored savages, and tolerates its worst abuses in civilised states'.

Head back to Laura Place, walk along Argyle Street and turn right down Grove Street for 150 metres until, as the street curves to the right, you come to a large classical building on the right. This was the city prison, built in 1772, where many of Paine's supporters, and others fighting for their rights, ended up. So far, you have seen the homes of some of Bath's more famous residents – Pitt, Hannah More and Wilberforce – with plaques in their memory. All were opposed to Paine, and all form part of the officially sanctioned side of Bath's heritage, the side that is recorded and celebrated. When we start to look for the unofficial side, and for evidence of those who fought and suffered for the rights we take for granted today, we have to look much harder and follow trails that often go cold.

After the publication of the second part of *The Rights of Man*, the government acted quickly against Paine. In May 1792, a Royal Proclamation was issued:

> Whereas divers wicked and seditious writings have been printed, published, and industriously dispersed, tending to excite tumult and disorder by endeavouring to raise groundless jealousies and discontents in the minds of our faithful and loving subjects, respecting the laws, and happy constitution of government, civil and religious, established in this kingdom and endeavouring

The prison in Grove Street

to vilify and bring into contempt the wise and wholesome provisions made at the time of the Glorious Revolution: and since strengthened and confirmed by subsequent laws, for the preservation and security of the rights and liberties of our faithful and loving subjects: and whereas there is nothing which we so earnestly desire, as to secure the public peace and prosperity and to preserve to all our loving subjects, the full enjoyment of their rights and liberties, both religious and civil; we therefore being resolved, as far as in us lies, to repress the wicked and seditious practices aforesaid, and to deter all persons from following so pernicious an example, have thought fit, by the advice of our privy council, to issue this our royal proclamation, solemnly warning all our loving subjects, as they tender their own happiness, and that of their posterity to guard against all such attempts which aim at the subversion of all regular government within this kingdom, and which are inconsistent with the peace and order of society; and earnestly exhorting them at all times, and to the utmost of their power, to avoid and discourage all proceedings tending to produce riots and tumults: and we do further charge and command all our sheriffs, justices of the peace, chief magistrates in our cities, boroughs and corporations, and all other our officers and magistrates throughout our kingdom of Great Britain, that they do, in their several and respective stations, take the most immediate and effectual care to suppress and prevent all riots, tumults and other disorders which may be attempted to be raised or made by any person or persons which on whatever pretext they may be grounded, are not only contrary to law, but dangerous to the most important interests of this kingdom; and we do further require and command all and every our magistrates aforesaid, that they do from time to time, transmit to one of our principal secretaries of state, due and full information of such persons as shall be found offending as aforesaid or in any degree aiding or abetting therein; it being our determination for the preservation of the peace and happiness of our faithful and loving subjects, to carry the laws vigorously into execution against such offenders as aforesaid.

This blueprint for what amounted to a police state was swiftly followed by acts of parliament outlawing seditious writing. Paine evaded arrest by fleeing to France, but was tried 'on an indictment for publishing a scandalous, wicked and seditious libel against the king and constitution' in his absence. The report of his trial in the *Bath Chronicle* on 20 December 1792 included details of what occurred when a guilty verdict was pronounced:

> Immediately as the verdict was announced, a man in the crowd hissed (it was supposed) the jury, on which the court was thrown into tumult. The people cried out, 'Seize him! Hold him up!' nor would they be satisfied till he was taken into custody.

A few weeks before Paine's trial, the Association for the Preserving of Liberty had been founded in London. Similar organisations soon sprang up all over the country. The same issue of the *Bath Chronicle* that included the report of Paine's trial carried news that 'numerous parties from the neighbouring villages, and the frequenters of our markets, flock to the Guildhall to join the Loyal Bath Association; the signatures to which amount to nearly 7000.' Many of those who signed did so at the behest of their employers; failure to have done so would have entailed dismissal and denunciation to the authorities. The paper also reported on the first local outbreak of what would, over the following months, become one of the most terrifying instances of mob hysteria in Britain's history:

> Last night the effigy of Tom Pain [sic], placed in a cart loaded with faggots, with a seditious pamphlet in one hand and a pair of stays in the other, was drawn to the top of Beechen Cliff, and there, hoisted on a pole, his body being filled with combustibles, was set fire to and his head blown off; his carcase was then thrown into a large bonfire, and consumed amid the firing of cannon and the loudest acclamations of a numerous multitude. By the bursting of the cannon, Luke Lappam, a mason, was wounded in the breast, but not dangerously; he was taken to the casualty hospital.

The following week, the *Chronicle* reported that 'Tom Paine has been hung in effigy, and, with his seditious works, burnt, at Kilmersdon, Chilcompton, Midsummer-Norton [sic], and most of the neighbouring villages, amidst repeated and hearty shouts of "God Save the King".' On New Year's Day 1793, over a thousand people walked from Box up to Kingsdown in the rain to witness Paine being burnt in effigy, and the words of 'God Save the King' were 'given to every young person in the parish, as a future memorial of the loyalty of their fires'. At Keynsham, 'the ceremony of hanging and burning the effigy of Paine was conducted with a mock solemnity similar to that of the execution of a criminal.' In Lacock – that olde-worlde village so beloved of the makers of costume dramas – Paine's effigy was 'drawn on a sledge round the town and parish ... and afterwards hung on a gibbet 30 feet high, and then burnt amid the acclamations of an immense number of people who testified their love of the king and our glorious constitution'.

It goes without saying that expressions of anything less than whole-hearted support for these mock lynchings were extremely unwise. In a 'little village' identified only as being 'not five miles from Devizes', a fiddler was burnt in effigy because he refused to play 'God Save the King' as Paine went up in flames. Principled stands such as this were rare, however. Again and again, newspaper reports emphasised the solemnity and decorum that accompanied these burnings, assuring readers that they took place 'without the least outrage against any individual'. The authorities not only sanctioned but actively encouraged them. At Mells, for example, 'the populace were treated by Mr Horner, of the Park there, with a hogshead of strong beer.' Just occasionally, though, a blow was struck for the opposition. The *Bath Chronicle* for 24 January 1793, reported that

> a ludicrous circumstance attended the execution of Tom Paine's effigy at Saltford. A great crowd assembled, with drums beating, colours flying, etc, and the culprit was hung with due formalities; but lo! while they retired to regale over a refreshing pot, till the hour for conflagration, some rogue or humourist carried off the effigy with its clothes, to the great disappointment of the eager expectants.

Those who refused to be intimidated by these officially sanctioned demonstrations of patriotic fervour faced arrest. In 1794, Thomas Wyld, a 'gentleman's servant', who wanted to see the Duke of York's troops 'cut to atoms in the next campaign' and the abolition of what he called 'a damned arbitrary government', was given a six-month sentence for seditious speech. He did not serve his full sentence, however, as a 'wanted' notice published in the *Bath Chronicle* on 6 June indicates:

> Escaped last night out of the prison of this city: THOMAS WYLD, about 5 feet 6 inches high, dark long brown hair tied, a smooth face, pale complexion, slim made; by trade a hair-dresser, and lately lived with an American gentleman; had on a blue coat, corduroy breeches, and round hat; under sentence of imprisonment for speaking seditious words – aged 26 years ...

Several other prisoners escaped at the same time, including three deserters from the army.

Then there was George Wilkinson, an Irish republican and member of a local corresponding society. He worked for the bookseller Samuel Hazard, who published Hannah More's tracts. Wilkinson's trial was reported in the *Bath Chronicle* on 16 January 1794:

> At the quarter sessions for this city, on Monday last, George Wilkinson, a journeyman printer, was tried and found guilty of uttering the following seditious expressions: 'Success to the French and down with the Allies'; 'The King and his Ministers are villains'; and (alluding to the Declaration lately published on the causes of the war) 'That will make their villainy more clear'. He was sentenced to pay a fine of 20/- to the king, to be imprisoned for four months, and to find security for his good behaviour for one year.

His spell inside did not deter him. In 1804, he attempted to subvert the Bath Loyal Volunteers by joining them and trying to persuade them to go on strike. He was dismissed.

Benjamin Bull was a journeyman tailor who lived in Wine Street, off St James's Parade. He was arrested in August 1794 for giving away pirated copies of *The Rights of Man* to friends in the Market Place. One of these friends took a copy into the Guildhall and reported him. He was arrested and given twelve months for seditious libel. The loss of his liberty had a devastating effect on Bull, as a notice in the *Bath Chronicle* on 30 July the following year indicates:

SUBSCRIPTION towards the RELIEF of *BENJAMIN BULL, a Prisoner in Bath Gaol.*

THIS Man was tried, found guilty, and justly imprisoned, for dispersing Seditious Publications; the principles of which he has now solemnly renounced, and being *truly penitent* for his former errors, he is resolved (like an honest Englishman) to become a loyal subject to his King and Country; and earnestly recommends the same laudable conduct to his *late* associates, before (like him) they *lose* their LIBERTY!!!

"My shame and guilt confound me!
"Forgive me!——If hearty sorrow
"Be a sufficient ransom for offence,
"I tender it here; I do as truly suffer,
"As e'er I did *commit.*"
' Then we are paid,
' And once again we do receive thee honest.
' *Who by repentance is not satisfy'd,*
' *Is nor of heaven, nor earth.*'

BENJ. BULL is a *sickly* Taylor, *without* work, with a *Wife and five Children* almost *destitute of Food and Cloathing.* Donations for this unfortunate Family will be *properly* applied by the SHERIFFS of BATH.

	s.	d.		s.	d.
Sir Edw. Harington	5	0	Dr. Lee, M.D.	5	0
Mr. G. Crook	5	0	Mr. Nagle	2	6
W. Meyler	2	6	Lady H.	2	6
Rev. Mr. Wake	2	6	R. C.	2	6

Walk back along Grove Street, turn right across Pulteney Bridge and carry on up Bridge Street to the High Street. On your left is the Guildhall, built in the late 1770s, where the mayor and corporation held court. This august body had good reason to despise Paine, for he laid into them in his attack on chartered monopolies in Part One of *The Rights of Man*:

In these chartered monopolies a man coming from another part of the country, is hunted from them as if he were a foreign enemy. An Englishman is not free in his own country: every one of those places presents a barrier in his way, and tells him he is not a freeman – that he has no rights. Within these monopolies, are other monopolies. In a city, such for instance as Bath, which contains between twenty and thirty thousand inhabitants, the right of electing representatives to parliament is monopolized into about thirty-one persons. And within these monopolies are still others. A man, even of the same town, whose parents were not in circumstances to give him an occupation, is debarred, in many cases, from the natural right of acquiring one, be his genius or industry what it may.

Are these things examples to hold out to a country regenerating itself from slavery, like France? Certainly they are not; and certain am I, that when the people of England come to reflect upon them, they will, like France, annihilate those badges of ancient oppression, those traces of a conquered nation.

Paine returned to the subject of chartered monopolies in Part Two of *The Rights of Man*:

It is a perversion of terms to say that a charter gives rights. It operates by a contrary effect – that of taking rights away. Rights are inherently in all the inhabitants; but charters, by annulling those rights, in the majority, leave the right, by exclusion, in the hands of a few.

Charters ... are sources of endless contentions in the places where they exist, and they lessen the common rights of national society. The generality of corporation towns are in a state of solitary decay, and prevented from further ruin only by some circumstance in their situation, such as a navigable river, or a plentiful surrounding country. As population is one of the chief sources of wealth (for without it land itself has no value), everything which operates to prevent it must lessen the value of property; and as corporations have not only this tendency, but directly this effect, they cannot but be injurious.

Given Bath's decline in the mid-nineteenth century, these words were surely prophetic.

The Guildhall before it was extended in the late nineteenth century

One of the major causes of unrest in the late eighteenth century – more pressing even than agitation for the Rights of Man – was a chronic shortage of food. In 1795 a group of women boarded a barge loaded with grain at Broad Quay in Bath, to try to seize it. They sang 'God Save the King' but were dispersed by troops. In 1800 there was a food riot in the market place, with women seizing a trader's goods and selling them for a fair price. Despite their name, these food riots were generally orderly affairs, aimed at stopping profiteering at times of scarcity. Somewhat predictably, Hannah More wrote a ballad attacking the food riots, called 'The Riot: or Half a Loaf is Better than No Bread' – it is recorded that a 'very formidable riot' was quelled in Bath in 1796 when a 'quick-thinking gentleman' struck up a rendition of it.

Broad Quay, by the Old Bridge, where a group of women attempted to seize a barge loaded with grain in 1795

Carry on along Upper Borough Walls to Burton Street. It was on the corner of Burton Street, backing onto Old Bond Street, that John Cunningham Butler Campbell, the most prominent victim of the 1794 witch hunts, had a bookshop and circulating library. He was an American Methodist, who had set up in partnership with Thomas Gainsborough's nephew, and was also editor of the *Bath Advertiser*. He was a poet, democrat and anti-slavery campaigner. Between 1792 and 1794, he hosted meetings of the Bath Corresponding Society above his shop and displayed radical pamphlets and cartoons condemning the war with France in its windows. In 1794, he was removed as editor of *Bath Advertiser*, had his house attacked by a loyalist mob and went bankrupt after a well-orchestrated boycott of his business. He died in poverty in Chapel Court five years later, in June 1799, his wife and seven-year-old daughter having died the previous November.

Walk up Burton Street and turn right into New Bond Street. At the end, cross to the Podium, turn left along Walcot Street and walk along to the entrance to Beehive Yard. This was the yard owned by Henry Hunt, where the mass rally described in the previous walk started off. On 6 January 1817, the *Times* reported that

> Bath is to have a public meeting this day. A requisition to call a meeting was presented to the mayor, who replied that it did not meet with his approbation. In consequence the requisitionists appointed a general meeting to held in Mr Hunt's large yard, adjoining the new market, Walcott [sic] Street. The mayor and magistrates had therefore invited the inhabitant householders to attend at the Guildhall, to be sworn in as special constables. The troops that were sent to Bristol, previous to the late meeting there, were under orders to proceed to Bath.

The *Times* followed this with a report from its Bath correspondent:

> The meeting of reformers is just over, and the crowds are separating, and hitherto without much disorder. The mayor and magistrates had taken every precaution to prevent the peace of the city being disturbed by those clamorous sons of sedition; several hundreds of the respectable householders were enrolled as constables; and that well-ordered body, the Bath Chairmen (full 300 strong active fellows), were likewise sworn in and armed with staves. Several formidable troops of dragoons from Bristol and Trowbridge barracks had, for the last two or three days, gradually taken up their quarters in the city; as had the Mendip Yeomanry Cavalry, under the command of Colonel Horner and Major John Wiltshire. The Bath Rifle Corps were also in readiness, if their active service had been required. These defenders gave assurances of safety to the loyal and to the timid.
>
> About half past eleven, Hunt, in his curricle, arrived from his friend Parson Wood's at Newton St Loe, and drove through the streets by the Guildhall to Racey's late brewery yard, about the middle of Walcot Street (now Hunt's property, as assignee to Racey): not a single shout or any follower attended the orator's progress through the city. At the appointed spot of rendezvous the assemblage was, however, rather numerous, and still increasing, it was resolved to adjourn the meeting to the old Orange Grove; and the rout was facilitated in its progress by one of the severest storms of rain and hail that ever was witnessed. A carpenter's bench was placed under the east window of the Abbey church, upon which rostrum Hunt soon mounted, attended by one Hickman, a poor infatuated lad, the servant of a bookseller, as his secretary and reader. The orator went over his old topics of enormous taxation, ruinous wars, abominable sinecurists, the corrupt press, with a good deal of abuse on the Bath corporation, and other constituted bodies. His resolutions were read, and as much of them

The Orange Grove, where Henry Hunt addressed a meeting in January 1817. Despite the presence of large numbers of soldiers, everything went off peacefully. In August 1819, when he addressed a meeting in Manchester, a troop of cavalry charged into the crowd, killing at least eleven people. The representation of the massacre below shows what could so easily have happened at Bath if the authorities had panicked.

as could be heard appeared to be exact copies of what had been produced at Spitalfields and at Bristol, which were adopted by acclamations; and to each, about 200 double-fisted fellows and basket-women held up their hands. There were two or three speakers besides: one Young, a puritanic schoolmaster (a tenant of the orator's); little Hibbert, the engraver; and Carpenter, a picture-frame gilder ... Mr Hunt will certainly not add to his popular fame by this meeting: a set of more obscure despicable names than the 30 who signed the requisition to the mayor, the city could not possibly produce; and those who attended to support and applaud the orator were, from their appearance, really the very scum of the city ...

The post will not allow me to add more than that the mob is entirely dispersed, and the streets perfectly quiet.

Half past four o'clock.

Carry on along Walcot Street, take the third right down Walcot Gate and, if the gates to the mortuary chapel are open, go through them and head down to the right of the chapel to find the grave of John Thelwall along the bottom row. Thelwall is all but forgotten today – but after Tom Paine fled to France in 1792, he was the most important radical leader in the country. In 1792, he helped form the London Corresponding Society – the focus for radical thought – and in 1794 was tried for treason along with fellow members John Horne Tooke and Thomas Hardy. Although all three were acquitted, government officials continued to hound him. He was regarded by many as the most dangerous man in the country. Cartoons by Gillray and others portrayed him flourishing a butcher's knife and holding the torch of arson.

Thelwall wrote a best-selling sequel to *The Rights of Man* called *The Rights of Nature*. His lectures were attended by thousands, and, when the Seditious Meetings Act and the Treasonable and Seditious Practices Act (known as the 'gagging acts') were passed in 1795 – largely to shut Thelwall up – he got round the legislation by talking on Roman history – although he was actually talking about contemporary issues. His lectures were routinely broken up by hired thugs, however, and magistrates refused to intervene. On one occasion he only managed to escape by waving a gun at his attackers.

Thelwall was also a poet and in 1796 Coleridge (who, unlike Thelwall, was virtually unknown at the time) wrote to him, suggesting that, as they were 'pursuing the same end by the same means ... we ought not to be strangers to each other'. In 1797, Coleridge invited Thelwall down to stay with him and Wordsworth in Somerset. Wordsworth was favourably impressed, describing Thelwall as 'a very warm-hearted, honest man ... we like each other uncommonly well', while Coleridge dedicated a sonnet to

John Thelwall   Thelwall's grave in Walcot cemetery

him, declaring that he had been 'by thy fair example taught to glow with patriot zeal'. Thelwall, for his part, liked the two poets so much that he conceived the idea of renting a house near them, and enshrined his feelings in verse:

> Ah! Let me, far in some sequester'd dell,
> Build my low cot; and happy might it prove,
> My Samuel! Near to thine, that I might oft
> Share thy sweet converse, best-belov'd of friends!
> Long-lov'd ere known: for kindred sympathies
> Link'd, tho far distant, our congenial souls.

Thelwall's reputation and the government agents that followed him down to Somerset soon led the local populace to suspect they were harbouring a cell of revolutionary traitors in their midst. Fears of patriotic vigilantism soon made Coleridge and Wordsworth change their minds about the advisability of having Thelwall for a neighbour. 'Come, but not yet,' Coleridge wrote to him, 'I say it with a very sad, but a very clear conviction – at present I see that much evil and little good would come from your settling here.'

Thelwall never did return, and it was not long before Coleridge and Wordsworth began that disavowal of radicalism that was to lead to an espousal of Tory principles and support for the establishment. In 1801, Coleridge wrote to Thelwall,

> we are so utterly unlike each other in our habits of thinking, and we have adopted such irreconcilably different opinions in politics, religion and metaphysics (and probably in taste too) that I fear – I fear I do not know

LITERARY WALKS IN BATH

how to express myself – but such, I fear, is the chasm between us, that so far from being able to shake hands across it, we cannot even make our words intelligible to each other.

This cruel retraction, for a man who had taken on a police state and won, must have been one of the bitterest blows of all. 'The ordinary transactions of life have been interrupted,' he wrote, 'the intercourses of the closest relationship violated and impeded … The channels of vital sustenance have been dried up; and friendship (the last stay of the human heart) – even friendship itself … wearied and intimidated by the hostilities to which it was exposed, has shrunk from its own convictions.'

Thelwall went on to become well known as a lecturer on elocution, but never gave up his principles and in 1818, in response to the agitation for reform that followed the defeat of Napoleon, set up a journal called the *Champion*. He is buried in Bath because he died in the city in 1834, while giving a series of lectures on elocution at the Royal Literary & Scientific Institution.

We end not with the final resting place of John Thelwall, but with Tom Paine – and an explanation for the title of this walk. 'The Rhythm of Tom Paine's Bones' is a stirring song by Graham Moore, best known in a version recorded by Dick Gaughan. The reason behind the title, though, is a convoluted and bizarre one.

By the time a warrant was issue was issued for Paine's arrest in 1792, he had already fled to France, tipped off, so it is said, by William Blake. When he arrived, he was such a celebrity, due to his involvement in the American Revolution and support for the French Revolution, that – despite not being able to speak French – he was elected to the National Assembly. Things were already turning nasty in France, however, and before long there were calls for the king to be executed. Paine refused to go along with this; he was against the institution of monarchy, not the man who happened to be king. Again, as in America, he was prepared to suffer for his principles – and suffer he did. He was arrested and thrown into prison where he only escaped execution by an incredible stroke of luck.

Every evening, a guard walked through the prison chalking a sign on the doors of those prisoners due to be guillotined in the morning. One night, it was the turn of the door to Paine's cell, which had been left open to let some air in, as Paine was ill. During the night, the door was closed, hiding the mark. When the prisoners to be executed were rounded up, Paine was not among them. This temporary respite allowed him to survive a few vital days until the fall of Robespierre on 9 Thermidor (July 27) 1794 brought him a reprieve.

While in prison, Paine, then 57 years old, started a new work called *The Age of Reason*. It was an attack on conventional Christianity, as well as on the atheism of the French Revolution. Paine has often been labelled a godless atheist: in fact, he was a Deist or Unitarian – prepared to accept the existence of god but opposed to mysticism, religious revelation and religious dogma.

He stayed in France and was rehabilitated – even to the extent of discussing the invasion of England with Napoleon – but became increasingly disillusioned as he saw the country sliding towards dictatorship. Thomas Jefferson invited him back to the States, but when he arrived the public mood had turned against him. Attacked by mobs, he retired to the country, where he had a stroke and – at least according to his denigrators – drank a pint of rum a day. Principled to the last, he never did subscribe to the philosophy of winning friends and influencing people. Among the missives he fired off was one to George Washington which included one of the most glorious insults of all time:

> As to you, sir, treacherous in private friendship, and a hypocrite in publick life, the world will be puzzled to decide, whether you are an apostate or an impostor; whether you have abandoned good principles or whether you ever had any.

Tom Paine died on 8 June 8 1809 at 59 Grove Street in Greenwich Village, New York. He was 72 years old. Although the original building is no longer there, the present building has a plaque commemorating Paine's death. Many newspapers reprinted the obituary from the *New York Citizen*, whose tone can be gauged from a single sentence: 'He had lived long, did some good and much harm.' A more fitting tribute was made years later by the great American orator and Civil War veteran, Robert G Ingersoll:

> Thomas Paine had passed the legendary limit of life. One by one most of his old friends and acquaintances had deserted him. Maligned on every side, execrated, shunned and abhorred – his virtues denounced as vices – his services forgotten – his character blackened, he preserved the poise and balance of his soul. He was a victim of the people, but his convictions remained unshaken. He was still a soldier in the army of freedom, and still tried to enlighten and civilize those who were impatiently waiting for his death. Even those who loved their enemies hated him, their friend – the friend of the whole world – with all their hearts. On the 8th of June, 1809, death came – death, almost his only friend. At his funeral no pomp, no pageantry, no civic procession, no military display. In a carriage, a woman and her son who had lived on the bounty of the dead – on horseback, a Quaker, the humanity of whose heart dominated the creed of his head – and, following on foot, two negroes filled with gratitude – constituted the funeral cortege of Thomas Paine.

That modest funeral was not quite the end of the story, however. Ten years later, the great radical writer William Cobbett, on a visit to America, dug up and shipped Paine's bones back to England. The plan was to give Paine a heroic reburial on his native soil, but the bones were still among Cobbett's effects when he died over twenty years later. There is much dispute about what happened to them after that, although various people down the years have claimed to own bits of the great man, such as his skull and his right hand. Paine, who had no time for idolatry and relics, would surely have been highly amused, and with good reason, for it is the unflinching rationalism and humanity of his works, his belief in natural justice, and his stirring blend of utopian idealism and commonsense – not his bones – that constitute his legacy. Over two centuries after his death, dancing 'to the rhythm of Tom Paine's bones' – in the words of Graham Moore – can still provide inspiration for those fighting new threats to the Rights of Man.

8

VAPOUR, SHADOW, SMOKE AND CONFUSION
Jane Austen's Bath

The first view of Bath in fine weather does not answer my
expectations; I think I see more distinctly through rain. The sun was
got behind everything, and the appearance of the place from the top
of Kingsdown was all vapour, shadow, smoke and confusion.

Jane Austen, *Letter to her sister Cassandra, 5 May 1801*

Every September, Bath attracts some rather unusual visitors. Ladies attired
in high-waisted long dresses, sporting elaborately decorated bonnets, peer
into the shop windows of Milsom Street. Dashing gentlemen in many-
caped coats, fancy boots and top hats stroll along the wide pavements
of the Royal Crescent. Occasionally, they all come together for a grand
promenade – an amazing assemblage of frills, feathers and furbelows,
parasols and pantaloons, military magnificence and beribboned bosoms. It
is the Jane Austen Festival.

These eccentrically garbed people have come from all over the world
to recreate, for themselves and for others, a time long gone – the period
when Jane Austen lived in Bath. Some modern residents look upon this
gloomily, saying that it just adds to Bath's toytown image, keeping it stuck
in the past – others say it is just a bit of harmless fun, and that those
who participate are well aware they are taking a break from their otherwise
humdrum lives. This is probably true – the participants have no qualms
about photographing themselves with digital cameras, and keeping in touch
on their mobile phones. But how many of those who come realise just how
different Jane Austen's Bath was from the city they see now? We should not
delude ourselves that dressing up and walking the streets that she walked
will bring us any closer to her world. The past is not just another country
– it is another planet. This walk takes you to that planet, and explains what
Bath between 1797 and 1806 was really like.

Many changes have been for the better. Jane's impression from the
top of Kingsdown would no longer include smoke. In her day, the
chimneys belched forth dark clouds of sooty particles, which soon
changed the gleaming white stone to black, as the early twentieth-
century photograph on the left of Jane Austen's house at 4 Sydney Place

shows. It is hard for us to imagine exactly how smoky Bath was. In 1763, Gainsborough moved out of his 'house in the smoake' in the Abbey Church Yard, to the clean air of Lansdown Road, and then to the Circus. The Woods advertised their houses on the northern slopes as being much healthier because the air was so much fresher.

However, there are drawbacks to the modern world. There is still vapour – but all too often it is caused by chemical pollution. When Lunardi made his famous balloon trip in 1784, it is striking how far he could see in all directions. The emissions from factories, cars, goods vehicles and trains mean that, were Jane Austen to return to Bath today, she would doubtless wrinkle up her rather Roman nose at the cocktail of chemical smells to which our noses have become accustomed. By contrast, we would be horrified at the odour of Georgian Bath. Horses, then the main form of transport, have powerful emissions too. On top of that, there were slaughterhouses, and related trades such as tallow making, soap boiling and leather dressing to add to the mix. Above all, there would be the rich smell of brewing. In the early nineteenth century, Bath brewed more beer than Bristol. Nearly every pub offered home-brewed beer and there were several large breweries as well.

Another modern advantage is street lighting. Although we complain about light pollution, and have lost the magical view of the Milky Way flung across the sky like a glittering silk scarf, we can find our way about easily at night. By contrast, Jane Austen's Bath would have seemed very dark – it is no wonder that footpads were so active. We would also be astonished and alarmed at how many people carried guns. It explains why Bath embraced the technology of gas lighting as early as 1818, just twelve years after Austen left.

In the shadows of this lost world lurked the spectre of poverty. It was frighteningly easy to be comfortable one moment and facing destitution the next. The Austens did their best to keep up appearances when they found themselves in straitened circumstances after the death of Jane's father, the Rev George Austen. They rushed out to visit people who had said they would call on them, rather than let them see where they were reduced to living – which also helped to conserve their supplies of tea and sugar. Although her brothers offered money, and Henry Austen seemed optimistic about their prospects, Jane was aware that they were now dependent on relatives. 'I think we are just the kind of people and party to be treated about among our relatives,' she remarked lightly to her sister Cassandra in April 1805, adding, 'we cannot be supposed to be very rich'. It was, nevertheless, a humiliating position for them to be in.

So let us go back to this different world, and begin outside the lodgings which Jane shared with her mother, brother Edward and his family, in the south-west corner of Queen Square, at No 13. To guide us, we will use a map published in 1800 which you will find overleaf. Jane was an indefatigable walker and you will, in the course of the walk, have the option of following her on three excursions which stray beyond the borders of the map – to Beechen Cliff, Charlcombe and Weston.[1]

The first visit about which we have any certain knowledge is the one that Jane and her family made in 1799, although we know that she made an earlier visit in 1797, because she refers to her aunt and uncle Leigh-Perrot inviting them to Bath again, in a letter of 1798. In 1799, however, they did not stay with the Leigh-Perrots in the Paragon but took lodgings in this house in Queen Square. We would hardly recognise the square as it was then. On the west side, there were still the three Palladian villas designed by John Wood, with the middle one set back. The villas at either end consisted of three houses, while the central one consisted of two. The square was beginning to look dated architecturally, however. Even though Mrs Austen liked it, in *Persuasion* the Musgrove girls turn up their noses at it, saying:

> I hope we shall be in Bath in the winter; but remember, papa, if we do go, we must be in a good situation: none of your Queen-squares for us!

In 1799, every window would still have had its glazing bars, and window lengthening was only just beginning. Wood's chapel of St Mary was still standing in the south-west corner. The first demolition took place in 1830, when the central villa on the west side went, and the Greek Revival building which now houses the Bath Royal Literary & Scientific Institution was built on what had been its garden. The chapel went in the 1860s, to allow easier access to the new Midland Railway station.

Traffic would not have circulated around the square as it does now. Charlotte Street, in the north-west corner, was not created until about 1840 – before then, the square was much more of a backwater, where elegant people could perambulate. In addition, its magnificence was not marred by trees. Jane Austen told Cassandra that

> the prospect from the drawing-room window, at which I now write, is rather picturesque, as it commands a prospective view of the left side of Brock Street, broken by three Lombardy poplars in the garden of the last house in Queen's Parade.

Today, that same view is completely blocked by vegetation in the summer, though it is a little clearer in the winter. In Jane Austen's day, the square

---

1 The excursions, which appear in italics, go through fields and over rough paths, and involve steps. The main walk, however, while it includes several flights of steps, also has step-free alternatives.

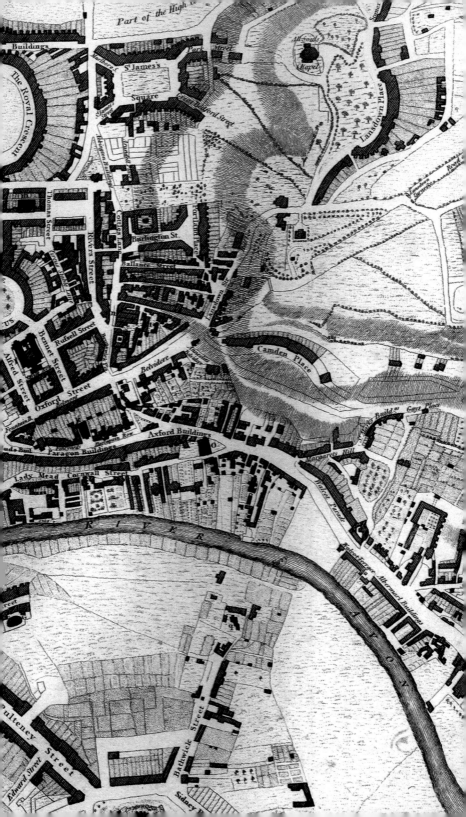

still retained its formal gardens, which made it look rather dated, compared with the *rus-in-urbe* style of Lansdown Crescent.

Despite being less fashionable than the streets higher up, there were still plenty of lodging and boarding houses in the square. This one was run by Mrs Bromley, who seems to have moved around the square. In 1792 she was at Nos 2 & 3, and in 1800 she was at No 12, where she stayed for some time. Jane's description of the rooms gives us a good idea what lodging houses were like:

> We are exceedingly pleased with the house; the rooms are quite as large as we expected. Mrs Bromley is a fat woman in mourning, and a little black kitten runs about the staircase.

Above: The chapel in the south-west corner of Queen Square, just across from No 13, where Jane Austen stayed in 1799

Below: Queen Square as Jane Austen would have known it – a map dating from 1775

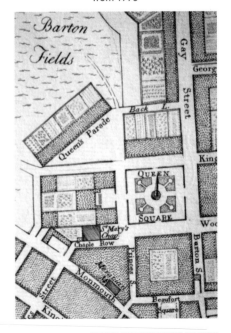

LITERARY WALKS IN BATH

Eliz[1] has the apartment within the drawing-room; she wanted my mother to have it, but as there was no bed in the inner one, and the stairs are so much easier of ascent, or my mother so much stronger than in Paragon as not to regard the double flight, it is settled for us to be above, where we have two very nice-sized rooms, with dirty[2] quilts and everything comfortable. I have the outward and larger apartment, as I ought to have; which is quite as large as our bedroom at home, and my mother's is not materially less. The beds are both as large as any at Steventon, and I have a very nice chest of drawers and a closet full of shelves — so full indeed that there is nothing else in it, and it should therefore be called a cupboard rather than a closet, I suppose.

The family had come for Edward's health, and we will shortly be visiting one of the spa facilities he tried. However, we now leap forward to 1801, when the Rev George Austen decided to move to Bath, hoping to take the house on the other side of Princes Street, facing No 13 Queen Square. This was not available, however, and they were forced to go house-hunting.

Head out of Queen Square down Chapel Row, carry on across Monmouth Street at the lights, continue down Charles Street to a set of pedestrian lights and cross to New King Street. Early in May 1801, Jane and her mother stayed with the Leigh-Perrots, leaving the Rev Austen and Cassandra at home in Hampshire. Jane and her mother were concerned about the cost of coming to Bath, and it was agreed that this part of town would be ideal. We know from accounts by Lady Nelson and Fanny D'Arblay that this area was cheaper. Lady Nelson wrote in 1797 of her house in New King Street:

> This house £90 a year: Gay Street £160, the higher you go the dearer.

This sentiment was echoed by Jane Austen, early in 1801, when she was still at Steventon. She was delighted to hear that New King Street had been rejected, however, as the houses were so small. Despite this, her mother insisted on looking at one, only to find it even smaller than they had imagined. After their visit, Jane wrote to Cassandra:

> One in particular out of the two was quite monstrously little; the best of the sitting rooms not so large as the little parlour at Steventon, and the second room in every floor about capacious enough to admit a very small single bed.

You can get an idea of what the houses were like by visiting the Herschel Museum at No 19. Jane Austen would be very surprised to learn that many of them are now divided into flats, some with bedrooms which do indeed just about admit a single bed. For the daughter of an Anglican clergyman, the proximity of the Wesleyan chapel in the street might have

1 Elizabeth Austen, Edward's wife.
2 This may be a misreading of 'dimity', a cotton furnishing fabric commonly employed for bed upholstery and curtains in the Georgian period. Alternatively, it may just be Jane being amusing.

been considered a drawback. She would doubtless have approved, however, of the organisation run from there, the Strangers' Friend Society, which aided the poor without asking the reasons for their distress – a very unusual attitude in those days. Today, the Percy Boys Club stands on the site.

Jane was more enthusiastic about the houses in Charles Street, because they were new, and nearer to Kingsmead Fields, where she could go walking. However, only this side of Charles Street remains. Turning to look across the road, you will see that all the streets shown on the map on pages 176-7, including Kingsmead Street, have disappeared. This part of Bath suffered badly during the two nights of bombing in April 1942.

Continue down Charles Street and cross to Green Park Station. Seymour Street, where Jane Austen and her mother looked at another house, once stood here. They were assured that the house would soon be available, and did not suffer from its proximity to the river, but the principal room was only 14 feet square and they thought it uninviting. This part of town was already unfashionable and during the Austens' brief stay in Bath became even more so. In April 1805, Jane Austen reported that the Stanhopes, who lived in Seymour Street, were lucky to have let their house, as there was 'an astonishing number of houses at this time vacant in that end of the town'. Nothing remains of Seymour Street as it was in 1801 – one side went when the Midland Railway built their station and the other was damaged beyond repair in the bombing of Bath.

Continue across the road to the corner of Green Park Buildings. Jane Austen and her mother then turned their attentions to Green Park Buildings, a curious arrangement of two straight terraces arranged in a V-shape. Only this west wing[1] survived the bombing of April 1942 – the east wing, on the other side of the main road, was destroyed by incendiary bombs. There are modern buildings there today, so we only have this wing to give us an idea of what the Austen family were looking at. Jane Austen and her uncle had already made one visit to No 12 – in the east wing – which would have been about two-thirds of the way down towards the river. At first, she seemed impressed, telling Cassandra that

> we walked all over it except into the garret; the dining-room is of a comfortable size, just as large as you like to fancy it; the second room about 14ft square. The apartment over the drawing-room pleased me particularly, because it is divided into two, the smaller one a very nice-sized dressing-room, which upon occasion might admit a bed. The aspect is south-east. The only doubt is about the dampness of the offices, of which there were symptoms.

---

1 If you look carefully, you will see that the word 'West' is just visible on the end of the building. If you consult the map from 1800 on page 176, you will notice that Green Park Buildings East and Green Park Buildings West are transposed.

A couple of weeks later, she wrote to Cassandra again:

> Our views on GP Buildings seem all at an end; the observation of the damps still remaining in the offices of an house which has been only vacated a week, with reports of discontented families and putrid fevers, has given the *coup de grace*. We have now nothing in view. When you arrive, we will at least have the pleasure of examining some of these putrefying houses again; they are so very desirable in size and situation, that there is some satisfaction in spending ten minutes within them.

To be fair, Mr Phillips, the owner of No 12, offered to raise the floor of the kitchen, which was in the basement, but, as Jane realised, this would have merely hidden the problem rather than solving it. As time went on, and their poor reputation became more established, the properties in this part of town became harder to let. In 1804, however, the family returned to Green Park Buildings to take lodgings at No 3 in the east wing, which was further from the river, and presumably less damp. It was here that George Austen died in 1805.

You will see how low the park in front of Green Park Buildings is – the basements have access to it. This was part of the area known as Kingsmead Fields, where Jane Austen planned to go walking.

Very few pictures of Green Park Buildings East, where the Rev Austen died in 1805, survive. Above on the left is an Edwardian postcard of No 4. The Austens lived next door at No 3, the remains of which can be seen on the right after the bombing raids of April 1942.

By now, Jane and her mother were becoming dispirited by their unsuccessful house-hunting, although it may well have been that they were trying to be too economical. As we shall see, when Cassandra and the Rev Austen arrived, they opted for a house in a much better location, which Jane had thought would be beyond their means.

To see how close the river was and some of the other problems associated with this area, **continue along Green Park Road (to the left of the park). Stop when you reach Avon Street, which runs northwards between a coach park and a car park.** The river curves in a slow meander around this part of town, and early developments such as Avon Street soon went down in the world. The towpath, which you see on your right, floods readily even today, despite all the flood prevention measures in place.

This is a part of Bath which Jane Austen would not have frequented. At the bottom end of Avon Street was Narrow Quay, with Broad Quay a little way upstream. The river was a major traffic artery, made navigable to Bristol in 1727, and here were warehouses, stores, stables and malthouses. Many boats would have been moored up here, loading and unloading a variety of cargoes. It would have been very vibrant, but also noisy and at times downright rowdy. Across the river, the Lower Bristol Road would have been busy with pack trains and caravans – the delivery vehicles of their day.

Although just around the corner from places she would have known well, it is unlikely, given its reputation, that Jane Austen ever visited Avon Street

And what of Avon Street itself? In the eighteenth century rich and poor often lived in close proximity. The modern idea of zoning simply did not exist. Some areas, however, became so notorious that they blighted streets close by. The Avon Street area – which included Corn Street, Back Street and Little Corn Street – was just such a place. It became a byword for prostitution. As early as 1762, less than 30 years after the first houses were built as grand lodgings, the High Sherriff of Wiltshire, Henry Penruddocke Wyndham, wrote warmly of the pleasures of Mother Addams' brothel in Avon Street; by 1771, when Smollett referred to 'the nymphs of Avon Street' in *Humphrey Clinker*, his readers would have had no trouble understanding what he meant. Yet parts of it were still salubrious enough in 1767 for the Rev John Penrose to visit its second-hand shops with his wife to buy pieces of silk which had 'never been made up and were as good as new'. However, the year before, he had described it as a street of ill-fame, and avoided using it. Like the Rev Austen, Penrose was not flush with cash, and the chance of a bargain was enough to overcome his scruples.

In 1786, one of Avon Street's more respectable inhabitants, Mr Mansford, wrote to the council complaining of the smell and the failure of the council to keep it clean:

> I am sorry that present circumstances makes your attention necessary in Avon Street, which with the quantities of all kinds of nastiness thrown out by its inhabitants for a whole week together and the interspersion here and there of a group of pigs makes a perfect dung muckson from one end to the other. Because 'tis Avon Street once a week is thought sufficient for the scavenger to clean it, but from the disorderly practices of most of its inhabitants makes it necessary it should be swept etc, every day, which I shall leave to your consideration.

By 1821, over 1500 people – around 5% of Bath's population – were crammed into Avon Street's 88 houses. It is hardly surprising if the poor and dispossessed sometimes took to the streets. Fanny Burney and the Thrales had left Bath in a panic when the mob went on the rampage in 1780, and it was at Broad Quay that 200 women boarded a boat loaded with grain in 1795 to prevent it sailing. In 1800, when the Austens were thinking of moving to Bath, Williams' malthouse on the quay was burnt down. Breweries and malthouses frequently did burn down – they were highly combustible – but an anonymous threat sent a few days earlier indicates that this was almost certainly arson. Today, thanks to clearances – by the Luftwaffe and Bath City Council – barely a trace of the old Avon Street, or the alleys, courts and quaysides that lay around it, survives – which, given the miserable lives of many of its inhabitants, is probably just as well.

Before leaving this spot, look across the river to the hill rising above the buildings. This is Beechen Cliff, 'that noble hill whose beautiful verdure and hanging coppice render it so striking an object from almost every opening in Bath'. Later, you will have the chance to enjoy the view which Henry Tilney shared with Catherine Morland in *Northanger Abbey*, by taking an optional excursion through Lyncombe Vale to the top of Beechen Cliff.

Cross over and walk up Avon Street, which today, in marked contrast to its former character, is largely taken up with the City of Bath College. **When you reach James Street West, cross (using the zebra crossing a little way along to the left) and carry on up Avon Street.** Just before you reach Kingsmead Square, you can see the sole surviving house from the old Avon Street on the left.

Carry on along the east side of Kingsmead Square before turning right and right again into Westgate Buildings. Cross over and carry on past the gardens of St John's Hospital to a building at right angles to the street with 'Chandos Buildings' carved above its ground-floor windows. The large block opposite was built by the Bath Co-operative Society in 1934. The eighteenth-century buildings it replaced were, by the time of their demolition, very run down. This slide from their original elegance had already begun in Jane Austen's day, largely due to the proximity of Avon Street. When the Austens first went house-hunting, however, a friend of theirs, Miss Lyford, gave such a glowing report of her mother's stay in Westgate Buildings in 1797 that Mrs Austen was keen to

Westgate Buildings, built between 1760 and 1771, the home of Anne Elliot's friend Mrs Smith

see them. Jane wrote to Cassandra that, although Westgate Buildings were 'quite in the lower part of town', they were 'not badly situated themselves; the street is broad, and has rather a good appearance'. The Rev Austen, however, ruled them out without even seeing them.

By the time Jane wrote *Persuasion*, Westgate Buildings had come down in the world considerably; Anne Elliot's friend Mrs Smith is staying there, 'in lodgings near the hot baths, living in a very humble way, unable even to afford herself the comfort of a servant, and of course almost excluded from society'. When Anne's father finds out she has visited Mrs Smith there, he is outraged, and leaves us in no doubt as to his opinion of this part of town:

> Upon my word, Miss Anne Elliot, you have the most extraordinary taste! Everything that revolts other people, low company, paltry rooms, foul air, disgusting associations are inviting to you ... Westgate-buildings must have been rather surprised by the appearance of a carriage drawn up near its pavement ... A widow Mrs Smith lodging in Westgate-buildings! A poor widow barely able to live, between thirty and forty – a mere Mrs Smith, an every-day Mrs Smith, of all people and all names in the world, to be the chosen friend of Miss Anne Elliot, and to be preferred by her to her own family connections among the nobility of England and Ireland!

The building you are standing by – now part of St John's Hospital – was built by John Wood as an elegant lodging house for James Brydges, Duke of Chandos – a distant relative of Mrs Austen. Known as Chandos House, it originally looked out over the city walls across open country, but, as Bath continued to grow, was soon hemmed in by far less desirable buildings. By the mid-nineteenth century, as the area continued to decline, it became a pub – the Chandos Arms.

Carry on past Chandos House, past another small garden, and turn left along a broad alleyway towards the new spa. The building at the end of the alleyway on the right was once the Hetling Pump Room – if you carry on round the corner you can still see its name above the ground-floor windows. It was here that Jane came with her brother Edward in June 1799 to take the waters. He had been consulting Dr Fellowes, who lived three doors along from the Leigh-Perrots, and told him that he wanted to try an electrical cure, to which Fellowes made no objection. This probably involved brushing the skin with metal rods through which flowed a mild current. Known as Perkins tractors, these were very fashionable, and supposed to cure a variety of ailments, although Jane reported that no one in the family believed they would have any effect. This may have been because Edward was something of a valetudinarian. However, Fellowes may have heard from another Bath doctor, John Haygarth, of the results of his trials using wooden tractors painted to look like metal, which proved just as effective. A year later he published a report *On the Imagination as a Cause & as a Cure of Disorders of the Body*, debunking the whole idea. He had discovered the placebo effect.

Across the street from the Hetling Pump Room is the Hot Bath, which then would not have had the serpentine extension, added around 1830, which rather spoils John Wood the Younger's charming building of 1775. To your left is the Cross Bath, designed by Thomas Baldwin and radically altered by John Palmer when Bath Street was built in 1791, destroying buildings dating from the sixteenth century, if not earlier. So in 1799 this was a newly redeveloped area, the oldest buildings being only about 25

years old. In 1813, Jane Austen wrote to Cassandra that members of the Bridges family were taking the waters at both these baths, and that Louisa Bridges was bathing there. However attractive Bath Street might have looked, however, it hid, on its north side, a vast network of stables and other buildings linked to the White Hart Inn at the other end of the street. These were not only used by grooms, ostlers and those connected with the coaching business; they were also a rendezvous for prostitutes, and anyone living in Bath would have been aware of this.

In 1801, Mr Chamberlayne, a distant relative of Mrs Austen, was staying with his wife in Bath, in what Jane refers to as the Charitable Repository. The Repository of Works of Industry and Ingenuity for the Benefit of the Poor, founded in 1796 by a committee of charitably minded ladies, was in Cumberland House in Bath Street. Some of the goods – mainly fancy items – were made and brought in by poor people themselves, and sold directly for their benefit. Other items were given by genteel ladies – Jane expressed the hope that Mrs Chamberlayne would sell her black beaver bonnet here.

Head east along Bath Street, cross to the other side of Stall Street and turn to look back at Bath Street. On the right-hand corner once stood one of Bath's busiest inns, the White Hart, which dated back to at least 1503. It was completely refronted in 1791 as part of the improvements to this part of town, but behind the new façade lurked the old inn.[1] Although it could be noisy, it was still very fashionable. In addition to the normal noises of a busy inn, the Harmonic Society held rowdy meetings here[2]. When a friend of the Austen sisters, Fanny Cage, stayed here in 1813 before moving into lodgings, she found the noise terrible.

In *Persuasion*, when Charles Musgrove brings his wife and mother to Bath, they come to the White Hart as well, and it is while Mary Musgrove is looking out of one of its windows that Austen gives us a clear pointer to Mrs Clay's immorality. She has already told us that Mrs Clay has freckles. This does not bother Elizabeth Elliot, although the more worldly-wise Sir Walter is shocked. This reaction would not have seemed as peculiar in the eighteenth century as it does today. Freckles were often considered an indication of venereal disease. As if to confirm this is what Austen had in mind, we are later told that Mrs Clay uses Gowland's Lotion. In Georgian newspapers, abortifacients and remedies for the pox often masqueraded as cosmetics. The principal ingredient of Gowland's Lotion was an oxide of mercury, commonly used to treat venereal disease, and its efficacy in treating 'scorbutic eruptions' was another nod to those who understood its real purpose. Two years before *Persuasion* was written, it had been denounced in *Reece's Gazette of Health*. With Jane Austen's more knowing readers already suspecting that Mrs Clay might not be all she seems, we are told that, as Mary Musgrove looks out of the window of the White Hart, she sees Mrs Clay and Mr Elliot walking up Bath Street. As the White Hart's stables, behind Bath Street, were notorious for sexual assignations, we are left with the unspoken suggestion of what they may have been up to. It comes, therefore, as no surprise when Mrs Clay runs off with Mr Elliot to be his mistress, which, in the Georgian era, was tantamount to becoming a prostitute.[3]

The shop under the colonnade on the left-hand corner was where Jane Leigh-Perrot was accused of shoplifting in 1799. The shop, owned by a

---

1 A photograph of the White Hart can be found on page 226.
2 For more on the Harmonic Society, see the Georgette Heyer walk.
3 Mrs Clay's name too, with its earthy connotations, may have been carefully chosen.

Mrs Smith but run by her sister, Miss Gregory, was a haberdasher's which sold, amongst other items, lace. What is not in dispute is that Jane Leigh-Perrot, who was in town with her husband, bought some black lace which was made up into a parcel. Later that day, Miss Gregory accosted the Leigh-Perrots in the street, demanding to know if there was some white lace in the parcel. When the parcel was opened, a card of white lace was found. Mrs Gregory took the lace, and no more was said. A couple of days later, a menacing anonymous letter arrived at the Leigh-

Looking west along Bath Street around 1900, with the shop where Jane Leigh-Perrot was accused of shoplifting on the left. The ivy-covered fountain on the right – erected in 1859 – has now been removed to Terrace Walk.

Perrots' house, telling her that all her friends and acquaintances would soon be advised of the theft. Similar letters followed but the Leigh-Perrots ignored them. Six days later, Mrs Gregory and the shopman, Filby, went to the magistrates and swore out a warrant for her arrest on a charge of grand larceny. Not content with charging her with the theft of the white lace, they charged her with stealing the black lace as well. Jane Leigh-Perrot was unceremoniously carted off to Ilchester Gaol to await trial. After several weeks in confinement, she was declared innocent, to the joy of her family, and the disgust of modern conspiracy theorists, who claim that this was a case of one law for the rich and one for the poor, but this is to ignore several important facts.

Filby did not make a good witness. He and Miss Gregory said they had tried to report the theft to the magistrates at the time, but found no one available. No evidence was offered to show the truth of this. What they did do was to spend three hours with a newspaper man, Mr Gye, who had a pecuniary interest in the shop, leaving the shop unattended save for a girl. They also left the card of white lace with him.

LITERARY WALKS IN BATH

At the trial, two women, neither of whom knew the Leigh-Perrots, testified that they too had found extra items in packages bought at the shop. In the first case, prior to Jane Leigh-Perrot's visit, Miss Gregory served the customer with gloves. Two days before Jane Leigh-Perrot's alleged offence, the lady returned to the shop with an extra pair she had found wrapped up with the others and handed them back to Filby. Filby, on oath, first of all said he did not remember her at all, and was sure he would have done because the shop was not busy. Then he said he did not remember her because there were so many customers in the shop, he could not remember them all. He made a similar reply to the testimony of another customer about an extra veil – in this case, after Jane Leigh-Perrot had been arrested. The lady was quite clear she had returned it to him because she had told him that, in view of what had happened to Jane Leigh-Perrot, he ought to be more careful.

As Jane Leigh-Perrot pointed out later, while all the staff could remember with remarkable clarity everything they did and she did when the alleged crime took place, they apparently could not recall things that happened just five minutes before and after. She could have added that, although both Gregory and Filby said the prisoner was a stranger to them, they had no trouble in picking her out in the street. To any reasonable person, the whole affair stinks – and luckily for Jane Leigh-Perrot, who could have been, at worst, condemned to death and, at best, transported, the jury was made up of reasonable people. Frank Mackinnon, a High Court judge who made a careful study of the case, also believed her to be innocent, with the whole thing a plot to extort money. As he pointed out, if she had been guilty, continuing to plead not guilty was a very high risk strategy, as in those days the prosecution could have been bought off at any time. It is also telling that Miss Gregory and Mr Filby seem to have smartly removed themselves from Bath after the trial, with Mrs Smith taking over the shop.

However, say those determined to find her guilty, there was a later case when she was accused of stealing some plants. Careful examination of what was actually said, however, shows that this truth now universally acknowledged is based on what looks like malicious gossip. What she may have done is to try to get her hands on a seedling – it can have been no more than that since it was allegedly wrapped in her pocket handkerchief. While, strictly speaking, this is theft, it should be remembered that keen gardeners are prone to this – some gardens open to the public ban ladies from carrying large bags in order to prevent it.

The trouble with Jane Leigh-Perrot was that, although she and her husband were happily married, she was an outspoken woman who knew her own mind at a time when women were expected to be subservient to their husbands. As a result, poor James Leigh-Perrot was condemned as a 'Jerry Sneak of a husband' by a clergyman who accused him of buying off her prosecutor – precisely the thing the Leigh-Perrots chose not to do. As for elderly ladies being prone to shoplifting – another popular piece of modern evidence against her – recent events have shown that apparently pointless shoplifting is not confined to women or the elderly. When women do indulge in this kind of mysterious behaviour, they almost always fit a particular profile, which in no way resembles Jane Leigh-Perrot.

Despite this, there were plenty in Bath prepared to believe her guilty, which may have been one reason why Jane Austen was so opposed to coming here – and, perhaps, why her aunt was so keen for the family to come.

Head south along Stall Street and stop at the crossroads at the top of Southgate Street. In May 1801, Jane went for a walk with Mrs Chamberlayne to Lyncombe and Widcombe. As the Chamberlaynes were staying in Bath Street, the quickest – though by no means the most salubrious – route would have been along Southgate Street and over the Old Bridge. The old Southgate Street, which dated from medieval times, has completely disappeared. Two centuries ago, however, you would have found butchers, slaughterhouses, tallow chandlers, tinplate workers, tripe-sellers and a large brewery along here. Busy inns stood alongside seedy alehouses where prostitutes gathered to drink and pick up clients. It was a rambunctious sort of place, loud with the clatter of hooves, the cries of street-sellers, the squeals of animals on their way to slaughter and the sound of laughter as drunken men and women stumbled from pub to pub. In *Persuasion*, when Lady Russell and Anne Elliot are driven along Southgate Street, Lady Russell positively relishes this cacophony:

> Everybody has their taste in noises as well as in other matters; and sounds are quite innoxious, or most distressing, by their sort rather than their quantity. When Lady Russell not long afterwards, was entering Bath on a wet afternoon, and driving through the long course of streets from the Old Bridge to Camden Place, amidst the dash of other carriages, the heavy rumble of carts and drays, the bawling of newspapermen, muffin-men and milkmen, and the ceaseless clink of pattens, she made no complaint. No, these were noises which belonged to the winter pleasures; her spirits rose under their influence; and like Mrs Musgrove, she was feeling, though not saying, that after being long in the country, nothing could be so good for her as a little quiet cheerfulness.

Anne Elliot feels rather differently, however, and in 1838 that indefatigable chronicler of Bath's changing scene, Captain Rowland Mainwaring, described this route as 'at all times ineligible for female pedestrians of respectability'. So it is unlikely that Jane Austen and Mrs Chamberlayne would have come this way.

Southgate Street holds no such terrors today, so, if you want to follow their footsteps to Lyncombe Vale and the dizzy heights of Beechen Cliff, **head south along the left-hand side of the street. Cross at the end, carry straight on past the bus station and cross a footbridge over the river. Go under the railway, then bear left and walk alongside the river until you come to the first lock on the Kennet & Avon (K&A) Canal.** *When Jane Austen walked along the canal with her uncle in May 1801, they almost certainly joined it here, although they would have got here by crossing Pulteney Bridge and heading south alongside the river – which is also the route she probably took with Mrs Chamberlayne. On another occasion, Jane and her uncle walked all the way to Combe Hay to see the caisson lock, an experimental boat-lift, being tested on the Somersetshire Coal Canal (SCC), which leaves the K&A at Dundas Basin. Although you can follow the route she took, the caisson lock has long gone. The ground where it was built was a fine clay, known as fuller's earth, which caused the sides of the lock to bow in, and the experiment was abandoned. Despite this, the SCC became the most remunerative canal in the country – a reminder that Jane Austen's Bath adjoined the Somerset coalfield, and heavy carts and boats laden with coal would have been a common sight.*

Carry on along the canal towpath. After going under a bridge, take the path leading up to the right, turn right along the road and follow it round to the pedestrian lights. Cross over, turn left and then right up Prior Park Road. *We have now strayed beyond the limits of the 1800 map. The cottages on your right were built by Ralph Allen for his stonemasons in 1737, and the White Hart across the road was built around the same time. Jane Austen would be surprised to see the hart over the door – in her day, it stood over the White Hart in Stall Street.*

As you continue up the street, you pass Prior Park Buildings (built around 1820) on the right, with a stream running in front of them. By now, Jane Austen and her friend were walking through open fields, not past houses on one side and a garden centre on the other. As you carry on, however, you will see fields to the right. The car dealership on your left was originally a mill. **Turn right along Lyncombe Vale, taking the pavement on the left-hand side which leads onto a causeway high above the road, with a millstream alongside it.** *This is the 'raised narrow pavement' which Jane Austen and Mrs Chamberlayne walked along 'for many yards together'. Jane Austen wrote to her sister that 'the walk was very beautiful', and some of the buildings she would have seen survive amid more modern houses. Lyncombe Vale Farm, on the left, dates from the early eighteenth century, as does Lyncombe Hall, which you can glimpse through the trees on the right.*

LYNCOMBE VALE. BATH

Carry on and turn right at the junction. *If you look down to the left at the junction, you will see a tall eighteenth-century building, now a school but originally Lyncombe Spa. At the top of Lyncombe Vale Road, you will see Lyncombe Hill over to the right. This is probably the way Catherine Morland and the Tilneys would have walked up from Widcombe on their way to Beechen Cliff. We will be heading back down Lyncombe Hill shortly, but for now follow their footsteps as they continue uphill, discussing theories of the Picturesque.* **Turn left up Greenway Lane, and, when the road bears left, go through a kissing gate by an old barn on the right. Follow the path ahead, then, after passing through a gap in the hedge, head diagonally up the field, go through a kissing gate and turn left up to Beechen Cliff** *to see the view of Bath that Catherine rejects 'as unworthy to make part of a landscape'. With the foreground now dominated by the new Southgate shopping centre, modern seekers after the Picturesque may well agree with her.*

Retrace your steps to Greenway Lane and head back to the city down **Lyncombe Hill. At the bottom, turn right, cross two sets of pedestrian lights, cross the footbridge over the river and go through the tunnel under the railway. Cross to the Royal Hotel and head north along Manvers Street. Cross to the left-hand side at the pedestrian lights and carry on before turning left along Henry Street and right into Old Orchard Street to the old Theatre Royal.**

If you decide to miss out the excursion to Beechen Cliff, turn left at the bottom of Stall Street into New Orchard Street, and then turn left along Old Orchard Street to Bath's original Theatre Royal. It is here that General Tilney catches his first sight of Catherine Morland and, misled by

LITERARY WALKS IN BATH

from their ladies' suppers during the 'calamitous scarcity of flour'. The newspapers were full of recipes substituting rice for flour, farmers were encouraged to grow root vegetables and the poor were exhorted to grow potatoes. This may have seemed like good advice, but over-reliance on potatoes, which was soon common throughout Europe, had catastrophic effects when the potato crop failed, most notably in Ireland, in 1845.

Farm receipts were also badly affected by the poor harvests, and this may have been one of the reasons the Austen family moved to Bath. Not only was George Austen ageing and finding it difficult to fulfil his parish duties, but a significant part of his income came from Cheesedown Farm, which he had held the lease of since 1764. As the farm also provided most of his family's food, the drop in his income was of great concern to him. One option would have been to raise his tithes, but this would have been very unpopular; instead, he made over the curacy of Steventon to his son James, keeping the tithe income for himself, and selling off the lease of the farm. Bath was a wise choice, as its declining popularity meant that property prices and rents were falling, but the family's circumstances explain why they were so concerned about being able to afford lodgings in a pleasant part of the city.

By the end of May 1801, Jane Austen and her mother had had no luck finding suitable lodgings and were getting somewhat disheartened. Then they espied an advertisement:

> ## TO BE DISPOSED OF,
> THE LEASE of No. 4, SYDNEY-PLACE, three years and a quarter of which are unexpired at Midsummer.——The situation is desirable, the Rent very low, and the Landlord is bound by covenant to paint the two first floors this summer.—A premium will therefore be expected.
> For particulars apply to Messrs. Watts and Forman, Cornwall-Buildings, Bath. '804]

A few days later, Cassandra and the Rev Austen arrived, checked how much 'very low' actually was and decided that this was the very place. It was cheap, of course, because so little of the lease was left.

Continue along the High Street, turn right down Bridge Street and carry on across Pulteney Bridge to Argyle Street, known in Jane Austen's day as Argyle Buildings. The Austens would have walked along here many times during their stay in Bath, and would have seen urgent repairs being carried out to Pulteney Bridge. Floods in 1799 and 1800 undermined the central pier on the north side and the whole of that side had to be taken down and rebuilt by John Pinch, the surveyor to the Pulteney estate, in a plainer style. The building adjoining Pulteney Bridge on the south side, with steps leading down to the river, was the Argyle Inn and Tavern, sometimes known as the Argyle Coffee House. It opened in 1791, and by 1800 was being run by John Gould, who had previously sold wines and spirits at 18 Pulteney Bridge. It offered good accommodation for gentlemen travellers, with meals available and newspapers to read. Underneath it was the Argyle Tap, where sedan chairmen and servants could refresh themselves.

As you **continue along Argyle Street**, you will see the United Reformed church on the opposite side. This was built in 1789 by a group expelled from the Countess of Huntingdon's Connexion on the Paragon (which you will be seeing later). The countess was an enthusiastic Methodist until she fell out with Wesley and started her own sect. She was not prepared to tolerate criticism or views that differed from her own, and, when the breakaway group found a new home in Morford Street, she acquired the lease and evicted them. When they built this chapel it was set back with a courtyard in front. However, in 1804 it was extended forward into the courtyard; the current façade was added in 1821.

Continue into Laura Place. Rather to Jane Austen's surprise, her father had high hopes of living in 'one of the short streets leading from Laura Place or Pulteney Street', which she considered would be 'above our price'. These houses were among the grandest on the Pulteney estate: in 1800 the Duke of Northumberland stayed at No 11 Laura Place, and in 1802, William Pitt the Younger stayed on the corner of Johnstone Street. No wonder Austen had the dowager viscountess, Lady Dalrymple, living here.

LITERARY WALKS IN BATH

There was, however, someone well known to the Austens living near Laura Place, who might have influenced the Rev Austen's desire to move here. In 1760, when he was a tutor at Oxford, one of his former pupils, James Nibbs, asked him to be a trustee in his marriage settlement which included plantations in Antigua owned by his family since the 1670s. George Austen remained a trustee for the wealthy Mr Nibbs, and made him godfather to his first son, whom he christened James after him. James Nibbs called his second son George – possibly after the Rev Austen – and sent him to the school run by the Rev Austen at Steventon. In 1783, George Nibbs went up to Oxford with James Austen.

James Nibbs gave George Austen a portrait of himself, which Jane referred to in a letter to Cassandra when the family was deciding what to do with their belongings in preparation for their move from Steventon to Bath in 1801. He died in 1795 at his country seat, Beauchamp House in Devon, and was buried in Washfield church. After his death, his widow, Barbara Nibbs, moved to Bath and settled at 6 Great Pulteney Street. She later moved to 12 Henrietta Street, just around the corner. She died in 1813 and was buried in the Abbey.

It seems almost certain that, given their strong family ties, and with a portrait of Mr Nibbs as a treasured heirloom, the Austens, when they came to Bath in 1801 would have visited Mrs Nibbs on a regular basis. It also seems likely that the Rev Austen would have been in contact with her before moving to Bath, and may have asked her advice on finding a suitable place to live. Had he done so, 'one of the short streets leading from Laura Place or Pulteney Street' seems likely – given her own choice of residence – to have been the answer.

When, over a decade later and long settled back in Hampshire, Jane Austen wrote *Mansfield Park*, she seems to have had Mr Nibbs in mind. Beauchamp – the name of his country seat – finds an echo in Bertram, the surname of Sir Thomas, master of Mansfield Park. The Austen family would surely have relished this private joke. Sir Thomas Bertram – like Mr Nibbs – is an absentee plantation owner with estates in Antigua. Sir Thomas's eldest son is prodigal, but eventually sees the error of his ways. Mr Nibbs' eldest son was similarly prodigal, but in his case there was no reconciliation, and, after he had 'reduced himself by imprudence to great streights [sic] and debts', his father disinherited him. Mr Nibbs' second son, however – who had lodged with the Austens at Steventon and gone to Oxford with Jane's eldest brother – was the total opposite: like Edmund Bertram, he became a country parson – in his case at Cutcombe in Somerset. Such parallels cannot be coincidental – one wonders how many more there were between the real-life Nibbs and the fictional Bertrams, and what subtexts, likely to have been known only to the Austens and a close circle of acquaintances, exist in this most enigmatic of novels.

As you **continue along the right-hand side of Great Pulteney Street**, you pass, at No 76, the house where Hannah More lived. As you saw in the previous walk, although More was an anti-slavery campaigner and worked to improve the condition of the poor, she was also a believer in 'the rich man in his castle, the poor man at his gate'. Education, she held, should encourage the poor to accept their lot, as they would have their reward in heaven. She also believed that women should be a moral force rather than trying to exercise their intellect – although she was more than happy to display her own. Not surprisingly, Jane Austen was not an admirer. When More published *Coelebs in Search of a Wife*, Austen wrote that

> the name Caleb ... has an honest, unpretending sound, but in Coelebs there is pedantry and affectation. Is it written only to classical scholars?

In another letter, she came straight to the point – she did not want to read the book because 'I do not like the evangelicals.' The ever-fashionable Jane, who enjoyed dancing and company, would also have scorned Hannah More's suggestion that anyone enjoying such pleasures was sinful.

The Duchess of York – whom Austen accused of pushing up the price of salmon – also lived in Great Pulteney Street. In July 1801, there was great excitement when it was announced that the king was coming to Bath. Two houses in Great Pulteney Street were turned into one, and the rooms redecorated to create a veritable palace. In September, however, the king decided that he felt so well at Weymouth that a visit to Bath was not required, and the houses were returned to their owners – Lady Dunwelly and Mr Whalley. It was a sign of the times that even the king preferred bathing in the sea to Bath's hot springs.

If you look across Great Pulteney Street, you can see where Barbara Nibbs lived. The doors to Nos 2 to 6 have been replaced by windows, as these houses now form part of an apartment complex, but No 6, as you would expect, was to the left of No 7.

Carry on along the right-hand side of Great Pulteney Street. Four doors along from Edward Street, you come to No 49, which the Leigh-Perrots, after years of lodging in the Paragon, bought in 1810. Although it did not have the views the other house did, there was a level walk into town from here for the ageing couple, and, as most of the work on the Pulteney Estate had ground to a halt, there was little threat of them being disturbed by building work.

Great Pulteney Street features in both of Jane Austen's Bath books. The Allens, who bring Catherine Morland to Bath, have lodgings here, and it is here that Lady Russell and Anne Elliot see Captain Wentworth, after Anne begins to realise that perhaps he still loves her. She wonders what her friend, who persuaded her to part from Captain Wentworth years before, will say. However, Lady Russell pretends she has not seen him, saying that she was looking at some curtains, which makes Anne blush for her.

At the end of Great Pulteney Street, cross at the pedestrian lights to the Holburne Museum. This was built as the entrance to Sydney Gardens,

which opened in 1795. Jane Austen would struggle to recognise it today, as it has been drastically altered over the last two centuries. Inside, there is no trace of the banqueting hall, billiard room or coffee room, where you could read the country and London papers. To reach the gardens, you had to go through the front door – assuming you had a ticket – and carry on through a large archway at the back of the building. If the front was severely Palladian, the back was all curvaceous lightness – a horseshoe of dining boxes curving away from the building around an area with a moveable extension known as the 'elegant orchestra' – or what we would call a bandstand. Beyond it, winding paths led to attractions such as a grotto, a rill, a sham castle – and a famous labyrinth, twice the size of that at Hampton Court, which led down to a grotto, and was the work of 'an intelligent native of Scotland'. Jane Austen confided to Cassandra, while she was still house-hunting, that 'it would be very pleasant to be near Sidney gardens – we might go into the labyrinth every day.'

If the Holburne is open, go through the colonnade to the right, across the lawn at the back and through a gate into the gardens – if not, turn right and then left into the gardens, following the path round to stand at the back of the Holburne, looking up the main drive. Public breakfasts were held in the gardens every morning, leading Jane to remark, during her visit in 1799, that we 'shall not be wholly starved'. There were also concerts and firework displays[1] as well as public celebrations. On 4 June 1799, a gala to celebrate the king's birthday came to nothing due to rain, but it was held two weeks later to great acclaim. The programme gives an idea of what

1 For more on Sydney Gardens see pages 274-6.

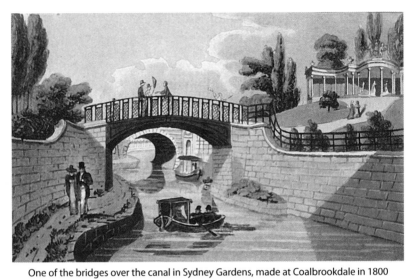

One of the bridges over the canal in Sydney Gardens, made at Coalbrookdale in 1800

A map of 1810 showing the canal running through Sydney Gardens. Sydney Place, where the Austens lived from 1801 to 1804, lies between the gardens and Daniel Street

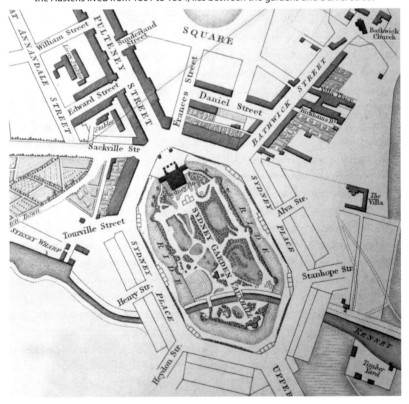

passed for popular entertainment in Bath at the time. It included overtures by Haydn and Pleyel, arias, glees and comic songs, and a performance by Mr Rossignol, a noted bird impersonator, who imitated a blackbird, a canary, a thrush, a skylark, a titter-wren[1], a nightingale and a variety of other birds. After the concert, there was a 'capital display' of fireworks by Signor Invetto, who exerted 'the utmost of his skill to produce new and astonishing effects'. It is hard for us to imagine, as we stand in this quiet park, how phenomenally popular it once was, with thousands cramming into the gardens on concert nights. However, if Austen's comments on the desirability of getting as far away from the music as possible are anything to go by, the standard may not have been that high.

Head diagonally across the lawn to your right and cross the cast-iron bridge over the railway, which, when it was driven through the gardens in 1841, destroyed Jane Austen's beloved labyrinth, along with much else. **Carry on uphill and cross the canal over another cast-iron bridge.** This, like the bridge you can see to the left, bears the date 1800, and was not here when Jane Austen first visited Bath. When she came to live in Sydney Place, however, it – along with the canal – would have been one of the gardens' newest attractions. **Turn left, then left again, recrossing the canal and the railway. Head down to the gate at the back of the Holburne, turn right and carry on through the gate out of the gardens. Cross, using the pedestrian lights, to the traffic island and then cross to the left and walk along Sydney Place, stopping outside No 4.** This comfortable house – in 'one of the short streets leading from ... Pulteney Street' – was where the Austen family came in June 1801 and where they lived for the next three years. Despite the rent being advertised as 'very low', it stretched the Austen family's finances to the limit. It was a prestigious address: next door but one, at No 2, lived Sir Hugh Dillon Massey, who represented County Clare in parliament and had been created a baronet in 1781, while at the far end of the row, No 14 was, by 1805, the home of Lady Nelson.

The terrace was almost new, having been built between 1792 and 1796, and the whole of the first floor was taken up by a drawing room, with views over Sydney Gardens at the front and open country at the back. Today, the back windows overlook Daniel Street, but, although work on the street had started several years earlier, only three houses at the west end (including the Pulteney Arms pub) had been completed. Work on the rest did not resume until 1810. Beyond Daniel Street, land that the Pulteneys had intended for further streets and squares was left as gardens or fields, eventually becoming

---

1 A dialect word for the wren or, occasionally, the willow warbler

Henrietta Park – an eloquent testimony to how fashionable society was now shunning Bath in favour of Brighton and other seaside resorts.

The lease ran out in September 1804, by which time Jane was staying in Lyme Regis with her parents, and Cassandra was with friends near Andover. The family had already chosen new lodgings in Green Park Buildings, but these were probably not ready, so it seems as though they took the opportunity to have a brief holiday.

Carry on to the end of Sydney Place, turn right into Sutton Street and then left into Henrietta Mews. Continue on with Henrietta Park on your right and stop just before the archway through to Henrietta Street. Behind the buildings on your right, a tree now stands on the site of Laura Chapel, where the Austen family worshipped, and which was demolished in 1909.[1] **Go under the arch and cross Henrietta Street** to look back at the two archways that once led into the chapel, with its name still carved above them. As you **head south along Henrietta Street to return to Laura Place**, you pass No 12, where Barbara Nibbs moved to from 6 Great Pulteney Street. Fanny Cage, the friend of the Austens who found the White Hart so noisy, sought refuge in lodgings at No 1. There was no pleasing her, however – after moving here, she complained that, while Bath might have been all right in season, out of season the streets were empty and the shops less gay than she had expected.

Turn right along Argyle Street and right again into Grove Street, carrying on until the road curves to the right beside a large Georgian building. This, as you saw in the previous walk, was not a grand townhouse but a prison – in eighteenth century Bath even prisons had to blend in. While the Austens were in Bathwick, passing the top of Grove Street on a daily basis, this building held the unfortunates who had been incarcerated for debt, as well as a large number of minor offenders. For centuries, the smallest debt could land you in prison, and, unless you could repay it, you stayed there, possibly for the rest of your life. In addition, any small sums you might raise were immediately taken by the gaoler, who charged you for the privilege of staying there. In the previous decade, there had been attempts to push an act through parliament to alleviate the distress caused by this inhumane system. It was not until 1813 that such an act was finally passed. Debtors in many gaols made petitions to parliament; on 1 December 1801 one was submitted by the debtors of Bath, praying for relief. In 1802, when James Neild reported on the prison on behalf of the Society for the Discharge and Relief of Persons Imprisoned for Small Debts, he was underwhelmed by the state of it:

1 For more information on Laura Chapel, see pages 272-3.

This prison is situated in Grove Street, and unfortunately built on very low ground; the ascent by a fine flight of stone steps.[1] The ground floor, on which there are three cells and a day-room, was so excessively damp, that the water was running down the walls of the passage and stair-case in large drops; the day-room was filled with every description of prisoners, three of whom, (women) slept in one of the cells, nine feet square and nine feet high, upon straw; ventilated by an aperture in the door. Above are three stories, five good size rooms on each; two of which are used by the keeper; the rest for debtors: one bed in a room, for which the prisoner pays 3s 6d per week.

Two rooms on the second story are free wards, one for men, the other for women. No work of employment furnished by the Corporation, there is painted on a board 'No strong liquors admitted, under the penalty of ten pounds or three months imprisonment'. The debtors have a small court-yard, through which you pass to go to the felons' yard, in the centre of which a double range of cells is built, with a fireplace in each. I was sorry to be informed that the wall was to be raised several feet, as it will make the little remainder of the felons' yard very unhealthy, for the want of fresh air; and, not being a paved or gravel bottom, almost useless. Though the city affords a very liberal supply of coals,[2] it is not sufficient to counteract the effects of the local situation.

In 1816, Jane's brother Henry might easily have found himself in a debtor's prison when the bank of which he was a partner failed, with substantial debts. His brothers Frank, James and Edward paid large sums to rescue him. Once again the spectre of poverty had stepped out of the shadows to threaten the Austens. In the end, it was the much denigrated Jane Leigh-Perrot who saved him, leaving him a large legacy in her will, which enabled him to retire.

There was a pub called the Ostrich near the prison, and another – the Rising Sun – which still survives further along the street. Grove Street was very unlike the genteel streets nearby, and it flooded with monotonous regularity. The architect and builder John Eveleigh had his offices and yard here, while just across the river was the ever-growing Northgate Brewery. This opened in 1777, and went on to become the biggest in the West of England, with malthouses on the Grove Street side of the river, some of which have been converted into flats called Northanger Court. One wonders what Jane Austen would make of that.

Head back along Grove Street, turn right across Pulteney Bridge and carry on up Bridge Street. Cross over at the top and carry straight on along Upper Borough Walls to the top of Union Street. Our route takes us along Upper Borough Walls because, during the Austens' time

1 Today the steps have gone and you enter by what was intended as the door to the basement.
2 It could well afford to do so, with coal pits just outside the city boundary.

here, the more elegant New Bond Street did not exist. In its place was a narrow thoroughfare called Frog Lane. If Jane Austen had stood at this spot on Upper Borough Walls as late as 1805, she would have looked south not along Union Street but into the stableyard of the Bear Inn, busy with horses, grooms, ostlers and coaches. There was even an undertaker's for guests who had left their visit to Bath too late for the waters to restore them to health. The books will tell you that Union Street was built in 1806, yet there are no entries for it in the ratebooks till 1808. Although Jane Austen left Bath in 1806, however, Union Street features in *Persuasion*, written some ten years later.

Continue past the block with a clock your right and turn right along Old Bond Street. Until New Bond Street was built in 1806, this was known simply as Bond Street. On the right-hand side there are still some Regency shopfronts. Perhaps it was in one of these shops that Sir Walter Elliot stood and 'counted eighty-seven women go by, one after another, without there being a tolerable face among them'. The street was longer then – the northernmost buildings on the east side were demolished around 1830.

Carry on up Milsom Street, crossing Quiet Street and stopping outside the second shop on the left, which in Jane Austen's day was Molland the pastrycook's. It is in Molland's that Anne Elliot encounters Captain Wentworth again, and realises that he is still interested in her. He flourishes his new umbrella at her, offering to see her home in the dry, but she walks off with Mr Elliot, leaving him overcome with jealousy.

By 1817, the shop was run by Mrs Molland, who had taken over from her husband Nicholas after his death in 1804. In 1801, they would still have been recovering from the flour crisis, although they also had a room to hire out for private parties, as well as providing outside catering. Not all Bath's pastrycooks and bakers fared as well as the Mollands. In 1801, for example, a pastrycook called William Gibbs tried to prevent the Corporation from fixing the price of bread by claiming that flour cost more in Bath than it did in other places. It transpired in court, however, that some of Bath's bakers and pastrycooks were not only buying cheaper flour elsewhere, but also snapping up the few bags of flour sold in Bath at high prices in order to keep the price of bread artificially high. Mr Gibb's appeal was thrown out. The price of bread was a constant worry for many people, including Jane Austen, who, in 1813, mentioned 'a fall in the price of bread by the bye' in a letter to Cassandra, expressing the hope that her 'mother's bill next week' would also be reduced.

Milsom Street, then as now, was a street of upmarket shops, particularly in the fashion trade, as we will see in the Georgette Heyer walk. But where was the print-shop, into which Admiral Croft gazed so earnestly? There were several booksellers, auctioneers, and circulating libraries, all of which sold prints. In 1805, however, there was a print seller called Joseph Fasana at 35 Milsom Street. He was still there in 1819, when he described himself as a jeweller and stationer. This shop fits very neatly with the account in *Persuasion*, but to find it, you must **continue up Milsom Street, crossing over outside Jolly's.**

On the right-hand side, you will notice, at No 38, the Highgrove Shop. What would Jane Austen have made of the Prince of Wales being a shopkeeper? She was shocked to find that the Prince Regent – the future George IV – was a fan of hers, who not only owned specially-bound copies of her books but asked, in 1815, to have *Emma* dedicated to him. Two years earlier, Jane Austen had declared bluntly in a letter that she hated him, so this must have been something of an embarrassment. She managed to decline an invitation to Carlton House but was forced to include the dedication. The words 'dutiful' and 'obedient' – not to mention 'humble' – must have suggested, to those that knew her, however, that she did so under sufferance, while the over-effusive repetition of 'His Royal Highness' strays perilously close to sarcasm:

Milsom Street around 1788, before most of its buildings were converted from lodging houses to shops

TO
HIS ROYAL HIGHNESS
THE PRINCE REGENT,
THIS WORK IS,
BY HIS ROYAL HIGHNESS'S PERMISSION,
MOST REPECTFULLY DEDICATED,
BY HIS ROYAL HIGHNESS'S
DUTIFUL
AND OBEDIENT
HUMBLE SERVANT,
THE AUTHOR

Three doors along is No 35, which was Fasana's print shop in Jane Austen's day. Above the first-floor windows you will see the words 'Brush Manufactory'. They date from when a brushmaker called John Strawbridge had the shop in the 1850s.

Following Anne Elliot and Admiral Croft's footsteps, continue to the top of Milsom Street. Opposite are Edgar Buildings, where the Thorpe family had their lodgings. Across the street, at No 9 – now Martini Ristorante – was Ham's Ware-rooms, which offered a new assortment of elegant dresses. Throughout her life, Jane Austen remained interested in the latest fashions, and her letters are full of comments on what was being worn, and seeking advice from Cassandra on whether she should buy a new dress or restyle an old one. Whatever else Jane Austen was, she was never a frump. Like her characters, she too must have lingered in Milsom Street, gazing in the windows, and perhaps purchasing silk to make a new gown, or ribbons to dress a bonnet.

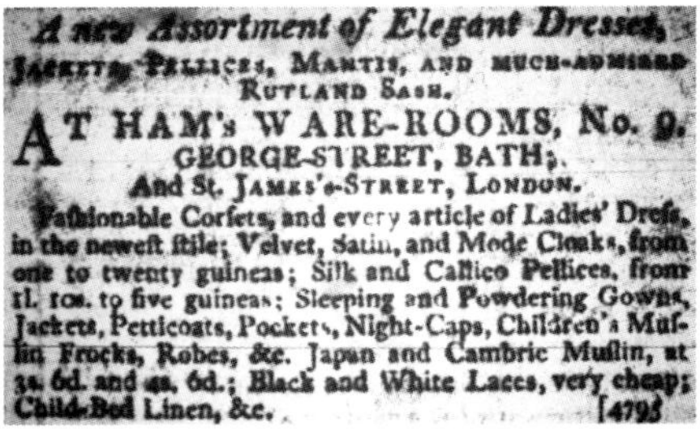

Anne Elliot would now have crossed over to walk up Lansdown Road to Camden Place. We, however, will turn right, cross the top of Broad Street and carry on past Bladud's Buildings. At the end of Bladud's Buildings, you will see a flight of steps down to Walcot Street. Just past this is No 1 The Paragon. In 1797, the Leigh-Perrots rented this property from Richard Atwood, and stayed here until 1810, when they bought their house in Great Pulteney Street. However, as James Leigh-Perrot was one of the shareholders in the Upper Assembly Rooms, it is likely that they had already made regular visits to the city before 1797. We know he was here in 1764, for he was witness to his sister's marriage to George Austen in Walcot Church.

The person who usually greeted the Austen family on their arrival at No 1 was Frank, who may have been black. Jane referred to his 'black head ... waiting in the hall window', and, while this may simply mean that he had black hair, it is suggestive that he was always called Frank, while the other servants were referred to by their surnames, as black servants often did not have surnames. We know very little more about him, beyond the fact that Jane always got a warm welcome from him. On arriving in Bath in 1801, she wrote that he 'received us very kindly, and his master and mistress did not show less cordiality'. There is a sense that his welcome was the more genuine. But, if he was black, what was his status and where did he come from? As Jane Leigh-Perrot came from Barbados, it is often assumed that he was originally a slave, but he is never mentioned as one of their regular servants. Bath had a large black population, and as people taking lodgings often employed local servants, it is possible that he was a Bath resident and may have worked for Richard Atwood before the Leigh-Perrots took the house. Unless a hitherto undiscovered letter turns up, we may never find out more about him.

Jane Austen frequently found the company in this house boring – she hated the stupid private parties and what she called the 'old toughs' who came to visit. She was not alone in disliking No 1 – her mother was not keen on it because the stairs were too steep. Edward Austen's doctor, Dr Fellowes, lived three doors along at No 4.

Continue along the Paragon, stopping outside No 13 to look across the road. The Strawberry Hill Gothick building opposite was a chapel for the Countess of Huntingdon's Connexion. The countess was an extremely autocratic woman – witness her treatment of the breakaway group in Argyle Street – who liked to be surrounded by tame preachers. All this is very reminiscent of Lady Catherine de Bourgh in *Pride and Prejudice*, and Austen may have had her in mind when creating her character. Although the countess died in 1791, the Austens knew about her, and probably made fun of her, as many people did. The chapel now houses the Building of Bath Collection.

Continue along the Paragon, passing Axford Buildings. In January 1801, when they were house-hunting, Jane told Cassandra that 'we know that Mrs Perrot will want to get us into Oxford Buildings'. No such place ever existed. She may have been referring to Oxford Row, near the Assembly Rooms, on the west side of Lansdown Road, but probably meant Axford Buildings. Whichever it was, the family were united 'in particular dislike of that part of the town'. Perhaps they did not want the Leigh-Perrots too close to them, trying to organise their lives. Axford Buildings was also close to several fairly insalubrious pubs, while in nearby London Street there were two shoemakers, a pawnbroker, an ironmonger, a laundress, a wheelwright, a tailor, a chairmaker, two butchers, a baker, a carpenter and a brewer. It would hardly have been the quiet retreat the Austen family were looking for.

Continue on to Walcot Church. There has been a church dedicated to St Swithin on this site since 971 AD. In 1739, after the old church was badly damaged in a storm, John Wood the Elder offered to rebuild it, but to his disgust the church authorities chose a design by the churchwarden, Robert Smith. The new church, which probably used much of the material from the old one, was very small. It was here that George Austen married Cassandra Leigh in 1764. Forty years later, he was buried in the crypt of the church that succeeded it, designed by John Palmer in 1777. Although his grave is still in the crypt, thanks to his daughter's celebrity his tombstone has been moved to the churchyard, where you can see it through the railings to the left of the church. As you saw in the fifth walk, the same thing has happened to Fanny Burney's gravestone. Burney seems to have ignored Austen, the young kid on the block whose style made hers look dated, even though their families knew one another. However, Jane Austen did not ignore her, nor her son. 'Perhaps I may marry Mr D'Arbley [sic],' she remarked mischievously in 1813, when she was 38 and he was 19.

When Jane Austen came to Bath in 1799, Cassandra asked her to buy some hat trimmings. Jane wrote back to tell her what was in vogue:

> Flowers are very much worn, and fruit is still more the thing. Elizabeth has a bunch of strawberries, and I have seen grapes, cherries, plums, and apricots. There are likewise almonds and raisins, French plums, and tamarinds at the grocers', but I have never seen any of them in hats. A plum or greengage would cost three shillings; cherries and grapes about five, I believe, but this is at some of the dearest shops. My aunt has told me of a very cheap one, near Walcot Church, to which I shall go in quest of something for you.

Ten days later she reported back:

> We have been to the cheap shop, and very cheap we found it, but there are only flowers made there, no fruit; and as I could get four or five very pretty sprigs of the former for the same money which would procure only one Orleans plum – in short, could get more for three or four shillings than I could have means of bringing home – I cannot decide on the fruit till I hear from you again. Besides, I cannot help thinking that it is more natural to have flowers grow out of the head than fruit. What do you think on that subject?

Although we do not which 'cheap shop' she visited, Morse's artificial florists was in Walcot Buildings, a little way along the London Road – not that near the church, but nearer than any of the others listed in the 1800 *Directory*.

Cross at the pedestrian crossing and head up the flight of steps opposite the churchyard to a T junction with Upper Hedgemead Road.[1] In June 1799, Jane Austen took an evening walk up Beacon Hill and over the fields to Charlcombe, which, as she says, is sweetly situated in a valley. The first part of her walk is difficult to follow, as Beacon Hill is a rather vague term, and not used much today. The map of 1800 suggests that this path existed, so it is possible that they came this way, especially as a convenient route to Charlcombe is at hand.

Turn left along Upper Hedgemead Road, crossing to the right at the end and doubling back on yourself up Camden Crescent. Designed in 1788 by John Eveleigh, and originally called Camden Place, Camden Crescent's precarious position proved to be its downfall. As you can see, it is not complete – a section slipped away before it was finished, leaving the easternmost house looking like a romantic ruin – a ruin which finally collapsed sometime before 1829, although it was still one of Bath's 'sights' when Jane Austen was here. It is perhaps significant that she has Sir Walter Elliot living here, for financially he is in as rickety a position as the crescent itself.

If you walk to the east end of the crescent, you can, if you wish, continue to Charlcombe by turning up St Stephen's Road, taking the flight of steps up to the left, turning left along the road at the top and following it round to the right. Turn right up Mount Road and

CHARLCOMBE

---

1 For a step-free route, carry on past the steps, bear left up Margaret's Hill beside the park, turn left into Lower Hedgemead Road and carry on up to the junction with Upper Hedgemead Road, where you turn left.

carry on up Mount Beacon. When you reach the green, follow the path along by the hedge on your right. When you reach the road, bear right and follow it as it heads downhill, bearing left along Summerfield Road. When you come to a T junction, turn left along Solsbury Way. In Jane Austen's day, you would now have been walking through fields. *When Solsbury Way makes a sharp bend to the right, bear left along Charlcombe Way. This eventually leads to Charlcombe Lane, which you follow to Charlcombe.* Legend has it that the church here was founded in AD675 and was the mother church of Bath. The gardens below the church contain a holy well, which is believed to have been a holy site in pre-Christian times. *To return, retrace your steps, staying on Charlcombe Lane rather than turning off along Charlcombe Way, and carry straight on along Richmond Road at the junction. This eventually joins Lansdown Road by St Stephen's Church, where you cross and continue downhill, turning right opposite the Old Farmhouse pub down Morford Street.*

If you decide not to make the excursion to Charlcombe, head back along Camden Crescent to Lansdown Road and cross at the pedestrian lights a little way downhill. Turn right uphill before turning left down Morford Street, opposite the Old Farmhouse pub. If you look over to the right near the bottom of Morford Street, you will see the red roof of a church on the site of a riding school run by Jonathan Dash in 1800.

Turn left at the bottom of Morford Street and walk along to Christ Church. This was completed a year after Jane Austen's first known visit to Bath in 1797, as a free church for people who could not afford pew rents. The long building facing it across the car park is the surviving part of another riding school run by Dash. It was probably at one of these riding schools that, in 1805, Jane Austen saw Miss Chamberlayne looking hot on horseback, and where she saw Miss Lefroy riding in 1797. Between the riding school and the church, set back at the top of a flight of steps, is a Royal Tennis Court dating from 1777 and built to a design by the Duc d'Orleans. It now houses the Museum of Bath at Work, which traces the history of Bath's industries and shows what life was like for the vast majority of the city's inhabitants.

Cross into Rivers Street and turn left down Russel Street to the Assembly Rooms. Originally called the New or Upper Rooms, these were financed by a tontine, a system whereby, as the shareholders died, their shares went into a pot until the surviving shareholder took everything. Among the shareholders were Lord Clive, Mr Leigh-Perrot, and William Hoare the artist.

The arches on the north side once housed fashionable shops. In the heyday of the Rooms, over 1,000 people would pack into the ballroom on ball nights. Even as late as the 1790s, the Rooms were still crowded, as we know from the descriptions in *Northanger Abbey*. By 1801, however, Jane Austen was complaining about how few people were attending the balls, with many of those who did attend turning up late after going to private parties.

As early as 1799, there were concerns about the type of people attending the balls. James Leigh-Perrot was one of ten subscribers who called a general meeting to discuss the conduct of one of the other subscribers. In December 1801, it was reported in *The Times* that 'certain upstart tradesmen ... have mixed with the people of fashion, and that one, at a public assembly, had the impudence to ask a young lady of family to go down a dance with him; and that this young fellow had, that very morning, been waiting on the said family with an assortment of ribbons and laces.'

In November that year concerns were raised about the sort of company now coming to Bath. A correspondent in *The Times* wrote that, 'there is every species of character and caricature – lords without money – gentlemen without manners – complexions without health, and beauties without paint. Here are plenty of minor poets, and though not many common beggars, there are many petitioning reduced old gentlemen and ladies, poor widows, etc.' Perhaps a retired clergymen in straitened circumstances with two unmarried daughters was the sort of unfashionable society he had in mind. No wonder Jane Austen considered Bath snobbish. You can still visit the Rooms, as well as the Fashion Museum in the basement, which has a fine collection of clothes from the seventeenth century to the present day, including many Jane Austen would recognise.

Head west along Bennet Street and through the Circus to Brock Street. At the end, turn right into Upper Church Street and left along Crescent Lane. Cross Julian Road at the zebra crossing, turn left and then right into St James's Road, which leads into St James's Square. This square was still new in 1805 when Jane Austen and her mother walked here from Gay Street. The following year, they tried to move here. They wanted only rooms, however, not a whole house. This posed something of a problem, as Mrs Austen explained to James Austen's wife in April 1806:

> We are disappointed of the lodgings in St James's Square, a person is in treaty for the whole house, so of course he will be prefer'd to us who want only a part – We have look'd at some others since but don't quite like the situation – hope a few days hence we shall have more choice as it is supposed many will go from Bath when this gay week is over.

As it turned out, she and her daughters were among those who left shortly afterwards.

Turn left to walk along the south side of the St James's Square, turn left into Marlborough Street and right along Julian Road, before crossing Cavendish Road and carrying on to the zebra crossing. Although there are still open spaces on either side of the road here, in Jane Austen's day they were fields rather than a park and a golf course. This is probably the way she would have walked to Weston. She made several visits to Weston, although she was rather rude about the village itself. In a letter to Cassandra she wrote that she had walked there and liked it very much. 'Liked *what* very much? Weston? – No, walking to Weston.' This is rather unfair, for, despite much rebuilding in later years, Weston still has a village atmosphere and some interesting old buildings.

If you want to follow the route to Weston taken by Jane Austen and Mrs Chamberlayne in May 1801 – which is still surprisingly rural in parts – follow the Cotswold Way signpost up the footpath to the right beside a metal fence. As you climb, there are views of Cavendish Place and Crescent – both built after Jane Austen left Bath – over to the right. She would, however, have known Lansdown Crescent, which you can see above them. **When you reach Sion Hill, turn left.** *Gothic Cottage, which you pass on the right, was virtually new when Jane Austen came this way, having been built in 1797.* **Follow the road round as it curves uphill, and turn left at the T junction along Summerfield Road. Carry on down a footpath between stone walls, cross the lane at the bottom and carry on down another footpath. Go through a kissing gate, cross a brook and carry on through a meadow. Keep straight on, following signs for the Cotswold Way. Shortly after going through a gate into another meadow, the Cotswold Way branches off to the left. Follow it across the meadow, through a kissing gate and downhill to Weston churchyard**, *which Jane Austen and Mrs Chamberlayne crossed 'with as much expedition as if we were afraid of being buried alive'.* **Follow their footsteps through it, passing the church** – *rebuilt since Jane Austen's day* – **and bearing left downhill when the path forks. Carry on along Church Street, and when you reach Trafalgar Road** (*with an old cigarette advert on the wall ahead*) **turn left, cross over and double back along the High Street. At the end of the High Street, cross and head up Crown Hill to the left of the war memorial. Continue past the Old Crown** – *an inn since at least 1712, with a sign for 'Home Brew'd Beer' on its wall* – **along Weston Park,** *laid out – and covering the fields Jane Austen would have known – in the mid-nineteenth century.* **At the T junction, cross over, turn right, walk along to Weston Road and turn left. Carry on past the entrance to the park and eventually you will return to the point you started from.**

Whether you have made the excursion to Weston or not, you should now cross the zebra crossing and turn left to walk back to the **Marlborough Tavern**, built for the sedan chairmen who would doubtless have been in need of refreshment after carrying heavy visitors up to their lodgings from the city centre. **Turn right down Marlborough Buildings**, regarded as highly desirable in Jane Austen's day. This is where Colonel Wallis and his wife take lodgings in *Persuasion*.

When you reach Nos 13-15 – built before the rest of Marlborough Buildings as a stand-alone development and more highly decorated than the rest – **cross and walk along the Royal Crescent, stopping outside the central house.** This, as you saw in the fourth walk, was one of the grand parading places of Bath. The fashion for *rus in urbe* could be indulged here, with a well-paved walk set against an elegant background, but with a view of fields and countryside. There were even sheep and cattle to complete the Arcadian scene – although the ha-ha prevented them from getting too close. People came here to meet their friends and chat, so when Jane Austen and her mother found in 1804 that it was hot but not crowded, they went for a walk in the fields instead. In *Northanger Abbey*, however, Catherine Morland, walking here with the Thorpes and her brother, discovers that John Thorpe has cancelled her meeting with Henry and Eleanor Tilney, runs after them to put matters right, but is held up by the press of the crowd.

The fields below the ha-ha were known as Crescent Fields and it is here that Lady Willoughby presented 'the colours to some corps of Yeomanry or other' in June 1799. The yeomanry were often the butt of jokes, hence Jane Austen's dismissive comment. They were volunteer cavalry regiments, called in to support the army in cases of riot and civil unrest, and not always well-trained or disciplined.

If you want an idea how Bath's wealthiest residents lived, the Royal Crescent Hotel offers tea or coffee all day, and afternoon tea from 3pm. Alternatively, you can visit No 1, which is a museum owned by Bath Preservation Trust and fitted up as it would have been in the eighteenth century.

Continue to the end of the Crescent, turn right down the tarmaced footpath and left along the Gravel Walk.[1] During the eighteenth century, Bath was almost an extension of London. Anyone who was in society had been there and knew it intimately. Thus, at the end of *Persuasion*, Jane Austen is able to include a little joke which is easily missed by modern readers. Captain Wentworth and Anne Elliot, having finally got back

1 For a step free walk, continue down to Royal Avenue, turn left and walk through the park.

together and declared their love for each other, are supposed to be walking back to Camden Place from Union Street. Instead of walking up Milsom Street and Lansdown Road, however, 'soon words enough had passed between them to decide their direction towards the comparatively quiet and retired gravel walk, where the power of conversation would make the present hour a blessing indeed, and prepare it for all the immortality which the happiest recollections of their own future lives could bestow'. This is an enormous detour – suggesting that they have a great deal to talk about. The Gravel Walk was built as a sedan chair route to the Royal Crescent, but led through fields – the park was not laid out until 1830 and there were no steps at the end. A reminder of earlier days can be found on the left, where a Georgian Garden, laid out at the back of No 4 The Circus in the 1760s, was restored to its original condition in 1985.

After walking down the steps, turn left along Queen's Parade Place to Gay Street. The entrance to Queen's Parade Place was widened in the late nineteenth century by demolishing the end house on the left – No 1 Gay Street. It is this house that Jane Austen mentioned in a letter to Cassandra in January 1801, as her mother had 'no disinclination' to it, and it 'was lower rented than any other house in the row, from some inferiority in the apartments'. Perhaps it was this inferiority that contributed to its subsequent demolition.

Turn left up Gay Street and stop outside No 11. If you look across the road, you will see No 25, now a dental surgery. After the death of Jane's father, they gave up the house in Green Park Buildings and came to stay

The north side of Queen Square in the late eighteenth cehtury

       LITERARY WALKS IN BATH

here. Although it was much smaller than what they were used to, it was still genteel and situated in the upper town. From here, Jane Austen was able to indulge in her favourite pastime of walking, sometimes making several excursions in one day. However, her concerns over conserving their supplies of tea and sugar suggest that money was a problem, and they did not stay here long.

Retrace your steps down Gay Street (past the Jane Austen Centre) and, when you reach Queen Square, cross diagonally at the lights and walk down the east side. Carry on down Barton Street and take the second left into Trim Street. This is where Mrs Austen and the girls finally found lodgings in 1805, before leaving for Clifton the following year 'with what happy feelings of escape'. They had never wanted to come here. When house-hunting in 1801, Jane Austen told Cassandra that her mother had promised to 'do everything in her power to avoid Trim S^t altho' you have not expressed the fearful presentiment of it, which was rather expected'. We do not know which number they lived at. It may no longer exist, as much of the north side was demolished in the 1960s, and replaced with an uninspired modern building. In Jane Austen's day, it was in one of the busiest parts of the city and would have been noisy. Although there was a ladies' boarding school

Trim Street in the early twentieth century. The early eighteenth-century buildings beyond the archway were demolished in the 1960s

and dancing academy here, there were also the sort of tradesmen who would not normally have been the Austens' neighbours, such as a butcher, a carver and gilder, and a carpenter. One thing that might have interested Jane Austen was the showroom of William Smith, the 'Father of English Geology'. At No 2, on the corner of Trim Bridge, his collection of fossils and maps was on display, and Jane's inquiring mind would surely have found his cabinet of curiosities irresistible. She would have been even more excited by the opening of the new Theatre Royal in nearby Beauford Square on 12 October 1805. Yet, despite this, the Austen ladies clearly disliked Trim Street and were anxious to move – Mrs Austen headed one letter 'April 1806, Trim Street *still*'. As soon as they received a small legacy, they went in search of more suitable lodgings, although, when this proved difficult, Frank Austen came to the rescue, inviting them to come and live with him and his new wife in Southampton. And so they left Bath for good – or did they?

To ponder that question, **walk back along Trim Street and carry on into Beauford Square.** On the south side of the square is the Theatre Royal, where Charles Musgrove secures a box in *Persuasion*. He tells his mother that it will hold nine people – a clear indication that Austen had this theatre in mind, rather than the old Theatre Royal, whose boxes were smaller. She would, despite her family's straitened circumstances, almost certainly have visited the new theatre, so this is hardly to be wondered at. However, other references in *Persuasion* indicate that she kept up with changes that took place in Bath after she left. She could, of course, have learned of them from hearsay, letters and the gossip of friends, but she may well have returned herself. The Leigh-Perrots continued their visits to Bath and other relations lived nearby. In 1814, she wrote to Martha Lloyd, 'how many alterations you must perceive in Bath.' This sounds like someone who had seen the changes herself – she does not say she has heard about them. And there are long gaps in her correspondence and in what we know of her life, so subsequent visits cannot be ruled out.

The Austens eventually settled in Chawton, in Jane's beloved Hampshire, where she spent the last eight years of her life. She was happiest observing rural life. As she wrote in a letter to James Stanier Clarke in 1816, she could only write about domestic life in country villages, and could no more write a romance than an epic poem. 'I must keep to my own style and go in my own way,' she explained. However, that does not mean she did not like experimenting, and the letters to Cassandra often show her doing just this. One starts out as a parody of Hetty Thrale, and in another she tells her that, 'I am going to write nothing but short sentences. There shall be two full stops in every line.' She does not keep up this Hemingwayesque style for more than a couple of paragraphs, but it shows that she was constantly pushing the boundaries. Her naturalistic style makes her perhaps our first modern novelist, yet she is persistently misunderstood. Her social satires, sharply observed, are seen as romantic novels, although there are few people as unromantic as Jane Austen. She is criticised for cosiness, when no one painted more distinctly the unhappy position of women, especially middle-class women, in her time. For those who recognise this, however, it can be an unsettling experience. As WH Auden wrote:

> It makes me most uncomfortable to see
> An English spinster of the middle-class
> Describe the amorous effects of 'brass',
> Reveal so frankly and with such sobriety
> The economic basis of society.

So did Jane Austen love or hate Bath? Her views were probably mixed. Even today – as you will have discovered if you taken any of the optional excursions – it is easy to leave the city behind and walk through woods and fields, as she loved to do. Bath still has a wide variety of shops, including some fashionable if expensive ones, and there is no doubt that Jane enjoyed shopping. Yet she was aware of the misery that existed in poorer parts of the city, and hinted at this, especially in *Persuasion*. A country village did not have child prostitutes thronging its streets, nor brothel-house keepers lurking to pick up innocent country girls – something Austen referred to on a visit to London. While there was poverty in the country, there was usually a helping hand from the clergyman or the great house, or wealthier neighbours. There was no correspondent from *The Times* suggesting that your father and his family were not quite the company the city was looking for. There was a protective family about you, and no need to pretend that you were richer than you were, for propriety's sake.

For Jane Austen, however, everything she observed ended up in her writing. Though her time in Bath may appear to have been unproductive, what she saw and absorbed was crucial to the novels. Quite what she would make of the adulation she receives today in Bath, however, is anyone's guess. Given her sense of humour, the chances are she would laugh merrily.

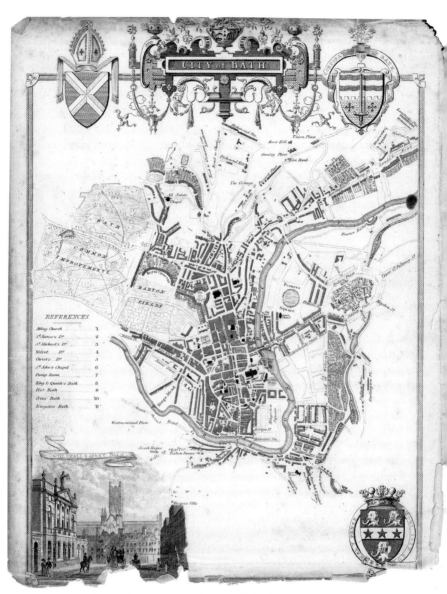

Bath around 1825, showing a host of projected developments – Upper Great Pulteney Street and Frances Square in Bathwick, Kingston Square south of the Parades, Lansdown Square behind Lansdown Crescent, and Worcester Square north of the London Road. Apart from the opening of Royal Victoria Park in 1830, the city had hardly changed when Dickens visited in 1835. None of the projected developments ever materialised; Bath, one of the fastest growing cities in the country for much of the eighteenth century, had ground to a standstill. The years that followed were marked by decline and a faded gentility. From being a place people came to for fun, it became a place they retired to. Hardly surprising that Dickens evinced such a visceral loathing of it.

9
PICKWICK, PUBS AND PENNY READINGS
In the Footsteps of Charles Dickens

Jane Austen's dislike of Bath pales into insignificance beside that of a writer who, at one time, was even more celebrated in the city. Charles Dickens' hatred of 'this mouldy old roosting place' is well documented, but the details of his early visits to Bath are shrouded in mystery, largely due to the efforts of those who have tried to prove he was actually very fond of the city. Sifting fact from legend is well nigh impossible. Tantalising snippets of information jostle for our attention with second-hand reminiscences and absurd flights of fancy, so that our image of Dickens in Bath is, for the most part, a shadowy and tentative one.

Our walk starts at **the Saracen's Head in Broad Street**, where, as far as many guidebooks are concerned, Dickens' association with Bath begins and ends. Trying to establish the details of his connection with this inn, however, encapsulate the problem of pinning down his connection with the city.

It is generally accepted that it was here that Dickens stayed when he came to Bath as a parliamentary reporter in 1835. A letter in the *Bath Chronicle* of 28 May 1935, from Alexander McDougall of 13 Rivers Street, sums up the evidence:

> I have come to the conclusion that Dickens first visited the city of Bath in May 1835, although some are inclined to think he came here before. To my mind one thing is really certain, and that is that in May 1835 he put up at the Saracen's Head in Broad Street, from which no doubt he would pay visits to the old White Hart, and often meet the Pickwicks, as Mrs Hurt, the landlady of the Saracen's Head at the time, has given far too detailed and circumstantial an account of this visit to this inn to be invented or doubted.

Further details come from a speech given by Mr Snowdon Ward at a prestigious Dickens dinner – of which you will hear more later – in 1903:

> Many years ago the landlady of the Saracen's Head perfectly remembered a young gentleman coming. When he came there was no room in the house proper, and he had to be sent across the yard to sleep above the outbuildings. At night the young man took his candle and walked across the yard, but just as he came to the outside of the room his light was blown out. He went back to the bar, relit his candle and just as he got to the steps again out went the candle. This he repeated several times

221

and, said the landlady, 'the young gentleman never said a single swear.'

The *Bath Chronicle* of 7 February 1903 added the following information:

At the old Saracen's Head Inn in Broad Street, the visitor is still shown the curious old mug which the novelist used to use, and in the upper storey of the rear portion of the premises, beyond the courtyard, there is the bedroom once occupied by Dickens, containing to this day the original old four-poster. In another room, low and raftered, is to be seen the stiff wooden armchair in which Dickens once sat.

The stairs up which – so legend has it – Dickens climbed to his room at the back of the Saracen's Head. This area was redeveloped and incorporated into the inn in the late twentieth century.

The Pickwick Curio Stores once occupied the right-hand side of the Saracen's Head

LITERARY WALKS IN BATH

In the early twentieth century the right-hand side of the inn was occupied by an antique shop called the Pickwick Curio Stores. A framed notice giving details of Dickens' visit can still be seen in the pub today, and the story even turns up in prestigious publications like the new Pevsner guide to Bath, which includes the information that 'Charles Dickens stayed here in 1835 when he was a Parliamentary reporter.'

What none of these accounts mentions is that, if Dickens did stay here, he certainly wouldn't have wanted to. It is surprising, to put it mildly, that an up and coming parliamentary reporter, with a keen sense of his own worth and status, used to staying in the best inns available when travelling around the country, should have opted for the Saracen's Head. It was, it is true, a coaching inn, but a coaching inn of a fairly lowly sort. When a council official inspected it in 1903 – admittedly almost 70 years after Dickens' alleged visit – he noted with some alarm that it had 'no urinal, customers making use of the stable'. And in 1835 it would have been more than usually dirty and inconvenient, because the new St Michael's Church was being built right next to it.

The other thing to say about the story is that it is not supported by Dickens' own statements. He is supposed to have stayed there in May 1835 when Lord John Russell visited the city to make a speech. This was part of a grand political tour through the West of England, and followed on from a speech he had given in Exeter a couple of days earlier. Dickens, along with another reporter called Thomas Beard, covered the speech at Exeter for the *Morning Chronicle*. Instead of following Russell to Bath, Dickens headed back to London with his report in an unsuccessful attempt to get it into print before the report appeared in the *Times*. He took the direct route from Exeter to London, via Wincanton, travelling on top of the coach for at least part of the journey. 'I feel the effects of the rain severely,' he wrote to Thomas Beard on 4 May 1835, 'I came up by slow coach, left Wincanton at nine on Saturday evening and reached town at eleven yesterday morning. I have a slight touch of rheumatism and am perfectly deaf. I hope to God I shall soon get rid of the latter complaint.'

Dickens did, however, come to Bath six months later. On 9 November Lord John Russell made another speech in Bristol. The following evening the Bath Friends of Reform held a celebratory dinner at Todd's Riding School on the Upper Bristol Road in Bath. Dickens and Beard were sent to report on both events. The story of the efforts he took to meet the *Morning Chronicle's* deadlines is a fascinating one. On 8 November, he wrote to Thomas Fraser, sub-editor at the *Chronicle*, from the George & Pelican Inn at Newbury:

We go down to Bristol today, and if we are equally fortunate in laying the chaise horses, I hope the packet will reach town by seven. As all the papers have arranged to leave Bristol the moment Russell is done, we have determined on adopting the same plan – one of us will go to Marlborough in the chaise with one Herald man, and the other remain at Bristol with the second Herald man to conclude the account for the next day. The *Times* has ordered a chaise and four the whole distance, so there is every probability of us beating them hollow.

As a result of these meticulous arrangements, the report of Russell's speech appeared in the following day's *Morning Chronicle*, beating the *Times* and providing a major coup for the young reporter.

Before leaving Bristol, Dickens wrote to Fraser again from the Bush Inn, one of the city's top hostelries, where Mr Pickwick would later stay:

The report of the Bath dinner shall be forwarded by the first Bath coach on Thursday morning – what time it starts we have no means of ascertaining till we reach Bath, but you will receive it as early as possible ... Beard will go over from here tomorrow morning, and I shall come back by the mail from Marlborough. I need not say that it will be sharp work, and will require two of us; for we shall both be up the whole of the previous night, and shall have to sit up all night again to get it off in time. As soon as we have had a little sleep, we shall return to town as quickly as we can, for we have (if the express succeeds) to stop at two or three places along the road, to pay money and express satisfaction. You may imagine that we are extremely anxious to know the result of the arrangement. Pray direct to one of us at the White Hart, Bath, and inform us in a parcel sent by the first coach after you receive this exactly at what hour it arrived. Do not fail on any account.

Not only does Dickens fail to mention the Saracen's Head, he states categorically that he can be contacted at the White Hart, one of Bath's most prestigious inns. Which seems to blow the Saracen's Head story out of the water – or does it? Dickens only expressed his intention of staying at the White Hart; nowhere does he say he actually stayed there. What if he turned up at the White Hart and found there was no room at the inn – perhaps he hadn't booked a room, or perhaps the landlord simply ignored his booking in favour of more lucrative custom. There were, after all, around 700 people – many of them titled – from all over the West Country in town for the Reform Dinner. Dickens was a lowly, 23-year-old journalist. And what if, having been turned away, humiliated, from the White Hart, he found it was a similar story all over town – until, that is, somebody suggested he try the Saracen's Head, where they managed to find him a room over the stables?

Such a theory not only fits the facts – and the legend – it also explains why Dickens had such a deep-rooted aversion to the city. To someone less thin-skinned an uncomfortable night in a dingy hostelry might have been shrugged off, put down to experience – but Dickens' hypersensitivity ensured that this unfortunate introduction to Bath laid the foundation for an unshakable loathing. His hypersensitivity is not surprising. At the age of 12 his father had been imprisoned for debt, and Dickens had been forced to exchange the comforts of a middle-class home for the squalor of Warren's Blacking Factory, earning six shillings a week to help support his family. Even though he was now a successful journalist, to turn up in Bath and be forced to sleep over the stables of one of the roughest inns in town would have been mortifying.

Head south from Broad Street into the High Street, which, when Dickens first visited the city, was packed with coaching inns – all much better than the Saracen's Head. On the corner of Bridge Street was the White Lion, dating from the seventeenth century, where Dickens

stayed on his last visit to Bath in January 1869. Writing to his friend and biographer, John Forster, from the inn, he declared that 'the place looks to me like a cemetery which the dead have succeeded in rising and taking. Having built streets of their old gravestones, they wander about scantily trying to look alive. A dead failure.'

The White Lion in the High Street, demolished in 1891 when the site was redeveloped

You'll be hearing more from Dickens in a similar vein later. For now, though, **head along the High Street, turn right along Cheap Street and left along Stall Street to the corner of Bath Street – the site of the White Hart Inn**.

Although Dickens failed to secure a room at the White Hart, Samuel Pickwick experienced no such difficulty. When Dickens visited Bath in 1835, he was not only a political reporter – he was also an aspiring novelist. He had already written a series of humorous pieces for the *Morning Chronicle* under the name of Boz, but, while well received, they had failed to bring him the recognition he craved. In April 1836, however, six months after his visit, the first monthly instalment of *The Posthumous Papers of the Pickwick Club* was published by Chapman & Hall. The first three instalments were received politely, but it was with the fourth, in which Dickens introduced Sam Weller, that *The Pickwick Papers* suddenly became the publishing success of the year. Dickens gave up his day job to concentrate on cultivating his reputation as the most celebrated writer of the age.

The White Hart in Stall Street, demolished in 1867. The colonnade at the east end of Bath Street can be seen on the left.

LITERARY WALKS IN BATH

It was in the thirteenth instalment of *The Pickwick Papers*, published in March 1837, that Mr Pickwick and his entourage decided to visit Bath. On the evening of their arrival, Dickens records, 'Mr Pickwick and his friends, and Mr Dowler and his wife [whom they had travelled down from London with], respectively retired to their private sitting-rooms at the White Hart Hotel, opposite the Great Pump Room, Bath, where the waiters, from their costume, might be mistaken for Westminster boys, only they destroy the illusion by behaving themselves much better.'

It is also at the White Hart that Mr Pickwick, the following morning, is introduced to the Master of Ceremonies,

> a charming young man of not much more than fifty, dressed in a very bright blue coat with resplendent buttons, black trousers, and the thinnest possible pair of highly-polished boots. A gold eye-glass was suspended from his neck by a short, broad, black ribbon; a gold snuff-box was lightly clasped in his left hand; gold rings innumerable glittered on his fingers; and a large diamond pin set in gold glistened in his shirt frill. He had a gold watch, and a gold curb chain with large gold seals; and he carried a pliant ebony cane with a gold top. His linen was of the very whitest, finest, and stiffest; his wig of the glossiest, blackest, and curliest. His snuff was princes' mixture; his scent *bouquet du roi*. His features were contracted into a perpetual smile; and his teeth were in such perfect order that it was difficult at a small distance to tell the real from the false.
>
> 'Mr Pickwick,' said Mr Dowler; 'my friend, Angelo Cyrus Bantam, Esquire, MC; Bantam: Mr Pickwick. Know each other.'
>
> 'Welcome to Ba-ath, Sir. This is indeed an acquisition. Most welcome to Ba-ath, sir. It is long – very long, Mr Pickwick, since you drank the waters. It appears an age, Mr Pickwick. Re-markable!'
>
> Such were the expressions with which Angelo Cyrus Bantam, Esquire, MC, took Mr Pickwick's hand; retaining it in his, meantime, and shrugging up his shoulders with a constant succession of bows, as if he really could not make up his mind to the trial of letting it go again.
>
> 'It is a very long time since I drank the waters, certainly,' replied Mr Pickwick; 'for, to the best of my knowledge, I was never here before.'
>
> 'Never in Ba-ath, Mr Pickwick!' exclaimed the Grand Master, letting the hand fall in astonishment. 'Never in Ba-ath! He! he! Mr Pickwick, you are a wag. Not bad, not bad. Good, good. He! he! he! Re-markable!'

One person whom Mr Pickwick fails to meet, however, is the landlord of the White Hart. In itself, this may not seem that significant – until you realise that it was the real-life landlord of the White Hart – the same man who may have turned Dickens away with a flea in his ear a few months earlier – who almost certainly gave Dickens the name of his central character. Moses Pickwick was not only the landlord of the White Hart; he also owned the coaches that ran between the White Hart and London, and it is in this guise that the fictional Mr Pickwick first stumbles across him. His party is about to set off from the White Horse Cellar in London when Sam Weller rushes up and begs to speak to him 'with an air of the deepest mystery':

'Well, Sam,' said Mr Pickwick, 'what's the matter now?'

'Here's rather a rum go, sir,' replied Sam.

'What?' inquired Mr Pickwick.

'This here, sir,' rejoined Sam. 'I'm wery much afeerd, sir, that the proprieator of this here coach is a playin' some imperance with us.'

'How is that, Sam?' said Mr Pickwick; 'aren't the names down on the way-bill?'

'The names is not only down on the vay-bill, sir,' replied Sam, 'but they've painted vun on 'em up, on the door o' the coach.' As Sam spoke, he pointed to that part of the coach door on which the proprietor's name usually appears; and there, sure enough, in gilt letters of a goodly size, was the magic name of Pickwick.

'Dear me,' exclaimed Mr Pickwick, quite staggered by the coincidence; 'what a very extraordinary thing!'

'Yes, but that ain't all,' said Sam, again directing his master's attention to the coach door; 'not content with writing up Pickwick, they puts 'Moses' afore it, vich I call addin' insult to injury, as the parrot said ven they not only took him from his native land, but made him talk the English langwidge arterwards.'

But, having arrived at Bath, not only does Mr Pickwick fail to seek out his namesake; he is never mentioned again. Perhaps Dickens thought he had made his point – perhaps he thought he had gone far enough? Whatever the reason, after his introduction to the Master of Ceremonies, **Mr Pickwick crosses the road to the Pump Room**, where he signs his name in the 'register of the distinguished visitors' and takes the waters. **Thither we will follow him**, to ask – not for the last time – how well Dickens knew Bath when he wrote *The Pickwick Papers*? Which hill, for example, is Mr Pickwick supposed to walk up and down? And why does the description of the Pump Room sound as though it has been lifted from a guide-book rather than based on observation?

Mr Pickwick began to drink the waters with the utmost assiduity. Mr Pickwick took them systematically. He drank a quarter of a pint before breakfast, and then walked up a hill; and another quarter of a pint after breakfast, and then walked down a hill; and, after every fresh quarter of a pint, Mr Pickwick declared, in the most solemn and emphatic terms, that he felt a great deal better; whereat his friends were very much delighted, though they had not been previously aware that there was anything the matter with him.

The Great Pump Room is a spacious saloon, ornamented with Corinthian pillars, and a music-gallery, and a Tompion clock, and a statue of Nash, and a golden inscription, to which all the water-drinkers should attend, for it appeals to them in the cause of a deserving charity. There is a large bar with a marble vase, out of which the pumper gets the water; and there are a number of yellow-looking tumblers, out of which the company get it; and it is a most edifying and satisfactory sight to behold the perseverance and gravity with which they swallow it. There are baths near at hand, in which a part of the company wash themselves; and a band plays afterwards, to congratulate the remainder on their having done so. There is another pump room, into which infirm ladies and gentlemen are wheeled, in such an astonishing variety of chairs and chaises, that any adventurous individual who goes in with the regular number of toes, is in imminent danger of coming out without them; and there is a third, into which the quiet people go, for it is less noisy than either. There is an immensity of promenading, on crutches and off, with sticks and without, and a great deal of conversation, and liveliness, and pleasantry.

Sam Weller's opinion of the waters is less circumspect than his master's. When the Master of Ceremonies' footman asks him if he has tried them,

'Once,' replied Sam.
'What did you think of 'em, Sir?'
'I thought they was particklery unpleasant,' replied Sam.
'Ah,' said Mr John Smauker, 'you disliked the killibeate taste, perhaps?'

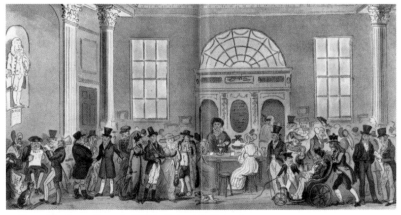

Above: The Pump Room in 1826 by Robert Cruikshank
Left: An early nineteenth-century view of the Pump Room from Stall Street

'I don't know much about that 'ere,' said Sam. 'I thought they'd a wery strong flavour o' warm flat irons.'

'That IS the killibeate, Mr Weller,' observed Mr John Smauker contemptuously.

'Well, if it is, it's a wery inexpressive word, that's all,' said Sam. 'It may be, but I ain't much in the chimical line myself, so I can't say.' And here, to the great horror of Mr John Smauker, Sam Weller began to whistle.

The Pump Room has another Dickens connection in the form of a bust of the author on a pedestal. For the story of how it got there we must turn to *Bladud* – the 'Bath Society Newspaper' – for 13 September 1905:

A bust of Charles Dickens by Mr Percy Fitzgerald has been presented to the city by that gentleman, and has been placed in the Pump Room. The bust stands upon a pedestal decorated with relief modellings by Mr Fitzgerald, who has attempted, by what measure of success the spectator must decide for himself, to represent Bath scenes in *Pickwick Pap*ers. The bust is no doubt a creditable piece of work for an amateur, but whether it is quite suitable to the environment is a matter for individual taste to determine.[1]

The paper then goes on to discuss Mr Fitzgerald's literary credentials:

The admiration of Mr Fitzgerald for Dickens is well known. He has just published *More About Bozland*, and the *Morning Post* in its notice of the work says: 'It is more in the nature of a popular account of many of the novelist's most popular books, adorned with occasional criticisms, and mingled with scraps of ascertained or conjectural biography suggested by passages in the novels, than a life in the usual sense of the word. It is written, of course, in the style familiar to Mr Fitzgerald's many admirers, wherein notes of admiration stand as thick as the hop poles in the hop gardens of that beautiful county of which the author, in relation to his present subject, has naturally so much to say. "How strange it is … !" "How often … !" "How amazing it is … !" "How grateful we should feel … !" – such passages are so abundant as to leave a stronger impression on the mind than any others when the book is closed. As for its matter, it adds very little of consequence to what was already well known to Dickens enthusiasts, but to those whose acquaintance with the novelist is mainly confined to *Pickwick* and the more widely read of its successors, the genial gossip with which it is filled will afford considerable satisfaction, while every reader must be struck by the obviously sincere and deep affection of Mr Fitzgerald for his friend, and, we may add, master.' In one part of the book we are told that Mr Fitzgerald 'takes pains to convince us that the greengrocer's shop, where, according to Dickens, the Bath footmen held their "swarry," was not a greengrocer's shop but a tavern'. 'Mr Fitzgerald's own inaccuracies,' says the *Morning Post*, 'are not infrequent, though usually quite trivial'.

---

1 Mr Fitzgerald also made a bust of Jane Austen, which was put on display in the Pump Room. It lasted less than a week, before an outraged member of the Austen-Leigh family ordered it to be removed. Its fate is unknown.

We will be coming across Mr Fitzgerald later, for he was responsible for many of the legends concerning Dickens' visits to Bath. He wasn't the only one, however. If you **retrace your steps along Stall Street, carry on up Union Street, turn left into Upper Borough Walls and take the first right into Trim Street, you will find, on the left-hand side towards the end of the street, a blocked-up doorway with the dates 1724 and 1897 over it**. This was once a pub which a columnist in the *Bath Journal* on 21 October 1899 revealed to be one of Dickens' favourite haunts in the city:

> This was a public house known as the Caledonian, which [was] carried on for some years by a Mr A Snodgrass [and] was very liberally patronised by the class of smaller tradesmen as well as by the more respectable of the artisan and working class … It was at the period of the tenancy of Snodgrass at the Caledonian that Dickens … was in the habit of frequently visiting Bath, meeting literary friends, and picking up some of his amusing, aye, and even detestable objectionable personages. Not only did he visit the Caledonian, but also the Marlborough Tavern and the New Inn, Rivers Street, licensed houses of the old sedan chairmen, and the St James's Hotel, St James's Square, and the Beaufort Arms, Princes Street, houses patronised by the coachmen and flunkies of the gay families then residing in this city. Snodgrass, host of the Caledonian, was an intellectual, matter-of-fact, hard-headed Scotchman, with the initial A signifying not Augustus but Alexander.

It was in this way – the writer goes on to claim – that Dickens came up with the character of Augustus Snodgrass, one of Mr Pickwick's travelling companions. There certainly was an Alexander Snodgrass at the Caledonian Tavern, but whether Dickens ever encountered him is unknown.

If you carry on along Trim Street and continue into Beauford Square, you come to the **original front entrance of the Theatre Royal**, opened in 1805. It was here, in December 1837, a couple of months after the final instalment of *The Pickwick Papers* had appeared, that a play based on the book, called *Sam Weller or the Pickwickians*, was performed. Bizarrely, it included the 'Procession of Her Gracious Majesty Queen Victoria, on the occasion of her Royal Visit to the City [of London] to dine with the Lord Mayor and Corporation'.

Such theatrical adaptations were performed throughout the country. Bath was not alone in its enthusiasm for Dickens – and Sam Weller – but, because part of the book was actually set in Bath, that enthusiasm was particularly heartfelt – despite Dickens' none too glowing depiction of the city.

Bath's reaction to *The Pickwick Papers* can be gauged from the reviews that appeared in the *Bath Chronicle*. When the first instalment appeared in April 1836, the paper's reviewer seemed rather baffled by it:

This appears to be a squib against the British Association for the Encouragement of the Arts, Sciences, Literature, etc ... If this be really not its drift, we must leave the solution of the enigma to some other Oedipus. It is very diverting in some scenes and the wit, though somewhat obscure, is at least harmless.

He greeted the next instalment rather more enthusiastically:

The second part of this humorous publication is as full of sly and racy fun as the first. Intimate acquaintance with that strange piece of patchwork – human life – peeps forth at every turn.

By the time the thirteenth instalment – in which Mr Pickwick comes to Bath – appeared the following April, *The Pickwick Papers* was a runaway success. The *Chronicle's* reviewer wrote:

The present number rivals many of its predecessors in humour and pungency. It is moreover particularly interesting to Bathonians, the hero being conducted down to Bath and being introduced to the Master of Ceremonies, to the Card Assemblies and to the Balls. The characters, we presume, are not of the present day exactly, as we do not recognise them by the description. The 'swarry' of the servants is keen in satire and rich in humour, and the flight of Mr Winkle is as comic an incident as these droll papers have as yet recorded.

Somehow, the savagery of Dickens' satire seems to have been lost on the reviewer, as it was lost, presumably, on those who flocked to see Mr Pickwick represented on stage at the Theatre Royal a few months later.

If you **carry on along Beauford Square and turn right up Princes Street**, you will come **to Beauford House**, the subject of one of Percy Fitzgerald's most implausible concoctions. This was, until quite recently, another pub, called the Beaufort Arms and it was here, according to Fitzgerald, that Sam Weller came to the footman's 'swarry'. This is what he had to say about it:

The place of meeting for the 'swarry' has now been quite settled. There can be no doubt it was the old tavern, the Beaufort Arms, in the street that turns out of Queen Square, Bantam's house. This venerable and not unpicturesque house, we feel, must have been the scene of meeting. And yet there are some difficulties owing to Boz's little disguises. For instance, he says that on leaving Bantam's they walked towards High Street. This was walking in the other direction. Then they turned down a by-street and so got to the greengrocer's shop.

Now to hold a 'swarry' in a greengrocer's shop seems a rather odd and inappropriate thing. Of course the selection was in the nature of a private club and therefore required premises of its own. But still the greengrocer ... could not be expected to have the necessary conveniences, as indeed the description of his borrowed knives and forks shows. Why then did not Boz say boldly it was the Beaufort Arms? No doubt he felt some delicacy in naming it.

So, although Percy Fitzgerald admits that they walked in the wrong direction and that Dickens clearly said that the 'swarry' takes place in a greengocer's shop, he insists that it was held in the Beaufort Arms. True, a great deal of drinking takes place, but the only reference to its source comes near the end of the episode, when the revellers send out for last drinks 'before the public-house [shuts] up'. It was common practice, until well into the twentieth century, for people to send out for drinks from a local pub.

The Beaufort Arms in Princes Street, the venue – according to Percy Fitzgerald – for the footman's 'swarry' in *The Pickwick Papers*

Unfortunately, Mr Fitzgerald's story is still widely current. In the early twentieth century, a guide to the city contained the information that a room in the pub, known as Sam Weller's Room, was frequently visited by tourists. Michael and Mollie Hardwick, in *Dickens' England*, published in 1970, wrote: 'The inn where the footmen of Bath met together to enjoy themselves, and where Sam Weller partook of the "friendly swarry" was the Beaufort Arms, just off Queen Square. Dickens, for some reason, called it a greengrocer's shop.'

Which just goes to show that, if you want to believe something badly enough, despite all the evidence to the contrary, you will. And if you repeat it often enough you may even get other people to believe it as well. In Percy Fitzgerald's defence, it could be argued that he was a friend of Dickens, first meeting him in 1863 and thereafter visiting him at Gad's Hill on several occasions. So his information could have come first-hand from Dickens. The problem is that Dickens was an intensely secretive man, who threw up smoke screens to keep his private life from public scrutiny. So successful was he in this that only now has the image he created of himself as a paragon of virtue started to crumble. He was a master fantasist, one of the greatest writers of fiction the world has ever seen, and he applied his gifts not only in his writings but in his life as well. When it came to his romantic entanglements, cover stories were obviously essential, but at other times he seems to have let his imagination run riot simply for the hell of it. So it is quite possible that – prompted no doubt by Percy Fitzgerald – he came up with a list of locations in Bath that inspired the incidents in *The Pickwick Papers*. The problem is, in the absence of corroborative evidence, it is often impossible to determine whether he was telling the truth or not.

A short walk up Princes Street brings us to Queen Square, where the Master of Ceremonies lived and where Sam Weller set off – in the opposite direction – for his 'swarry'. It is possible that Dickens chose this location for the Master of Ceremonies' house because it was one of the best-known locations in Bath and the sort of place you would expect a Master of Ceremonies to live. However, it is just possible he may have been indulging in another dig at Moses Pickwick.

The real-life Master of Ceremonies at the time was a Colonel William Jervais. In 1836, he lived at 5 Ainslie's Belvedere on Lansdown Road. By 1837 he had moved to 7 Portland Place. However, there was someone living at 12 Queen Square who had a close connection with *The Pickwick Papers* – Eleazer Pickwick, Moses' uncle, who had handed the business on to Moses some years earlier. This raises the intriguing possibility that the Master of Ceremonies in *The Pickwick Papers* was based not on Jervais but on another member of the Pickwick family.

The connection between the real life Mr Pickwick, who ran the White Hart, and his fictional counterpart is a peculiar one. It forms the pretext for the incident at the White Horse Cellar in London, where Sam Weller is alarmed to see the name of Pickwick on the side of the coach, but when the party arrive at Bath, not only does Mr Pickwick fail to meet his real-life counterpart – the coincidence of their having the same name is never mentioned again.

It is generally claimed that Dickens used the name of Pickwick in a spirit of genial good humour – but the element of gentle humour in Dickens is one of his overrated virtues. Savage caricature, fuelled by resentment at real or imagined slights, was at least as much a part of his make-up. If Dickens' encounter with Moses Pickwick in November 1835 was less than cordial, he would have been unlikely to remember him with affection – and perhaps his portrait of the Master of Ceremonies was a veiled attack on another member of his family – even if he never actually met him.

Head north out of Queen Square up the right-hand side of Gay Street, turn right along George Street and carry on to the York House Hotel on the corner of Broad Street. A Travelodge today, it was, in the early nineteenth century, one of the finest

THE YORK HOUSE, BATH,
FOR GENTLEMEN AND FAMILIES,

hotels in the country, and, apart from his first visit to the city, in 1835, and his last, in 1869, Dickens seems to have stayed here every time he came to Bath.

Crossing George Street at the pelican crossing and heading up Bartlett Street, you come to the Assembly Rooms, which also feature memorably in *The Pickwick Papers*. Built by John Wood the Younger betwen 1769 and 1771, they had been Bath's only Assembly Rooms since the Lower Rooms, which predated them, burnt down in 1820.

One of the Master of Ceremonies' main duties, when greeting Mr Pickwick on his arrival in Bath, is to invite him to that evening's ball. 'Ball nights in Ba-ath,' he tells him,

> 'are moments snatched from paradise; rendered bewitching by music, beauty, elegance, fashion, etiquette, and – and – above all, by the absence of tradespeople, who are quite inconsistent with paradise, and who have an amalgamation of themselves at the Guildhall every fortnight, which is, to say the least, remarkable.'

This attitude to tradespeople gives us one of the strongest hints as to the origin of Dickens' antipathy for Bath. It may even have been based on personal experience. Dickens was certainly a tradesman when he first came to Bath, being an unknown reporter, and would have been fairly put in his place had he tried to gain admittance to a ball. It had all been very different in Beau Nash's day, when anyone who could afford a ticket could attend a ball – an arrangement which drew forth satirical comments from writers as diverse as Smollett and Sheridan – but by the nineteenth century, snobbery allied to false gentility had led to the exclusion of those who did not have – or did not appear to have – the right credentials.

The description of the company Mr Pickwick finds when he gets to the Assembly Rooms is a savage satire on a society Dickens clearly loathed – although it is, for some reason, generally regarded as gentle humour:

In the tea-room, and hovering round the card-tables, were a vast number of queer old ladies, and decrepit old gentlemen, discussing all the small talk and scandal of the day, with a relish and gusto which sufficiently bespoke the intensity of the pleasure they derived from the occupation. Mingled with these groups, were three or four match-making mammas, appearing to be wholly absorbed by the conversation in which they were taking part, but failing not from time to time to cast an anxious sidelong glance upon their daughters, who, remembering the maternal injunction to make the best use of their youth, had already commenced incipient flirtations in the mislaying scarves, putting on gloves, setting down cups, and so forth; slight matters apparently, but which may be turned to surprisingly good account by expert practitioners.

Lounging near the doors, and in remote corners, were various knots of silly young men, displaying various varieties of puppyism and stupidity; amusing all sensible people near them with their folly and conceit; and happily thinking themselves the objects of general admiration--a wise and merciful dispensation which no good man will quarrel with.

And lastly, seated on some of the back benches, where they had already taken up their positions for the evening, were divers unmarried ladies past their grand climacteric, who, not dancing because there were no partners for them, and not playing cards lest they should be set down as irretrievably single, were in the favourable situation of being able to abuse everybody without reflecting on themselves. In short, they could abuse everybody, because everybody was there. It was a scene of gaiety, glitter, and show; of richly-dressed people, handsome mirrors, chalked floors, girandoles and wax-candles; and in all parts of the scene, gliding from spot to spot in silent softness, bowing obsequiously to this party, nodding familiarly to that, and smiling complacently on all, was the sprucely-attired person of Angelo Cyrus Bantam, Esquire, the Master of the Ceremonies.

Things do not improve when Mr Pickwick is introduced to some of them. Mr Dowler, who has accompanied him to the ball, asks the Master of Ceremonies if there is anybody of note there:

'Anybody! The *elite* of Ba-ath. Mr Pickwick, do you see the old lady in the gauze turban?'

'The fat old lady?' inquired Mr Pickwick innocently.

'Hush, my dear sir – nobody's fat or old in Ba-ath. That's the Dowager Lady Snuphanuph.'

'Is it, indeed?' said Mr Pickwick.

'No less a person, I assure you,' said the Master of the Ceremonies.

'Hush. Draw a little nearer, Mr Pickwick. You see the splendidly-dressed young man coming this way?'

'The one with the long hair, and the particularly small forehead?' inquired Mr Pickwick.

'The same. The richest young man in Ba-ath at this moment. Young Lord Mutanhed.'

'You don't say so?' said Mr Pickwick.

'Yes. You'll hear his voice in a moment, Mr Pickwick. He'll speak to me. The other gentleman with him, in the red under-waistcoat and dark moustache, is the Honourable Mr Crushton, his bosom friend. How do you do, my Lord?'

'Veway hot, Bantam,' said his Lordship.

'It *is* very warm, my Lord,' replied the MC.

'Confounded,' assented the Honourable Mr Crushton.

Bad turns to worse when he is persuaded to join three ladies for a game of cards:

Poor Mr Pickwick! he had never played with three thorough-paced female card-players before. They were so desperately sharp, that they quite frightened him. If he played a wrong card, Miss Bolo looked a small armoury of daggers; if he stopped to consider which was the right one, Lady Snuphanuph would throw herself back in her chair, and smile with a mingled glance of impatience and pity to Mrs Colonel Wugsby, at which Mrs Colonel Wugsby would shrug up her shoulders, and cough, as much as to say she wondered whether he ever would begin. Then, at the end of every hand, Miss Bolo would inquire with a dismal countenance and reproachful sigh, why Mr Pickwick had not returned that diamond, or led the club, or roughed the spade, or finessed the heart, or led through the honour, or brought out the ace, or played up to the king, or some such thing; and in reply to all these grave charges, Mr Pickwick would be wholly unable to plead any justification whatever, having by this time forgotten all about the game. People came and looked on, too, which made Mr Pickwick nervous. Besides all this, there was a great deal of distracting conversation near the table, between Angelo Bantam and the two Misses Matinter, who, being single and singular, paid great court to the Master of the Ceremonies, in the hope of getting a stray partner now and then. All these things, combined with the noises and interruptions of constant comings in and goings out, made Mr Pickwick play rather badly; the cards were against him, also; and when they left off at ten minutes past eleven, Miss Bolo rose from the table considerably agitated, and went straight home, in a flood of tears and a sedan-chair.

In 1851, Dickens returned to the Assembly Rooms, not to attend a ball, but to act in a play called *Not As Bad As We Seem* by his friend Edward Bulwer-Lytton. The cast included many famous names, most of whom were strangers to the acting profession – artists such as Augustus Egg and John Tenniel and writers such as Wilkie Collins and Douglas Jerrold. The proceeds of the play were to go towards the recently established Guild of Literature and Art.

The play had more than its share of problems. At the opening night in London, Dickens had to hire a plain-clothes detective to mingle with the audience after he was tipped off that Bulwer-Lytton's estranged wife,

Rosina, planned to turn up in disguise and throw eggs at Queen Victoria, who was in the audience. Then, when the play travelled down to Bath, somebody forgot to send the wigs down from London until it was almost too late. As the play was a seventeenth-century costume drama, this spelt potential disaster:

> By six o'clock on the evening of the performance no news of the wigs had been received. The boxes containing them had been left by Wilson at Chaplin and Horne's offices [in London] on the Saturday evening too late for the goods train that night. Sunday was a *dies non*. The wigs however were sent off by the one o'clock train on Monday midday and it occurred to the superintendent that if he sent a message by the early afternoon express to London dropping him at Reading, he might catch the goods train there and so transfer the boxes to an express train down which would reach Bath in time for the evening performance. By singular good fortune these arrangements were successful and on behalf of the company Mr Wilson expressed gratitude to the stationmaster for having relieved an awkward situation.

Unfortunately, it did not help that the play was terrible. Indeed, the extravaganza seems only to have been saved by the performance of a lively farce called *Mr Nightingale's Diary*, hurriedly penned by Dickens and another of the celebrity actors, Mark Lemon, which didn't finish until around one o'clock in the morning. It didn't, however, stop the *Bath Chronicle* laying into *Not As Bad As We Seem* the following day:

> The stage was rather small, and this was a serious defect; for, as the characters were thrown too close together, the illusion occasionally was not perfect; it was impossible to imagine that the actors could not hear the asides, the soliloquies and the parts of the dialogue which were supposed to be secret.

That might have not mattered if the play had been any good. It wasn't:

> A Californian newspaper jocosely describes *Not As Bad As We Seem* as *Not as Good As We Expected*. This, we think, must be the popular opinion … The dialogue is not sparkling, nor is it always expressive, though occasionally it throws off suggestive thoughts. The incidents are not striking and the situations are few … The applause during the progress of the piece was not very encouraging, but it grew loud and enthusiastic at the end, and the company were afterwards called before the curtain.

Leaving the Assembly Rooms, walk through the Circus (not mentioned in *The Pickwick Papers*) **and along Brock Street to the Royal Crescent**. This is where Pickwick and his friends take lodgings, sharing a house with Mr and Mrs Dowler, after leaving the White Hart. Most famously, however, it is the scene of Mr Winkle's early-morning sprint. Having answered the door in the early hours, he is left stranded outside, wearing only a nightshirt, when the door slams to. To save his embarrassment, he takes refuge in a convenient sedan chair, only to find it occupied by Mrs Dowler. Mr Dowler then turns up and finds Mr Winkle in a state of undress in a sedan chair with his wife. Hearing Mr Dowler's threats, Mr Winkle

> bounced out of the sedan, quite as quickly as he had bounced in, and throwing off his slippers into the road, took to his heels and tore round the crescent, hotly pursued by Dowler and the watchman. He kept ahead; the door was open as he came round the second time; he rushed in, slammed it in Dowler's face, mounted to his bedroom, locked the door, piled a wash-hand-stand, chest of drawers, and a table against it, and packed up a few necessaries ready for flight with the first ray of morning.

This Benny Hill-style episode gives you some idea what Dickens' farce of some 16 years later might have been like. It also raises the question as to whether Dickens had ever seen the Royal Crescent. He describes Winkle as running round the Crescent, keeping ahead of his pursuers, and, as he comes round the second time, rushing back through the door he had come out of. None of which squares with the layout of the Royal Crescent, although it does sound very like the Circus. Such a gaffe argues a knowledge of Bath's topography so rudimentary as to be almost non-existent, and suggests that Dickens chose to set part of *The Pickwick Papers* in Bath because he liked the concept of the place and created an imaginary city out of a passing acquaintance with it, using descriptions of the Pump Room and the Assembly Rooms from guidebooks to create a feeling of verisimilitude. Others – notably Percy Fitzgerald – have claimed that Dickens had a profound knowledge of Bath, but, given Mr Winkle's nocturnal escapade, these arguments do not seem very convincing.

Head along Upper Church Street (at the east end of the Royal Crescent), turn left into Crescent Lane and cross Julian Road at the zebra crossing. Turn left and then right into St James's Road, and head across St James's Square to Park Street. Although well off most tourist itineraries, then as now, Park

Park St Bath.

Street is one of the few places in Bath mentioned in *The Pickwick Papers*. Mr. Pickwick and his friends discover it shortly after arriving in the city:

> Having taken a short walk through the city, and arrived at the unanimous conclusion that Park Street was very much like the perpendicular streets a man sees in a dream, which he cannot get up for the life of him, they returned to the White Hart.

A few years after publishing that description of Park Street, Dickens came to know this corner of Bath well, as he made frequent visits to see Walter Savage Landor who lived at **35 St James's Square**, which can be found **in the south-east corner of the square**.

Landor had lived in Bath as a young man, and returned after a long absence in November 1837. A famous writer at the time, he is largely forgotten today. There are several reasons for this – he was a classicist and many of his writings rely on a knowledge of Greek and Latin texts; he was also very involved in the political, literary and social milieu of his day, and filled his works with references to people and events totally forgotten today.

Landor lived in Italy for many years; it was his separation from his wife that precipitated his return to Bath. Although Bath had changed greatly since the days of his youth, he still cherished memories of what it had once been like before fashionable society abandoned it to invalids and elderly people like himself. Dickens, of course, had no such memories to draw on. He saw Bath as it was in the second third of the nineteenth century, distinctly down at heel, with all the snobbish affectation that came with the reversal in its fortunes.

In April 1839, Landor wrote to Forster asking him to tell Dickens that 'he has drawn from one more tears and more smiles than are remaining to me for all the rest of the world, real or ideal.' The following January, Landor met Dickens while visiting London. 'I made a new acquaintance,' he wrote, 'in a very popular, and what is much better, a truly extraordinary man – the author of *Nicholas Nickleby* … Dickens is really a good as well as a delightful man.' Landor was around 65; Dickens was not yet 30. So, while Dickens was very much a Victorian, Landor was a late Georgian or Regency figure. He was, in fact, an exact contemporary of Jane Austen and had lived in Bath at the same time as her. It is not known whether they met, although, as they both frequented balls, it is an intriguing possibility.

Before leaving London, Landor made Dickens promise to come down to Bath to celebrate his birthday. In the event, Dickens missed the party,

Dickens in 1839

Walter Savage Landor

but travelled down a few weeks later. He wrote to Forster on 27 February 1840:

> I waxed rather stupid yesterday and consequently must keep close today … You write to Landor, I suppose? Mitton has taken places, but at what hour the coach starts, this deponent knoweth not, though he verily believes it is 10 from the railroad.

He left for Bath two days later, with John Forster and Daniel Maclise. The railroad was the Great Western, which had opened as far as Twyford the previous July. Although some travellers from London to Bath were still making the whole journey by coach, others went by train as far as Twyford and took the coach from there. Dickens' letter indicates he took the latter option.[1]

After dining with Landor the following day, Dickens wrote to his wife:

> My dearest Katie,
> We reached here in safety last night, after a very pleasant ride, during a great part of which (the day being so very fine) we came outside, stopping to lunch vigorously at two o'clock, and arriving here shortly before eight. We were alone at dinner, and although desperately learned and frequently first-person-singularish, we were much better than I had expected. Indeed, I was not bored – for which I am very thankful and devout this morning.
> We sleep at the York House – the largest hotel here – where the beds are very good and very warm. Of course, I arranged both the room and my luggage before going to bed, and had everything very tidy.

So the best Dickens could say about dinner with Landor (which he clearly doesn't seem to have looked forward to) was that he wasn't bored. It does not sound like the rip-roaring success some commentators have suggested. Forster's description of the evening indicates that at times they had difficulty keeping their faces straight. Landor, he recalled, proudly showed them a new picture he had bought – a lion supposedly by Rubens. Although they were very polite as he went on about how wonderful it

1 A few weeks earlier, as described on page 120, Charlotte Barratt had made a similar journey to attend Fanny Burney's funeral.

was, 'as they walked back to their hotel at midnight the usually quiet streets of Bath rang with their inextinguishable laughter, with which were mingled "Roars for the Lion!"' Maybe it was this memory which inspired Dickens to describe Landor, rather oddly, as 'like 40 lions concentrated into one poet'.

But the dinner with Landor had another, far-reaching, consequence, for it was here that Dickens conceived the character of Little Nell. This is one of the few legends about Dickens in Bath that is supported by documentary evidence. According to Forster, Landor himself 'confirmed the fact, and added that he had never in his life regretted anything so much as his having failed to carry out an intention he had formed respecting it; for he meant to have purchased that house, 35 St James's Square, and then and there have burnt it to the ground, to the end that no meaner association should ever desecrate the birthplace of Nell. Then he would pause a little, become conscious of his absurdity, and break into a thundering peal of laughter.'

There is evidence from Dickens' own letters as well. On 4 March, just after arriving back in London, he wrote to Forster:

> I think of lengthening [Master Humphrey's Clock], finishing the description of the society, and closing with the little child-story, which is *sure* to be effective, especially after the old man's quiet way.

The following day, he wrote again:

> What do you think of the following double title for the beginning of the little tale? *Personal Adventures of Master Humphrey: The Old Curiosity Shop.* I have also thought of *The Old Curiosity Dealer and the Child*.

At the time, Dickens only envisaged *The Old Curiosity Shop* as a short story. It actually begins like a short story, narrated in the first person. Only after the first part had appeared, did he see the potential of the tale, drop the first-person narrative, and set out to write a full-blown novel.

On the back of the story that Dickens came up with the character of Little Nell while talking to Forster and Dickens at 35 St James's Square, however, has grown up another story, that Dickens based Little Nell on a girl he saw in a shop at the back of Landor's house. In 1973, for example, Herbert van Thal, the author of *Landor: A Biographical Anthology*, wrote that, 'behind Landor's lodging was a small shop, and there, it is said, the *Old Curiosity Shop* took fire.' A variant of this legend is that Nell was based on the daughter of Landor's landlord. A correspondent in the *Bath Chronicle* on 21 December 1973 stated that 'the late T Sturge Cotterell … suggested that the original of Little Nell could have been the daughter of the landlord of No 35. And Mr Cotterell knew a woman who had actually known Dickens in Bath and took him into Royal Victoria Park to see a dwarf who hired donkeys for children to ride. The dwarf – nicknamed Donkey Prior – had a temperament as ugly as his appearance and the park authorities often threw him out. The woman assured Cotterell that Dickens was so impressed by this character that it gave him the inspiration for Quilp.'

We will be returning to this mysterious woman – and Mr Sturge Cotterell – later. And, perhaps, the story that Little Nell was based upon a girl who lived at what is now known as Curiosity Cottage is true. What is certainly true is that Dickens, despite any reservations he may have had about Landor and his predilection for pictures of lions, was well aware of Landor's standing in the world of literature, and was keen to cultivate his friendship. A year later, when his second son was born, he opted for the sincerest form of flattery and, as well as asking Landor to be his godson, christened him Walter Landor Dickens.

Shortly afterwards, Dickens visited America where he met Henry Wadsworth Longfellow. When Longfellow made a reciprocal visit to London in 1842, Dickens took him down to Bath to meet Landor. After his return to America, Longfellow wrote:

> In London I passed a very agreeable fortnight with Dickens. His wife is a most kind, amiable person, and his four children beautiful in the extreme. In a word, his whole household is a delightful one. At his table he brings together artists and authors; such as Cruikshank, a very original genius; Maclise the painter; Macready the actor &c &c. We had very pleasant dinners, drank Schloss-Johannisberger, and *cold punch,* (the same article that got Mr Pickwick into the Pound) and led a life like the

monks of old … Taking reluctant leave of London, I went by rail-way to Bath, where I dined with Walter Savage Landor, rather a ferocious critic, and author of five volumes of 'Imaginary Conversations'. The next day brought me to Bristol, where I embarked in the Great Western steamer for New York. We sailed (or rather paddled) out in the very teeth of a violent West-wind, which blew for a week with a vengeance. We had a very boisterous passage. I was not out of my berth more than twelve hours for the first twelve days. I was in the forward part of the vessel, where all the great waves struck and broke with voices of thunder. In the next room to mine, a man died. I was afraid that they might throw me overboard instead of him in the night; but they did not. Well, thus 'cribbed, cabined and confined', I passed fifteen days. During this time I wrote seven poems on Slavery. I meditated upon them in the stormy, sleepless nights, and wrote them down with a pencil in the morning. A small window in the side of the vessel admitted light into my berth; and there I lay on my back, and soothed my soul with songs.

This was Dickens' first trip to Bath by train (the line had been completed just over a year earlier), and he was so impressed that he came down again

a few weeks later, this time with his wife. It was Mrs Dickens' first visit to the city. As always, they were accompanied by Forster. They spent three days in Bath, during which time Landor showed them the sights, taking them on his favourite walk to the old church at Widcombe.

Dickens and Forster came again, for an overnight visit, on 30 January 1844, to celebrate Landor's birthday. This was the last time Dickens visited 35 St James's Square, for three months later Landor moved.

And so Landor's and Dickens' – and Little Nell's – association with 35 St James's Square came to an end. But it was not quite the end, as the two plaques on the wall of the building show. And it is at this point that we return to Percy Fitzgerald, the mastermind behind the 1903 Dickens Celebrations. The *Bath Chronicle's* coverage of the event, published on 7 February 1903, is a mine of disinformation:

This afternoon Bath paid fitting honour to the premier novelist of the British people – Charles Dickens. It was indeed appropriate that the date selected was the birthday of Dickens and the occasion was one of the greatest interest,

for the world loves Dickens, because Dickens loved the world. His connection with Bath may surely be called intimate. It was at No 35 St James's Square that the author lived, and was frequently visited by Walter Savage Landor.

A tablet to Dickens's memory was placed by the corporation of the City upon 35 St James's Square, which is the house where the novelist used to stay. This house is additionally interesting to the lover of Dickens because of the incontestable evidence in his own writings that it was here that the idea of the character of Little Nell first occurred to him.

The tablet was unveiled by Mr Percy Fitzgerald, president of the Dickens Fellowship, and he also unveiled a mural decoration to Walter Savage Landor, who was Dickens' greatest friend in Bath, at No 3 Rivers Street.

Top: Percy Fitzgerald unveiling the plaque to Dickens on 7 February 1903 – in the pouring rain

Left: Misinformation on an early twentieth-century postcard

After the Mayor's introductory remarks, Percy Fitzgerald – clearly no fan of political correctness – expressed the

> sincere pleasure it gave him to find himself in this ancestral and stately city of Bath. The hundred miles between this city and London he did not mind for he would gladly have travelled many hundreds of miles to come there, and join in that tribute to the great, good, glorious, and unsurpassable Charles Dickens, whom he knew so well and was his friend. He was sorry to say there were not many of Dickens' friends now about ... It was curious to note that this mortality among the friends of Dickens at the present moment were really no more than a score [sic]. There were Mr Markham Stone, the Academician, Mr Frith and a good many more he could name, and in this good city of Bath he had heard the names of Mr Tagart, whose name he had often heard in Dickens's circle, and Mr Charles Ellis, the veteran. In process of time he supposed even those survivors would be swept away, however disagreeable it might be for himself to contemplate it, and, as in the case of the 'Ten Little Niggers' (which used to be sung some years ago) 'there will be none'. He did not that day represent himself. He came as the president of a very important body lately founded in London, the Dickens Fellowship, whose aim was to propagate all of Dickens' ideas, and particularly those gracious and tender notions which were scattered through his works, particularly in the *Christmas Carol* and things of that sort; and to cultivate a knowledge of his life and works, criticisms and other things.

The plaque to Dickens on 35 St James's Square is, of course, something of red herring, for, as far as we know, he never so much as spent the night there. He went there for dinner on several occasions, it is true, but he always seems to have gone back to the York House Hotel to sleep. Knowing this, those responsible for the plaque distinguished it from the other plaques around the city by declaring that Dickens 'dwelt there' rather than 'lived there'. In the *Oxford English Dictionary*, 'dwell' is defined in several ways – 'to remain as in a permanent residence' is obviously the main one, but there is also the more archaic 'to abide for a time,' as well as more abstruse and forgotten usages. So, desperate for a Dickens' connection, the celebrants of 1903 chose an archaic usage of a familiar word and hoped no one would notice. As for Landor's plaque – which started out at 3 Rivers Street – more on that later.

A short walk up the east side of St James's Square brings us to Great Bedford Street, and to what is perhaps Bath's greatest Dickensian conundrum. No 7 Great Bedford Street was the home of Sophia Paynter. She was an old friend of Landor's and, when he moved back to Bath in 1837, it is likely that one of the reasons he chose St James's Square was to be near her. It is known that Dickens met Sophia Paynter while visiting

Landor in 1840. However, according to Reginald Wright, a former Bath City Librarian, who contributed a series of articles on Dickens to the *Bath Chronicle* in 1939, Dickens' acquaintance with her was not only of longer standing but much closer than has hitherto been suspected:

> Many of Dickens' friends knew Bath, and of these Walter Savage Landor is perhaps the most outstanding, but one of the most appreciative of his friends, about whom the biographers of Dickens have remained silent, was the Hon Mrs Sophia Paynter, who resided for many years at 7 Great Bedford Street. Her daughter was Rose, later Rose Lady Graves Sawle. She was present at a dinner with Landor and Dickens in London in 1839.

The problem is he does not say where he got his information from. All there is to go on are two clues. The first is a letter from Dickens to Sophia Paynter written in November 1842:

> I am afraid that the preparations for my new book will put a padlock on my locomotive powers, and keep me fast at home for some time. But, if I should get to Bath, rest assured that I have too pleasant a recollection of our old evenings there, and too earnest a desire to see you and Miss Paynter again, not to come very quickly up that very inaccessible hill, and inflict a cheery double knock upon your door, to which the street shall ring again.

The second is an extract from Sophia Paynter's daughter's memoirs, published in 1908:

> Dickens loved to wander about the back streets of Bath, picking up the queer names which appear so often in his books. We introduced him to the original of Quilp, a frightful little dwarf called Prior, who let donkeys on hire, and whose temper was as ugly as his person. He always carried with him a thick stick, with which he belaboured impartially his donkeys and his wife.

Like Little Nell, Quilp appeared in *The Old Curiosity Shop*, so neither of these scraps of evidence suggest Dickens knew Sophia Paynter before he met her at Landor's house in 1840. However, Reginald Wright seems to have been privy to other information concerning their relationship. He tells us, for example, that. in May 1837, Dickens was in Bath to witness the laying of the foundation stone of the obelisk in Victoria Park. 'Of the details of Dickens' visit,' he goes on, 'hardly anything is known. He had recently suffered the loss of his beloved sister in law, Mary Scott Hogarth ... A visit to his esteemed friend, Mrs Paynter must have brought him some consolation, as in his distress Dickens had come down to Bath alone.' A couple of years later, in March 1839, after travelling down to Exeter with his parents and fixing them up in a rented cottage, Dickens (according to Mr Wright) stopped in Bath to visit Sophia Paynter on the way back to London. He even quotes a report in the *Bath & Cheltenham Gazette* to the effect that Dickens was staying in Bath. However, he fails to give the date they published the report. A trawl through issues from around that time has so far failed to produce any result. It is, for now, a mystery, which must remain unsolved.

But perhaps Dickens himself has left us a clue to his early association with Bath in *The Pickwick Papers*, when he describes Park Street as 'very much like the perpendicular streets a man sees in a dream'. This is the only street in Bath – apart from the Royal Crescent – which he mentions by name, and, of all the streets to choose, it is one of the most obscure. Although it is not the street Sophia Paynter lived in, it is the one next to it, leading up from St James's Square – so was this perhaps a private joke inserted for the benefit of Sophia Paynter and her friends? And was his description of Great Bedford Street as 'that very inaccessible hill' a reference back to the description of Park Street in *The Pickwick Papers*?

Until such time as further evidence of Dickens' friendship with Sophia Paynter turns up, these intriguing scraps of information must remain just that – random pieces from a jigsaw so depleted that one can only guess at the overall picture. Dickens was a master at covering his tracks and, as far as his early connections with Bath are concerned, his success has been augmented by the willingness of Percy Fitzgerald and others to make up for an absence of facts with an abundance of fiction.

As you **head back down St James's Square**, look out for No 1 on the west side. It was here that Landor moved in April 1844. Towards the end of 1844, Dickens visited Italy, where he called on Landor's estranged wife at Fiesole and, at Landor's request, picked an ivy leaf to take back to him. In December 1845, he visited Landor at 1 St James's Square and presented him with the leaf.

Landor did not stay at 1 St James's Square very long. On 24 March 1846, he wrote to Forster:

> Alas, I must leave St James's Square … The people of my house are most impudent thieves – wine, umbrella, penknife … are carried off. However … I would rather have been pilfered to the amount of a dozen pounds a year, or even a score, than leave my old silk bed and derange the order of my pictures. I am going to No 3 in Rivers Street. I pay twenty pounds a year more for lodgings somewhat less elegant; but the mistress of the house bears a good character. It is horrible to live in a street. True, I look into a square and into a garden, right and left, and the only house nearly opposite has no window to overlook me.

Head back along St James's Street to Julian Road, turn left, cross at the zebra crossing, carry on to Upper Church Street, and turn right and

then left into Rivers Street. The house that Landor lived in – No 3 – was destroyed, like the church which stood on the large expanse of grass you have just passed, by bombing in 1942. Hence the removal of the plaque that once graced it to 35 St James's Square. Unlike the church, however, 3 Rivers Street was later rebuilt.

Dickens continued to visit Landor on his birthday, on one occasion catching the last train back to London rather than staying at the York House Hotel. Among the guests when he visited in 1850 was a writer called Eliza Linton who recorded her impressions of the evening:

> I found Dickens charming and Forster pompous, heavy and ungenial. Dickens was bright and gay and winsome, and while treating Mr Landor with the respect of a younger man for an elder, allowed his wit to play about him, bright and harmless as summer lightning. He included me, then quite a beginner in literature, young in years and shy by temperament, and made me feel quite at home with him; but Forster was saturnine and cynical. He was the 'harbitary gent' of the cabman's rank, and one of the most jealous of men. Dickens and Landor were his property – pocket-boroughs in a way – and he resented the introduction of a third person and a stranger.

A day or so later, Landor wrote to Forster:

> My thanks were not spoken to you and Dickens for your journey of 200 miles upon my birthday. Here they are – not visible on the surface of the paper, nor on any surface whatever, but in the heart that is dictating this letter. On the night you left me I wrote the following:
>
> > I strove with none, for none was worth my strife;
> > Nature I loved, and next to Nature, Art:
> > I warm'd both hands before the fire of Life;
> > It sinks; and I am ready to depart.

This remains one of Landor's best-known poems. It was also in 1850, however, that he published another, rather embarrassing poem praising Dickens, which ended with a reference to Little Nell:

> Write me few letters: I'm content
> With what for all the world is meant;
> Write then for all: but, since my breast
> Is far more faithful than the rest,
> Never shall any other share
> With little Nelly nestling there.

1850 marked the high point of their friendship, because for whatever reason – possibly because of the poem – Dickens now chose to use Landor as the model for the eccentric Boythorn in his next novel, *Bleak House*. Boythorn is not a villain – rather the opposite – but it is unlikely anyone would be flattered to find they were the model for this swaggering, comical figure. Landor certainly was not impressed. When someone asked him if he had read *Bleak House*, he replied, 'no! and never shall!' According to Eliza Linton, ever afterwards Landor was to speak of Dickens 'with a certain acerbity of tone'.

Landor continued to live at 3 Rivers Street until July 1858, when an unseemly and litigious squabble – just the sort of thing you could imagine Boythorn embroiled in – forced him to flee abroad. Dickens' visits, however, seem to have come to an end some years earlier, around the time *Bleak House* appeared.

Bleak House has another claim on our attention, for it is Dickens' other Bath book – although the references to the city in it are, it must be admitted, fleeting. Bath, which is described as 'that grass-grown city of the ancients', is home to Volumnia Dedlock,

> a young lady (of sixty), who [has] the honour to be a poor relation, by the mother's side, to another great family. Miss Volumnia, displaying in early life a pretty talent for cutting ornaments out of coloured paper, and also for singing to the guitar in the Spanish tongue, and propounding French conundrums in country houses, passed the twenty years of her existence between twenty and forty in a sufficiently agreeable manner. Lapsing then out of date, and being considered to bore mankind by her vocal performances in the Spanish language, she retired to Bath; where she lives slenderly on an annual present from Sir Leicester, and whence she makes occasional resurrections in the country houses of her cousins. She has an extensive acquaintance at Bath among appalling old gentlemen with thin legs and nankeen trousers, and is of high standing in that dreary city. But she is a little dreaded elsewhere, in consequence of an indiscreet profusion in the article of rouge, and persistency in an obsolete pearl necklace like a rosary of little bird's-eggs.

There is more in the same vein, including a memorable portrait of 'a hideous old General, with a mouth of false teeth like a pianoforte too full of keys, long the admiration of Bath and the terror of every other community'.

One of *Bleak House's* chief claims to fame is as the book in which the word 'boredom' was used for the first time. It also has another, rather obscure, Bath connection. For this, you have to turn to a review in the *Bath Chronicle* which claimed that Inspector Bucket, one of the characters in the book, was based on a famous real-life detective called Inspector Field. The reviewer went on to say that Dickens was writing a biography of Field. Two days later the story was picked up by the *Times*. A few days after that, the *Times* published a letter from Dickens himself:

> I observe two statements from a country paper copied into your columns of Saturday last. They represent me as having availed myself of that excellent police officer Mr Inspector Field in *Bleak House* and also as having undertaken

to write the said excellent officer's biography. Allow me to assure you that amid all the news in the *Times* I found nothing more entirely and completely new to me than these two pieces of intelligence.

Tempting though it is to regard this as a piece of duff reporting on the part of the *Bath Chronicle*, it seems that Dickens was being a little disingenuous. It is now generally accepted that he did base Bucket on Field. He had already based several stories on him, using his real name, as well as publishing an article called 'On Duty with Inspector Field' two years earlier. Field was also the plain-clothes detective whom Dickens had engaged to provide security at the opening night of *Not As Bad As We Seem*. So perhaps the *Bath Chronicle* was not so wide of the mark after all.

Carry on along Rivers Street and take second right into Catherine Place. Carry on past Bath Old Books (one of only two second-hand

bookshops left in the city and well worth a visit) **along Margaret's Buildings, turn left along Brock Street and cross the Circus to return to the Assembly Rooms.** It was here that Dickens gave a series of readings from his novels in 1867 and 1869. He had started giving public readings in 1853. Four years later he came up with the idea of charging people a penny to come to hear him. In 1858, about the time he separated from his wife, he embarked on the first of a series of reading tours. One of the first places he visited was Clifton, but he did not come to Bath for another nine years, and even then it was with extreme reluctance.

Dickens' penny readings were such a success that many people followed his example. Readings from great literature were the perfect formula for Victorian reformers, combining as they did entertainment with education. In Bath, penny readings were launched in 1859 by the Rev James Fleming of All Saints, Lansdown. By the time Dickens came to Bath, however, his charges had risen somewhat. Such is the price of celebrity. It was on 17 January 1867 that the *Bath Chronicle* announced that

> Mr CHARLES DICKENS will give two of his most popular readings on Friday evening, February 8th, and Saturday morning, February 9th.

Bath had changed greatly since his last visit – and not, as far as he was concerned, for the better. Landor was dead, and the White Hart, having lain derelict for several years, was due for demolition. The baths, after having been let to a private individual, had closed three years earlier. The post of master of ceremonies was vacant. It was one of the lowest points of the city's fortunes. After giving his readings, Dickens wrote to a Mrs Dickinson: 'Don't come to Bath. I hate the people and only read there at Chappell's solicitations … Privacy is impossible.' He would not have been too impressed either by the review in the *Bath Chronicle*:

> Mr Dickens as a writer is somewhat of a caricaturist; as a reader or actor he appears to air a more faithful imitation of nature … It is some years since we heard our great humourist read. Time has hardly been kind to him, for he looks much worn and the voice seems to have lost in power. It may be, however, that the apparent weakness of voice was nothing more than a difficulty to get the pitch of the room, though we noticed it at each reading.

Nevertheless, he was persuaded to return two years later to give two more readings. By now, the White Hart had been demolished and replaced by the new Grand Pump Room Hotel. Dickens could not stay at the new hotel, because it was not yet open, nor could he stay at the York House Hotel, which was closed. Instead, he stayed at the White Lion in the High Street, the site of which you saw earlier. Dickens was by now in poor health and this was his farewell tour. Indeed, it was brought to a premature end when he suffered a stroke. However, he did manage to get to Bath – although he probably wished he hadn't.

The *Bath Chronicle* of 28 January 1869 carried an advertisement for two readings on Friday 29 January and Saturday 30 January 1869. Friday's performance featured Boots at the Holly Tavern, Sikes and Nancy from *Oliver Twist*, and Bob Sawyer's Party from *The Pickwick Papers*. Saturday's featured *A Christmas Carol* and Mrs Gamp. The price of admission ranged from 1/- to 10/6.

The review of the two performances was, as before, lukewarm, and the reviewer once again claimed that Dickens was better as an actor than as a writer. Having struggled with the acoustics of the Assembly Rooms two years earlier, Dickens ordered a heavy curtain to be hung across the orchestra gallery, which 'greatly improved the acoustic properties for those in the lower half of the hall'.

It was Dickens' last visit to Bath. Eighteen months later he was dead, at the age of 58.

Just over 30 years later, on the day the plaques to Dickens and Landor were unveiled, the great and the good of Bath repaired to the Assembly Rooms, along with Percy Fitzgerald and other stalwarts of the Dickens Fellowship, for a grand Dickens Dinner. The report in the *Bath Chronicle* gives an idea of the true awfulness of the occasion:

The celebration of Dickens' birthday, and the unveiling of the two tablets were on Saturday evening consummated in a most fitting and enjoyable fashion by a dinner served in that apartment of the Assembly Rooms so closely wrapped up with the immortal name of Pickwick ... Everything was done so far as possible in true Pickwickian style. The menu card was of such an elegant character that it will form a pleasant souvenir of the delightful occasion ... On the inside of the cover was an excellent and lifelike portrait of Charles Dickens with the following appreciation of him by Landor: 'No mortal man exerted so beneficial and extensive an influence over the human heart. Everything that he writes is in the service of humanity. His genius was sent from heaven to scatter good and wisdom on earth.' ... The dinner appropriately included boiled mutton and caper sauce, with 'the usual trimmings'. Even the wines included the punch to which Mr Pickwick was addicted, so that during the evening the company was able to discuss Pickwick – and punch ... Behind the Mayor was placed the White Hart[1], and many of the company wore geraniums with ivy leaves, this being Dickens' favourite flower ... Mr Cotterell stated that the following telegram had been received from Mr Henry Fielding Dickens KC: ' Best of good wishes from self and family for success of Dickens's birthday celebration. Greatly regret cannot express in person my deep sympathy with movement.'

Percy Fitzgerald then made a speech which was a classic of special pleading:

When Boz went to Bath in 1832 [sic] this name struck him and remained in his memory – Moses Pickwick. Moses would hardly do, so he changed it to another Scriptural name, Samuel. When he sent his characters to Bath he thought he would do the coach proprietor, who had been so serviceable, a service in return, and accordingly gave him this good advertisement, actually mentioning his name and his coaches. Boz was ever good natured. Boz was the first, I think, to find out the significance or physiognomy of a place, treating it as though it were something. Every town has a particular character if you know how to get at it. He thus described Rochester, Canterbury, Ipswich, Yarmouth, Salisbury. But he was certainly most successful with Bath. The vividness of his picture is perfectly startling. I can only say for myself that on my first visit to Bath a great many years ago I found myself walking about as in a dream, saying to myself, 'surely I have been here before.' And coming to this room for a concert – the Passion music of Bach – I was all the time hearing the music of the dance, and seeing Mr Bantam and Mr Pickwick playing cards with the ladies.

---

1 This was the White Hart that had stood above the entrance to the inn in Stall Street. When the building was demolished, it was moved to the White Hart in Widcombe, where it can still be seen.

I may add that the late Charles Dickens the Younger always contended that his father had confused the Circus with the Crescent, because Boz describes Winkle as 'tearing round the Crescent,' and again speaks of his 'coming round' for the second time. This, he said, could not be said of a Crescent. But here 'round' does not mean going in a circle, but that when he got to the end he turned round and came back. Moreover, as we know the Circus has no less than three issues – any one of which Winkle might have turned down and so escaped notice – the word 'crescent' was before the writer's eyes and its meaning was obvious.

Percy Fitzgerald

Mr Snowdon Ward, who spoke next, dealt peremptorily with the thorny issue of Dickens' alleged hatred of Bath. He claimed 'that Dickens came to Bath much earlier than when Landor was responsible for bringing him and he carried away possibly interpretations full of interest and he did not care at all for the idea that in poking his genial fun at Bath he was in any way inimical to the city or its institutions'.

Bladud, the 'Bath Society Newspaper', recorded that 'during the evening punch was served and the company drank in solemn silence to the immortal memory of Charles Dickens. Miss Gertrude Taylor, who kindly gave her services, contributed several songs with a taste and sympathetic feeling, which delighted the company. Especially successful were the songs 'The Ivy Green' and 'Little Nell', the pathetic vein in the latter being brought out with exquisite tenderness.'

It all sounds in the worse possible taste, presenting a Dickens so anodyne as to be hardly worth reading. But Dickens was not the genial cove Percy Fitzgerald and his pals made out. He was savage, often unpleasant, and a good deal more interesting for it. He also, despite what anyone says, hated Bath. He made that quite clear on a number of occasions.

Dickens' most famous condemnation of Bath is the one he made in the letter to Foster during his last visit to the city in 1869, which was quoted earlier. On the same day, he expressed similar sentiments to George Dolby, who was accompanying him on the tour. In *Charles Dickens as I Knew Him,* Dolby recalled their visit to Bath:

> At Clifton, the following night was equally brilliant, and the public there (as usual) equally responsive. We had but one dread before us, and that was lest Bath should prove a damper on our spirits, to destroy the happiness and

brilliancy of out Western trip. To a certain extent it did, for we arrived there in a pouring rain, and when it rains in Bath you have about the gloomiest city in the world. Returning from a visit to the ticket agents, I found Dickens standing at the hotel window viewing the miserable streets. Assuming a comical attitude and approaching me in a melodramatic manner, he said in a hoarse whisper: 'Dolby, I have a new idea about this mouldy old roosting place. Depend upon it,' he continued, 'this place was built by a cemetery-full of old people who, making a successful rise against death, have carried the place by assault, and, bringing their gravestones with them, have contrived to build the city, in which they are trying to look alive. But' (shaking his head) 'it's a miserable failure.'

My reports from the ticket agents were not up to the usual standard of excellence, although it was considered 'good for Bath'. The agent explained the cause of what Dickens called 'the mouldiness of the let'. It seemed that one section of society wanted one particular reading and another section another, and so on. All of these objections, however, being 'boiled down', amounted to but one practical reason, which was that Bath could not *afford* to pay the prices of admission charged, notwithstanding that they were the same as those charged in other places in that part of the country. The result of the two Bath readings was, however, more satisfactory than the indications foreboded, and after all we felt we had passed one of the happiest fortnights of this reading life.

This damning indictment of Bath later reared its head in no less prestigious a setting than the council chamber of the Guildhall. In 1901, during a debate on the extension of Bath's boundaries, T Sturge Cotterell (one of those later responsible for the Dickens plaque in St James's Square), declared that Dickens had been misquoted. He added that he had taken Dolby to task over his remarks, and wrote a letter to the *Chronicle* to set the record straight:

It is now some years ago since I met George Dolby, and in the course of an interesting conversation I asked him particularly about this incident, and I well remember his answer, that never was Charles Dickens in a happier mood than when he left Bath in glorious sunshine the following day. The successful completion of his tour, coupled with the news that had reached him that morning of the promotion of his son in the Navy, gave him the greatest delight, and I am perfectly certain, said Mr Dolby, that his dismal remarks were quite obliterated from his mind.

Fair enough, but why Mr Cotterell should think that this negated his remarks on the city is hard to fathom. Did it not occur to him, for example, that Dickens was happy not only because he had received news of his son's promotion, but also because he was leaving a place he hated – and probably for the last time? It is commonly observed that criminals, on their release from prison, exhibit jubilation. Nobody, however, seems to have suggested that this indicates they have enjoyed their period of confinement. Mr Cotterell concluded his remarks with the following observation:

> I had hoped we had heard the last of this remark of Charles Dickens, which was not seriously spoken, and the reference does not do justice to the great novelist, who was such a broad-minded man. I have seldom heard it mentioned except by those who do not appreciate this city.

Well, with the greatest of respect, this is a load of nonsense. Dickens made it quite clear he hated Bath, and to argue otherwise seems perverse. And lest this should make present-day Bathonians twitchy, it should be pointed out that the city he knew was far removed from that of today, just as it was far removed from the Bath of Smollett or Jane Austen. It was a faded city living on past glories, where snobbery ruled. Its decline was already well advanced by the time of his first visit; by the time he bade farewell to it for the last time it was but a shadow of its former self.

10

BEAUX, BELLES, AND BLACK SHEEP
Bath through the eyes of Georgette Heyer

What a strange place Bath is! Poke fun at it and you will be praised and publicized. You may even get a centre and indeed an entire festival dedicated to your works. But write affectionately about it and you get ignored and despised. If you find this hard to believe, think, if you will about a certain internationally known author who was a close friend of the biographer Carola Oman and numbers the Booker Prizewinner AS Byatt among her fans. Her five novels about Bath – all still best-sellers – are an affectionate and historically accurate portrayal of the city in the Regency period. Wouldn't you think that Bath might be just the teensiest bit proud of her? After all, Austen, Dickens, and Smollett, none of whom liked Bath and satirised it relentlessly, are lauded and their links with the city promoted.

Such is not the case with Georgette Heyer. Mention her name to most Bath guides or local historians and you will be subjected to, at best, a pitying sigh and, at worst, a patronising sneer. Why should this be? Her prose is delightful, often containing mischievous references to Jane Austen, whom she greatly admired. Her meticulous historical research was ahead of its time and this alone should make her required reading for anyone interested in the Regency period. Her knowledge of costume was encyclopaedic and based on first-hand research at a time when the study of the history of fashion was in its infancy. Particularly interesting is her use of slang. Did the aristocracy really use working class cant? Indeed they did – fashionable grunge is nothing new. For the benefit of those not in the know, *The Dictionary of the Vulgar Tongue* appeared in 1811, its publication made necessary because 'our young men of fashion' had become 'as distinguished for the vulgarity of their jargon as the inhabitants of Newgate'. This slang was the language of bare-knuckle boxing – a subject about which you will learn little in Austen's novels, but on which Heyer was very well informed.[1]

---

1 Even Heyer's first biographer, Jane Aiken Hodge, could not believe that people spoke like that, quoting a term – inkle-weaver – as obscure. In fact, as the *Dictionary of the Vulgar Tongue* makes clear, it was then in common usage. Just because Jane Austen did not use cant does not mean it was not popular among the trend-setters in High Society. Heyer saw what all too many writers do not see – that Austen was writing about a restricted group in society – she was not an authority on the whole of Regency life, and her view was far from a complete one.

The problem with her novels is, of course, their plots, which are hardly demanding. It is generally possible to pick out the hero and heroine after just a few pages. They are usually – though not invariably – the ones at daggers drawn. However antagonistic they may be in the early chapters, you know things are going to end with a declaration of love. But isn't that precisely the plot of *Pride and Prejudice* by a certain Miss Austen? And if the heroine in one book sometimes seems a little like the heroine in another, they are always more likeable and certainly much feistier than prissy Fanny Price in *Mansfield Park*. Most of Georgette Heyer's women could – and probably would – have eaten Fanny's wimpish, vacillating suitor Edmund Bertram for breakfast. By and large, it seems that poor Georgette Heyer is the victim of simple snobbish prejudice.

This walk attempts to dispel some of that prejudice for those who remain unconvinced, while persuading any Georgette Heyer fans who have been intimidated into silence that their favourite author should be far better appreciated in Bath. Before we set off, however, we should make her acquaintance.

Georgette Heyer, born in 1902, was the eldest of three children, both she and her older brother George being named after their father. However, the family preferred her name to be pronounced the French way, with soft Gs. Her surname was pronounced 'Hayer', having been changed from 'Higher' by her father during the First World War to make it sound less German. He was, in fact, of Russian descent, which accounted for Heyer's striking looks, and also for her two brothers having Russian middle names.

George was so fond of his middle name – Boris – that he was known by it throughout his life, and it was thanks to him that Heyer began writing. He had a mild form of haemophilia, and often suffered from poor health. When she was seventeen, she wrote a story to amuse him during one of these periods. Her father was so impressed that he arranged for it to be published under the title *The Black Moth*, thus launching her career. Unlike Jane Austen, for most of her life Heyer wrote from necessity. Her father died in 1925, leaving no pension. The soon-to-be married Heyer took her brothers, then aged 19 and 14, under her wing. Her mother, too, was also financially dependent on her daughter, for which she never forgave Georgette, particularly as the money came from a career of which she disapproved.

Georgette Heyer's husband, Ronald Rougier, was a mining engineer and the first five years of their marriage were spent travelling and living abroad. On returning to England in 1930, Rougier found it difficult to get work. He invested in a utility company which failed, so decided to set up a sports shop in Horsham, where he employed Boris. It was not a great success, and Heyer's resources were further stretched as she was seeing her younger brother Frank through university. She was also paying for her mother to stay at a hotel in Horsham.

Rougier decided to become a barrister, and was called to the bar in 1939. Finally, he had a career in which he was successful, but many debts had been accrued along the way.[1] In addition, their only child, Richard, had been born in 1932, and Heyer was determined to give him a comfortable home. Then there was the Inland Revenue. Right up until her death, it seemed as though her dealings with 'the treasury sharks', as she described them, would never be settled. To be fair to the taxman, this was because neither Ronald nor Georgette were good at organising their financial affairs.

Today, Martin Salter, the face of the Jane Austen Centre, can research fashion and produce for himself an accurate Regency costume. As he strides out along the Royal Crescent, he could easily have stepped out of one of Georgette Heyer's novels. When she began writing, this would have been quite impossible. Her research in this field was years ahead of its time.

Despite everything, even when she was rushing off short stories to pay for things such as Boris's wedding, the quality of her prose and the standard of her research rarely faltered.

It is not surprising that she took her research so seriously. One of her friends from childhood – perhaps her closest friend – was the biographer Carola Oman, some of whose biographies, such as that of Nelson, are still considered classics. Heyer was not only an avid book collector; she also sought out old magazines and pamphlets to learn about fashion, a study regarded as trivial at the time but now widely respected. Curiously, however, the magazine where the characters in her books look up the latest fashions is called *The Ladies Home Journal*. No such magazine existed in Regency England; this is in fact the title

---

1 It should not be thought that Rougier was ineffective or a sponger. In fact, not only did he turn out to be a very successful barrister, he was always a tower of strength for his wife, as well as providing the plots for her detective stories.

of a late nineteenth-century American publication. As she was using contemporary magazines in the London Library, and making notes and drawings in her now famous notebooks, this cannot be a simple oversight. More likely, she was attempting to cover her tracks after discovering that her books had been plagiarised by Barbara Cartland.[1]

Literary influences were even more important. She makes subtle references to Fanny Burney, Richardson, and Sheridan, and did not disdain to read historical novelists from an earlier era, such as Baroness Orczy and Jeffrey Farnol. Her independently-minded heroines, some of whom, before meeting Mr Right, mock the institution of marriage, suggest that she knew early feminist works, such as Mary Wollstonecraft's *A Vindication of the Rights of Woman*. No wonder Germain Greer is another of her fans. Above all, though, Jane Austen's novels and letters are an abiding influence, with Elizabeth Bennet and Emma Woodhouse providing models for many of her heroines. And just as Jane Austen has a mischievous sense of humour, with in-jokes and sly references, so too does Heyer make mischievous references to Jane Austen's work.

Another important influence was the work of the Brontë sisters. The passionate affair between Catherine Earnshaw and Heathcliff in *Wuthering Heights* is echoed in the stormy relationship between Serena Spenborough and Ivo Rotherham in *Bath Tangle*. Serena even plans to marry a much gentler and kinder suitor, although here, as in most of Heyer's novels, the story has a happy ending. Charlotte Brontë's Mr Rochester – dark and brooding, with a murky past, but also witty and loving – also provided her with a model for several of her heroes, such as Miles Calverleigh in *Black Sheep* and Oliver Carleton in *Lady of Quality*.

Her five Bath books include her first Regency novel, *Friday's Child*, written in 1944, and her last, *Lady of Quality*, published in 1972, two years before she died. *Friday's Child* is a high spirited romp, in which the enchanting Hero Wantage and the dashing Anthony, Viscount Sheringham – known to his friends as Sherry – undertake a marriage which they believe at the time to be one of convenience but which, after many twists and turns, resolves itself into a love match. It was Georgette Heyer's favourite among her works. It echoes the light-hearted spirit of *Northanger Abbey*, but although, like Catherine Morland, Hero is an innocent abroad, Heyer made great use of her studies into the cant and boxing slang used by those in the highest society. Hero's naïve use of this language in polite society continually lands her in trouble.

---

1 Cartland shamelessly took the names of some of Heyer's characters, and also 'borrowed' her researches, particularly into fashion, without acknowledging the debt, but simple errors showed she had no real knowledge of her subject.

Just as *Persuasion* lacks the youthful sparkle of *Northanger Abbey*, so *Lady of Quality* is more thoughtful, dealing with issues such as the often hypocritical attitudes of Regency parents and guardians to the children in their care, and the way in which those children were manipulated into agreeing to an arranged marriage. Annis Wychwood, the heroine, is a feminist, who intends to lead her life in the way she chooses, despite the fussing of her brother. She has little regard for what people think. It is only when she meets Oliver Carleton, who shares many of her beliefs, that she falls in love. Heyer was at first dubious about the book, perhaps because she revealed her thoughts on marriage – her marriage had been one of friendship rather than romantic love, and in this book, such a marriage, between Annis's brother and his wife, turns out to be the happiest. One is left wondering, as her brother and his wife are left wondering, what the future will hold for Annis. It also contains the odd and slightly barbed remark: 'Only females admire handsome women: men infinitely prefer pretty ones!' Heyer herself was undeniably a handsome woman, and this comment suggests there were times when she would dearly have loved to be called pretty.

The Foundling, published in 1948, has a very different hero, the quiet, gentle but unexpectedly resourceful Duke of Sale. Its picaresque style harks back to a novel by another Bath resident – Henry Fielding's *Tom Jones*. This was followed in 1955 by *Bath Tangle*, written in a rush, under the influence of medication, and chiefly notable for the gloriously vulgar yet kind-hearted Mrs Floore. *Black Sheep*, perhaps the most pleasing of all her Bath novels, followed in 1966. It is full of hidden references to Jane Austen; not only does the heroine, Abigail Wendover, live close to where the Austen family lived from 1801 to 1804, but the description of her suggests that she was actually based on Jane Austen.

Armed with this knowledge, we can now set out to explore Georgette Heyer's Bath, on a route as convoluted as some of her plots, but taking in most of the key sites (and sights) in her Bath novels.

We start at Camden Crescent, which not only affords a fine view of the city, but establishes the first link between Jane Austen and Georgette Heyer. In Austen's last book, *Persuasion*, the heroine, Anne Elliot, finds herself living in a house in Camden Place taken by her sister and father. In *Friday's Child*, Hero Wantage takes refuge from her irate husband with Lady Saltash in Upper Camden Place, while in *Lady of Quality*, Annis Wychwood also lives here. Unlike Jane Austen, however, Heyer gives no description of either house. Although she must have visited Bath – her brother was a teacher at Downside, and she came at least once to visit his wife when she was in hospital in Bath – she did not know it intimately, and much of her information came from old maps and guidebooks. Not all of these are reliable, however, and this seems to have led her into an uncharacteristic mistake. Camden Crescent was never completed, due to a landslip, and the projected row of houses below it, to be called Lower Camden Place, was never built. The map on the right, however, taken from the *Improved Bath Guide* of 1813, which she appears to have referred to, shows Camden Crescent complete, with Lower Camden Place to the south.[1]

Using this map as a guide, Heyer has Hero take Lady Saltash's dog for a walk around Upper and Lower Camden Place, in the course of which she is abducted by the respectable Mr Tarleton. In *Black Sheep*, Lady Weaverham has lodgings in Lower Camden Place, while Annis Wychwood takes her nephew into the crescent-shaped garden below Upper Camden Place. As you can see, there is a considerable drop down to where this garden should have been – hardly the place for a gentle airing.[2]

Keeping the crescent on your right, walk downhill, crossing to the left beside a single-storey lodge, and turning left across Upper Hedgemead Road a few metres further on. If you were to turn right here up Lansdown

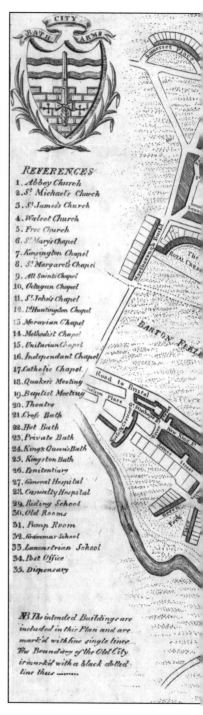

REFERENCES
1. *Abbey Church*
2. *St Michael's Church*
3. *St James's Church*
4. *Walcot Church*
5. *Free Church*
6. *St Mary's Chapel*
7. *Kensington Chapel*
8. *St Margaret's Chapel*
9. *All Saints Chapel*
10. *Octagon Chapel*
11. *St John's Chapel*
12. *Lady Huntingdon Chapel*
13. *Moravian Chapel*
14. *Methodist Chapel*
15. *Unitarian Chapel*
16. *Independant Chapel*
17. *Catholic Chapel*
18. *Quakers Meeting*
19. *Baptist Meeting*
20. *Theatre*
21. *Cross Bath*
22. *Hot Bath*
23. *Private Bath*
24. *Kings Queen's Bath*
25. *Kingston Bath*
26. *Penitentiary*
27. *General Hospital*
28. *Casualty Hospital*
29. *Riding School*
30. *Old Rooms*
31. *Pump Room*
32. *Grammar School*
33. *Lancastrian School*
34. *Post Office*
35. *Dispensary*

NB The intended Buildings are included in this Plan and are mark'd with fine single lines. The Boundary of the Old City is mark'd with a black dotted line thus ....

1 Upper and Lower Camden Place also appear on a map from 1793 on page 98.
2 As if to underline its unsuitability for a Regency lady, in 2011 a herd of pigs was introduced into this area to control the vegetation.

Camden Crescent in the early nineteenth century

Road, you would come to the turning to Lansdown Crescent, where Major Kirkby's valetudinarian mother had lodgings. To the Major's dismay, Serena thinks nothing of striding up the hill from town. In both *Black Sheep* and *Lady of Quality*, characters ride up to the top of Lansdown, taking this route out of town.

Turn left down Lansdown Road, cross over (using the pedestrian island) and carry on downhill. As you cross Julian Road, look across to Guinea Lane, now a one-way street, but up which Sherry, in *Friday's Child*, drives in his curricle before turning down Lansdown Road and turning right into Bennet Street. Before following him there, look across to the terrace below Guinea Lane, known as Belmont, which features in *Black Sheep*. Mr and Mrs Leavening, newly arrived in Bath, are looking for lodgings, and Miles Calverleigh tells them that he believes 'people speak well of Marlborough Buildings ... unless you would perhaps prefer the peace and quiet of Belmont?' Mrs Leavening tells him he has not the least notion where Belmont is, and he cheerfully concurs. This suggests he has been reading *Persuasion*, where Jane Austen speaks of Colonel Wallis 'living in very good style in Marlborough Buildings', as well as referring to the 'greater space and quiet of Belmont'.

Continue downhill and turn right along Bennet Street to the Assembly Rooms. Today this street has been made narrow by parked cars, but in *Friday's Child*, Sherry is distracted from picking his way between a hackney carriage drawn up on his left and a perch phaeton coming down on his right, by the sight of his wife with her hand on the arm of his friend

LITERARY WALKS IN BATH

George Wrotham. A collision occurs, and by the time Sherry has extricated himself, Hero and George have disappeared up Russel Street, opposite the Rooms, on their way back to Lady Saltash's.

Although these are now Bath's only Assembly Rooms, until the Lower Rooms burnt down in 1820 they were known as the New or Upper Rooms. When Lady Saltash brings Hero to a ball here, Hero forgets that she is pretending not to be married, and mistakenly heads for the peeresses' bench. Heyer correctly makes Mr King the Master of Ceremonies here – he took over in 1805 and stuck to the old rules, with, as Oliver Carleton observes, the dances ending at eleven o'clock. The newly-introduced waltz was not danced at either of the Rooms, which is why Annis Wychwood includes a waltz in her rout party for Lucilla, believing it a good thing for young girls to know something of the world before coming out – besides wanting to shock some of the gossips in Bath. The city was now tiresomely respectable, and the old dances – cotillions, minuets and country dances – were still the order of the day.

There is another very pointed reference to Jane Austen in *Black Sheep*. Just as Austen describes a concert in the Upper Rooms in *Persuasion*, so too, in *Black Sheep*, the company goes to hear Signora Neroli. By mentioning the mirrors in the Great Octagon, it is clear that Heyer had visited the Rooms, but anyone reading the two accounts will see that she is paying a graceful tribute to the earlier episode, without plagiarising it.

For those who enjoy the fashion in Heyer's novels, this is a good chance to visit the Fashion Museum.

Carry on along Bennet Street to the Circus and head across it to Brock Street, following Sherry and his friend Ferdy Fakenham on their way to the Royal Crescent. It is in the Crescent that the Dowager Lady Sheringham takes lodgings, bringing Isabella Milborne with her. Sherry had wanted to marry Isabella, marrying Hero instead after his proposal was rejected. Her mother wishes her to marry a duke, but in her heart of hearts she is in love with George Wrotham. She is known as The Incomparable, due to her beauty. Heyer is being mischievous here, for one of the top bareknuckle fighters of the day, Jack Randall, was known as The Nonpareil – she is using the argot of the ring to describe a beautiful woman.

Turn down the path opposite Upper Church Street at the end of Brock Street and then turn left along the Gravel Walk.[1] Although Heyer does not mention the Gravel Walk, she would have known about it because Anne Elliot and Captain Wentworth walk up it in *Persuasion*.

1 To avoid the steps at the end of the Gravel Walk, carry on, turning left into the Royal Avenue, and continue on at the end into Queen Square.

Walk down the steps at the end of the Gravel Walk, turn right and then left into Queen Square. Cross the road (you may prefer to use the zebra crossing down to your right), walk down the west side of the square and stand on the patch of grass at the corner.

As you saw in the Jane Austen walk, Queen Square has changed considerably since Regency times. When Gerard Monksleigh decides to elope with Emily Laleham, he hires a post chaise and waits for her in Queen Square. To reach the Bristol turnpike, the chaise would have had to go down Chapel Row – then much narrower because John Wood's chapel stood on this corner – before turning right into Monmouth Street.[1] So, to make a quick getaway, the chaise was probably waiting outside what is now the Francis Hotel. Emily was late, however, even though she did not have far to come – her grandmother, with whom she was staying, lived around the corner in Beauford Square.

To find Beauford Square, cross to 13 Queen Square (where Jane Austen once stayed), **walk down Princes Street and turn left at the end.** On the way, notice the early shop windows. Hanging bays were added to the front of ordinary houses, as trade for visitors increased, making more shops necessary. Georgette Heyer enthusiasts will notice that she always refers to this as Beaufort rather than Beauford Square. A glance at the map from the *Improved Bath Guide* will explain why. The houses in this square are not as grand as those in Queen Square and many other parts of the city. This suited the unpretentious Mrs Floore in *Bath Tangle*, perhaps one of Heyer's most delightful comic characters.

In many ways, though, *Bath Tangle* is the least successful of Heyer's Bath books. This is partly because Ivo Rotherham is truly unpleasant – his treatment of the unfortunate Emily is little short of sadistic[2] – and, were it not for Serena's refusal to take a snobbish attitude to Mrs Floore, but to accept her on her own terms, Serena would not be very likable either. It is the unexpected love which blossoms between Fanny Spenborough and Hector Kirkby which eventually captures our interest. But, in her desire to prove her worth as an historian, Heyer lets an abundance of historical facts get in the way of the story. For an historian, however, this flaw is what makes it a mine of information. It also gives us a clue to another book in Heyer's library – *Paterson's Roads*.

1 A photograph of Chapel Row as originally built can be seen on page 178.
2 Part way through writing the book, Georgette Heyer changed his name from the Marquis of Rockingham to Rotherham, admitting that she then felt like a stranger to her. Officially this was because the last Marquis of Rockingham had been 'that very dim Prime Minister', but there may have been another reason. Daphne du Maurier had used the name Rockingham for a villainous rake in *Frenchman's Creek*, and, mindful of her problems with Barbara Cartland, Heyer would not have wanted to have the same accusation levelled at her.

Paterson's Roads, compiled by Daniel Paterson, was first published in the mid-eighteenth century as a pocket-sized guide to Britain's main coach routes. By 1830, under new editors, it became a veritable tome, listing many inns, as well as details of sights along the way. The cross-country route that Serena suggests she and Ned Goring take to cut off the fleeing Emily and Gerard comes straight out of *Paterson's Roads*, as does her idea of the route they are likely to take. In other books, such as *Friday's Child,* when Heyer mentions an inn by name, it comes from *Paterson's Roads* – if she does not give its name, a quick check in *Paterson's Roads* shows that it is not mentioned there either. The Ship Inn, where Emily and Gerard pick up new horses and a postboy prepared to enter into the spirit of an elopement, is at Alveston, on the road from Bristol to Birmingham. There was indeed a road from Dursley to the Cambridge Inn, where Serena and Ned find they are not far behind, and the Bell Inn in Gloucester, where they finally catch up with the fugitives did, as *Paterson's Roads* helpfully informs us, allow post horses to be changed and stabled.

One of the reasons Mrs Floore likes Beaufort Square is because the Theatre Royal is on the south side. Opened in 1805 to replace the old theatre in Orchard Street, this was its main entrance. Not only can Mrs

Floore watch the people coming and going, she can also get to the theatre without having to call out the carriage. But which house might she have lived in? Those on the north side are quite small, even for Mrs Floore, who cared nothing for what people thought of her and did not flaunt her wealth.

The houses on the west side of Beauford Square

However, on both the east and west sides is a double-fronted house, with sufficient room for a drawing room on the first floor. The house on the west side would also have allowed Emily to watch out for Serena from the dining room window, while waiting to go for a ride with her.

Continue along Beauford Square and turn left at the end to walk back up to Queen Square. Continue up the the east side of the square and stop on the corner near the crossings. In *Friday's Child*, Hero Wantage has been told by her aunt that if she will not marry the curate, then she will have to be a governess in a school in Bath. After she runs away, Sherry guesses that she has gone to Bath to be a governess in 'some damned Queen's Square seminary'. From the mid-eighteenth century onwards, Bath was full of schools for young ladies and young gentlemen. One of the houses in Royal Crescent was built as a school. On 3 January 1771, Mrs and Miss Roscoe, 'removed from Bristol', placed an advertisement in the Bath Chronicle announcing that they had opened a 'ladies' school' in Brock Street 'till their house in Royal Crescent is finished'. On 3 October 1771, a further advertisement appeared:

> Mrs & Miss Rosco have moved their boarding school for young ladies from Brock Street to Royal Crescent, Bath. Their public dancing days are on first & third Wed every month.

The girls received instruction in 'writing, accounts, French, English grammar & all kinds of needlework'. Boarders paid £30 a year, day scholars one guinea a month and there was one six-week vacation a year from early August to mid-September.

The *Bath Directory* for 1819 listed two schools in Queen Square – one at No 15, on the west side, run by Miss Cook, and another at 41 Gay

Street, run by the Misses Evans. This is the house with the curved bay window on the corner of Gay Street. Perhaps it is here that we should imagine Fanny Wendover and Lavinia Grayshott coming tripping down from Lavinia's lodgings in Edgar Buildings for their lessons at Miss Timble's. It may have been on this very corner that Stacey Calverleigh waited, hoping to see Fanny, when she failed to keep her assignation with him.

Cross diagonally at the lights, turn right and head up Gay Street to stand outside No 8. As you walked up, you will have noticed the shops on the other side of the street. Although Gay Street was built as lodging houses, as with other well-placed central streets, shopkeepers soon recognised a good site and moved in, often imposing shopfronts on the buildings. In the lower part of Gay Street, some of these early shopfronts survive or have been replaced by modern ones; up here, in the upper part of the street, no such windows survive. This does not mean that there were no tradespeople running shops up here, because the 1819 *Directory* reveals that there were.

Fanny Spenborough is excited to find herself standing next to Madame D'Arblay at the ribbon counter in a shop in Gay Street. Although she is a great fan of *Evelina*, she is too shy to introduce herself to the former Fanny Burney. She is also afraid that she will want to talk about her latest book, *The Wanderer*, which Fanny Spenborough considers tedious – a judgement, sadly for Fanny Burney, shared by other readers.

The presence of Fanny Burney is one of many clues which dates this book to 1816. At the time, Fanny Burney was living in Great Stanhope Street, near Norfolk Crescent, in the bottom part of town. Also mentioned in *Bath Tangle* is Mrs Piozzi, the former Hetty Thrale. She had returned to Bath at about the same time as Fanny Burney, and was in very straitened circumstances, with lodgings in New King Street[1]. However, as you saw in the fifth walk, she managed to revive her fortunes by selling property, and at the time of the novel was living at 8 Gay Street.

Gay Street also features in *Lady of Quality*, when Annis takes Lucilla to a Servants Registry there. This seems to have been an invention to suit the story, although there was a servants' intelligence office (another name for a registry) in Queen Street.

Cross Gay Street, turn right downhill and then left along George Street. Edgar Buildings, set back facing the top of Milsom Street, is where Oliver Grayshott's kindly uncle, Mr Leonard Balking, finds lodgings for his sister and her daughter Lavinia in *Black Sheep*. It is really beyond her means, but her wealthy brother insists, despite her protests, on installing her in a suite of rooms which is 'the envy of many of her acquaintances'. However, since she makes no secret of the fact she owes it all to his generosity, only the ill-natured Mrs Ruscombe considers it 'an odd thing that an impecunious widow should be able to live as high as a coach-horse'.

In *Northanger Abbey* Jane Austen installs the Thorpe family, who are also not very wealthy, in Edgar Buildings, and Heyer may be making a sly reference to this when Mr Balking stigmatizes as poky another set of apartments in the house.

From Edgar Buildings you can look across to what is now the Bath Central Travelodge, but which was once the York House Hotel, where Charles Dickens stayed. Ivo Rotherham, Miles Calverleigh and Oliver Carlton also stay here, as does Sherry's friend, Ferdy Fakenham. It is also known to the Duke of Sale, but, while disguised as Mr Rufford, he chooses to stay elsewhere.

1 New King Street was also where the Stranger's Friend Society, founded by the Methodists in 1790, was run from the Wesleyan chapel. Maria Farlow, Annis Wychwood's talkative cousin, says that they would have rescued Lucilla had she been destitute but felt her parents would not want her to be an inmate there.

Cross the pedestrian crossing, turn right and walk along to the top of Milsom Street. This started out as a street of lodging houses. The first leases, granted in 1763, included covenants expressly forbidding them being converted to shops, but, by the early 1780s, some of the houses at the top end of the street had become shops and others soon followed, turning this into Bath's principal shopping street, although with some lodging houses still hanging on. There were two well-known circulating libraries in Milsom Street, Duffield's at No 12, and Godwin's on the corner now

Milsom Street as portrayed by Robert Cruikshank in 1826

occupied by a later building – once a bank but now Loch Fyne restaurant. Fanny Spenborough prefers the former but the Wendover ladies frequent Godwin's. It is in the doorway of Duffield's that Serena meets her former suitor, Major Kirkby.

Above all, Milsom Street was full of fashion shops – milliners, dressmakers, silk shops and so on. For the first time in this walk, here we meet some of the other characters from *The Foundling,* including the beautiful but dim-witted Belinda, from whom the book gets its title. Jane Austen

readers will guess that she is based on Harriet Smith in *Emma*, and, as if to emphasise the link, Heyer calls her heroine Harriet – Lady Harriet Presteigne. Belinda is enchanted with the goods on display in the windows, but, to Harriet's horror, sees a purple silk dress which she has always craved.

When Harriet's brother attempts to abduct her, she refuses to go until he has bought it for her, giving the schoolboy Tom Mamble, whom the Duke of Sale has also collected on his journey, time to rescue her.

It was not just Belinda who was entranced by Milsom Street – Lucilla Carleton 'became rapturous when she saw the very elegant hats, mantles, and dresses, displayed in Milsom Street' and made several purchases. It retains its fashionable status today.

Carry on down Milsom Street and turn left into Green Street. Christopher, Viscount Gaywood, Harriet's rake of a brother, has lodgings in Green Street. This seems a little unlikely, because the buildings are quite small and, by 1817, when the book is set, over a century old. However, perhaps a dashing beau with designs upon the women of the town – as he believes Belinda to be – would find other places a little too respectable. It would also have been very convenient for a drinking session, as the Old Green Tree has been a pub since at least 1750, and probably longer.

Turn left at the end of Green Street, walk up Broad Street, crossing above Saracen Street, and turning right into Broad Street Place (formerly Gracious Court) and descending the steps at the end into Walcot Street.[1] Opposite

Looking east along Green Street around 1820. The Georgian church of St Michael was replaced by the present building in the 1830s

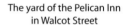

The yard of the Pelican Inn in Walcot Street

1 To avoid the steps, turn down Saracen Street, turn left into Walcot Street and stop outside Harvest.

is the site of the Pelican, where the Duke of Sale, still calling himself Mr Rufford, puts up, as does Ninian Elmore in *Lady of Quality*. In each case, the reason is the same – it is cheap but respectable. Recommending it to Ninian, Annis tells him that 'it isn't a fashionable hotel, but I believe it is comfortable, and provides guests with a good, plain ordinary.' In the eighteenth century, it had been one of Bath's top inns, with stabling for over 100 horses. Dr Johnson's biographer, Boswell, stayed here, and the Duke of Sale recalls how his tutor brought him to see it.

Cross Walcot Street and turn right past the Hilton Hotel and the Podium before turning left down Bridge Street, crossing Pulteney Bridge, and heading along Argyle Street to Laura Place. Named after Henrietta Laura Pulteney, Countess of Bath, this was the first part of the Pulteney estate to be developed in 1789, when hopes were still high that Bath would continue to be as popular as it had been for nearly a century. As we will see shortly, that proved not to be the case. The houses here were among the grandest on the Pulteney estate, and Jane Austen put the Dowager Viscountess Dalrymple and her daughter, the Honourable Miss Carteret, into lodgings here. This seems to have amused Georgette Heyer, who installed two dowager countesses here (thereby outranking Lady Dalrymple). The first is the Dowager Lady Ampleforth, Harriet Presteigne's rather racy grandmother, whom Harriet stays with; the second is Fanny Spenborough, who has lodgings with her step-daughter Serena. Serena – who is older than her stepmother – is unimpressed, wishing she was in the Royal Crescent or Camden Place, where there is more fresh air.

Selina Wendover considers Laura Place and Great Pulteney Street too expensive for her friends the Leavenings, although, as they are staying at the York House Hotel, money does not seem too much of problem for them. Mrs Stinchcombe and her daughters Corisande and Edith, who become great friends with Lucilla Carleton, also live here.

When Serena meets Hector Kirkby again after being parted for six years, they have so much to talk about that they pass through Laura Place and walk straight down Great Pulteney Street without noticing what they have done. However, as we will be walking back along Great Pulteney Street after visiting Sydney Gardens, we will first make a diversion.

Turn left along Henrietta Street. On the right, just past the entrance to Henrietta Mews, you will see two archways which once led to Laura Chapel. This was one of the most fashionable places of worship in Bath. In 1813, the *Improved Bath Guide* described it as 'an elegant, commodious building, and rendered comfortable in the winter season by fires in its recesses'. The Austen family worshipped here when they lived at the far end of Great Pulteney

Street, and Fanny Spenborough 'was content to visit the Pump Room each weekday and the Laura Chapel each Sunday'. It was demolished in 1909 and the archways now only lead to the houses on either side. The chapel was elliptical, and, as you **go through the archway to Henrietta Mews,** you can see – if you look over the wall to your left – that one of the back walls of the houses is curved, a ghostly reminder of what once stood here.

Take the next turning left into Henrietta Park. Looking at the map on pages 262-3, you can see that a grand square was planned for this site. It was never built. Instead, we have this quiet park. This change of plan eloquently conveys Bath's sudden slide out of fashion. The omens were there in the eighteenth century, but it was when the Prince of Wales

decided to patronise Brighton, and sea-bathing became the rage, that Bath began to look old-fashioned. Worse still, as far as fashionable society was concerned, it became horribly respectable – a suitable place for dowager peeresses, wealthy widows, spinsters and young ladies yet to come out into the world. The men who came were mainly retired army and navy officers, clergymen and strait-laced fellows like Mr Tarleton who, despite himself, is enraptured by Hero's innocent social blunders. In this small select pool swam the sharks – poverty-stricken rakes like Stacey Calverleigh and Denis Kilbride in search of heiresses to restore their fortunes. In this gossipy little world, anyone who dared step outside the bounds of propriety soon found their name on the tongues of malicious people like Mrs Ruscombe or the garrulous Miss Butterbank, as several of the characters discover.

Return to Henrietta Mews and at the end turn right up Sutton Street. Carry on to Sydney Place, turn left and walk along to No 4. From 1801 to 1804, this was the home of Jane Austen, who may have been the model for Abigail Wendover in *Black Sheep*. Jane Austen's niece, Caroline, described her aunt thus:

> Her face was rather round than long, she had a bright, but not a pink colour a clear brown complexion, and very good hazel eyes. Her hair, a darkish brown, curled naturally, it was in short curls around her face. She always wore a cap.

Edward Austen Leigh also mentions her hair and cap:

> Her curly brown hair escaped all round her forehead, but from the time of her coming to live at Chawton she always wore a cap, except when her nieces had her in London and forbade it.

Jane Austen herself said her long hair was plaited up and hidden out of sight, by her cap. Compare all this with Heyer's description of Abigail Wendover:

> Her hair was neither fashionably dark nor angelically fair, but of a soft brown. It was not cropped, after the prevailing mode; she wore it braided round her head, or in a knot from which curls fell about her ears. Occasionally, and in defiance of her niece's vehemently expressed disapproval, she tied a cap over it.

As if to confirm our suspicions, Abigail also lives in Sydney Place, although possibly not in this row. The Austens were not wealthy, and these houses were not nearly as grand as those in Great Pulteney Street. The Misses Wendover, however, are ladies of ample independent means. In the novel, everything suggests that their house was a large one. Could one, for example, really have held a rout party here? As you will see later, there was another part of Sydney Place – sometimes known as New Sydney Place – which was much grander, and this seems a more likely candidate. First, though, we will explore one of Bath's late Georgian delights, which figures in several of Heyer's novels, and was also one of Austen's favourite parts of Bath, Sydney Gardens.

Because of the constant flow of traffic past Jane Austen's house, you need to walk up to the lights, cross to the central island and cross to the right into Sydney Gardens. This entrance was only opened around a century ago. Originally, visitors entered through what is now the Holburne Museum, entry only being allowed to subscribers, or non-subscribers on payment of sixpence. The gardens opened in 1795, with the hotel at the entrance being completed in 1796. It was built because Bath, originally just a winter resort, now had a summer season as well, and these gardens, based on those at Vauxhall in London, were to provide a variety of entertainments. This is the tempting description of them that Regency visitors would have read in the *Improved Bath Guide*:

> Everything that taste and attention can effect to render this retreat agreeable to its visitors, may be found here; and perhaps no place in England of the same kind offers so many invitations as this to its pleasing shades.
>
> The amusements commence early in the spring with public breakfasts, promenades, and splendid illuminations, enlivened by music and every other fascination that labour and expense can provide. It is decorated with waterfalls, pavilions, and alcoves. The Kennet and Avon canal glides through this elysian scene, over which are two elegant cast-iron bridges after the

manner of the Chinese. A sham castle planted with several pieces of cannon, bowling-greens, swings, a labyrinth, formed by enclosed pathways, the principal one of which, after many intricate windings, leads to a fine Merlin Swing and a grotto of antique appearance.

After singing the praises of the ride, which encircled the gardens – the garden on your right and the tennis courts on your left are on part of the ride – it goes on to list further attractions:

There are generally four or five gala nights in the course of the summer, which for brilliancy, taste, and elegance, cannot be excelled: about 5000 variegated lamps are then lighted, and a splendid display of fireworks set off. On these occasions a company of three or four thousand persons frequently assemble to witness this enchanting scene, and present a spectacle the most sprightly and animating that the imagination can conceive.

Given all these delights – though contemporary reports suggest that the fireworks were sometimes more of a damp squib than a splendid display – it is no wonder that Georgette Heyer should have used this setting so often. It is clear that the Duke of Sale has read the *Improved Bath Guide*, as he sends Tom Mamble off there, complete with his sixpence, only for him to be dragged back before he has seen the grotto. Serena brings Emily Laleham here when she is trying to find out whether she really wants to marry Ivo Rotherham; Emily enjoys it until questioning by Serena reduces her to tears, and they take shelter in 'one of the shady arbours with which the gardens were liberally provided'. Emily makes another visit to the gardens in the evening, with Mrs Floore and Gerard Monksleigh, and he has great difficulty in coaxing her into another arbour to discuss the elopement, as she 'kept on stopping to exclaim at Merlin grottoes, or cascades, or festoons of coloured lanterns'.

However, just as a whiff of scandal permeated the original Vauxhall Gardens in London, so it did here. Tongues start wagging when Stacey Calverleigh takes Fanny Wendover unchaperoned around the gardens. Selina tells him, 'it was quite improper for a young female of breeding to wander round the gardens – to say nothing of the labyrinth! – without the vestige of a chaperon.' When Lucilla Carleton visits the gardens with Corisande and Edith Stinchcombe, she is chaperoned by her new lady's maid, Eliza Brigham. Even so, the charming Denis Kilbride, flirt and fortune-hunter, tells Lucilla about the evening entertainments there as he walks her home from Laura Place, presumably in the hope of meeting her there.

Carry on up through the gardens, crossing the railway – pushed through the gardens in 1841 – **and the canal before turning right and heading out of the gardens. Turn right downhill, and after crossing**

the railway you will see **New Sydney Place on the left-hand side of the road.** This impressive row, designed by John Pinch, was completed in 1807. *Black Sheep* is set around 1816, and the Wendover sisters have been in Bath since Fanny was eleven. She is now 17, so they could have moved here when the buildings were virtually new; it would have been the perfect place for them, their mother and their niece to retire to, with plenty of room. And it would have been here that Stacey Calverleigh had his first meeting with Abigail Wendover, during which each took an instant dislike to the other – which nevertheless does not prevent him from partaking 'of a light nuncheon' before heading back into town.[1]

We will now follow Stacey Calverleigh along Great Pulteney Street, through Laura Place, across Pulteney Bridge, up Bridge St and straight on along Upper Borough Walls. (You are not obliged to shrug your shoulders, as he does, at this point, but given that this is now a busy crossing, you are recommended to hesitate, if only to check that it is safe to cross.) **Continue in his footsteps as far as Burton Street**, where he turns right, but **where we carry on for a few paces to look up Old Bond Street**, whose serpentine Regency shopfronts may include the one from which Gerard Monksleigh emerges, only to bump into 'one of the perils that beset him' – Lady Serena – who inquires, with some surprise, what he is doing there. With her is Major Kirkby, and they set off for Laura Place, while Gerard heads down Parsonage Lane, which you can see further along Upper Borough Walls, beyond the Mineral Water Hospital.

Turn left along Union Street, not mentioned by Heyer although it sums up the attitude that allowed Bath to slip out of fashion. For centuries, this street was the site of the Bear Inn, one of the largest in Bath. As you saw in the third walk, it blocked the way between the upper town and the old city and visitors had to pick their way through the inn yard if they wanted the shortest route between their lodgings and the Pump Room or baths. For years there was talk of pulling it down and creating a thoroughfare, but, all the time the visitors kept coming, no one did anything. It was only when Bath started to be shunned by society in favour of Brighton that action was taken. By 1806, the inn was demolished and the new street well advanced. But it was too late. However, in Union Street, we have a genuine piece of Regency Bath. At the far end is Cheap Street, which Jane Austen tells us was always busy with carriages, horsemen and carts, a comment which Heyer picks up on, when Fanny Wendover's carriage is held up by 'the usual press of traffic in Cheap Street'. It is still a busy road today.

---

1 'Nuncheon' was a light meal taken at or shortly after noon.

Turn left along Cheap Street, and at the end turn left into the High Street and cross at the lights to the Guildhall. If you look back across the road, over to the left you will see All Bar One, once the Christopher Hotel and still with its old name above the second-floor windows. In the mid-eighteenth century, the landlord was a supporter of Wesley, and the Christopher continued to be a meeting place for Methodists well into the nineteenth century. Hence it developed a reputation for respectability, even if it was not up to the standards of comfort at the York House. This is doubtless why it is so attractive to Ninian Elmore's ultra-sensitive – and very manipulative – mother, Lady Iverley, who stays here with her daughter Cordelia. It was also known to the Duke of Sale, who chooses not to stay there as he is looking rather shabby. This upsets Belinda, who, having once delivered a bonnet there while serving as a milliner's apprentice[1] in Bath, 'had formed the opinion it was a very genteel, elegant hotel, in every way superior to the Pelican'. However, once he finds himself in funds, and returns to being the Duke of Sale rather than plain Mr Rufford, he moves from the Pelican to the Christopher.

Another inn which stood in the High Street – or the Market Place as it was once known – was the White Lion on the corner of Bridge Street, where Dickens once stayed. The northern extension of the Guildhall now occupies the site. In *The Foundling*, Mr Mamble is allegedly staying in the White Horse, but although there was a pub called the White Horse Cellar below Camden Crescent, it was quite rough. There was also, for a brief time, a pub called the White Horse in Stall Street, which we will come to later, but again, this seems an unlikely candidate. Heyer may have had the White Lion in mind, but called it the White Horse by mistake. What makes this more likely is that, after the Duke has been arrested, Mr Mamble is persuaded to send Tom's tutor, Mr Snape, back to the inn. This suggests it is not far away, and as the watch-house was probably in the vicinity of the Guildhall, the White Lion would indeed have been very close.

The Guildhall, in front of which you are standing, was built in the 1770s, with the wings added in the late nineteenth century. It does not feature in any of Heyer's books, which is surprising as Serena Spenborough is involved in politics, and this was the political heart of Bath.

Head back along the High Street towards the Abbey, crossing at the lights and turning left into Orange Grove. It is here that the Leavenings finally find lodgings – Mrs Leavening admits that the position is not

---

1 In the Georgian period, a milliners' apprentice was considered likely to become a prostitute, or 'Covent Garden nun', as Christopher Gaywood believes Belinda to be.

ideal, but it is very convenient, because she does not need to call a chair to go to the Pump Room or the Abbey. She is also confident that she will soon get used to the sound of the bells that Philip Thicknesse found so annoying.

Turn right at the end of the Orange Grove into Terrace Walk and cross to the triangular traffic island by the fountain where the Lower Assembly Rooms once stood. The *Improved Bath Guide* tells us that by 1813 the Rooms had been refurbished, although they must still have seemed dated compared with the Upper Rooms:

Orange Grove has changed enormously, with only the Abbey and the buildings on the south side surviving from Regency times. One of the grandest buildings was Nassau House on the east side. It was demolished in 1899.

> These Rooms have lately undergone very essential improvements, particularly at their entrance, which were for many years considered highly inconvenient, in consequence of the company being unable to drive up to the doors in their carriages. This objection is now removed, and a new street made which communicates with the Rooms from Stall Street, and from Pierrepont Street to the South Parade; two new entrances are also formed under some very handsome colonnades at the south and west end of the Rooms.

Georgette Heyer notes that the times allocated for balls were different at the two sets of Rooms. The Upper Rooms were more conservative, but at the Lower Rooms the balls went on till midnight. This was probably because the proprietor, Mr Finegan, was desperate to attract more trade.

Despite all Georgette Heyer's care, the *Improved Bath Guide*, though a mine of information about the times and types of balls, has led her into another error. None of the novels is set earlier than 1816, but throughout them all she refers to the Master of Ceremonies at the Lower Rooms as Mr Guynette, as stated in the *Guide*. However, he had smartly absconded in 1815. Although he passed himself off as a Frenchman, he came from Guernsey, but was married and had a family in Bath. All seemed to be going well, but the Rooms, despite their refurbishment, were struggling, and Finegan's financial woes were blamed on Guynette (or Guyenette, as his name was also spelt.) He was arrested for debt, but jumped bail and fled to London. A reward of £10 was offered for his arrest; the discrepancies between the description in the 'wanted' notice and the portrait on the

left suggest that he disguised himself in an attempt to evade capture:

> About 40 years of age, 5 feet 6 inches high, black hair with large mustachios, long black whiskers with dark complexion, is generally dressed in blue Cossack pantaloons, black coat with a blue regimental long great coat, braided in front; has a genteel appearance and address, walks very spright and quick.

Francis John Guynette, Master of Ceremonies at the Lower Rooms

He died, aged 70, in 1843. Life had not been kind to him – he set up as a builder, but was again declared bankrupt in 1830. Let us, instead, imagine him reigning over the Rooms and being charming to the ladies, especially the winsome Fanny Spenborough, or coercing unwilling gallants like Viscount Sheringham into dancing.

It is at the Lower Rooms that Hero and Isabel make one another jealous and play Sherry and George Wrotham off against each other, through misunderstanding their motives. As required by the organisers, Hero puts her name down on the day before the ball to dance a minuet, in which her partner is Mr Tarleton. In the end, George and Sherry make it up and walk off together, leaving the ladies unhappy and with 'an ardent desire to go home'. This is, of course, very different from the enjoyable evening Catherine Morland has when she meets Henry Tilney here for the first time, in *Northanger Abbey*. But all the dancing came to an end in December 1820 when the Rooms burnt down.

To the south, extending all the way to the river, is North Parade, where the terrible Mrs Nibley, with whom Lucilla had planned to find employment, lived. If you were to head south along Pierrepont Street, you would come to South Parade, where Mrs Floore is overcome by the heat, and where Madame Lisette – aka Eliza Mudford, the Misses Wendover's modiste – had her showroom.

We, however, will **head west along York Street** – the 'new street' mentioned in the *Guide* – **to Kingston Parade**. Until the early twentieth century, there were buildings here, including the Kingston Baths, which during the Regency period were run by Dr Wilkinson. He improved the baths, 'provided proper accommodation for wet and dry pumping' and a bath 'not exceeding 108°F' available at ten minutes notice. He also set up

LITERARY WALKS IN BATH

Remarkably, given the number of times Jane Austen's novels have been adapted for film and television over the years, there have been only been two Georgette Heyer film adaptations – a 1959 German version of *Arabella* and a spoof of *The Reluctant Widow*. In 1954, however, the centre of Bath was transformed into a Regency film set for *Lord Vanity*, based on a novel by Samuel Shellabarger and starring Robert Wagner and Joan Collins. Make-up and wardrobe tests were filmed, but the film was never made. These two photographs, evoking the world of Georgette Heyer's novels, show Bath Street and the colonnade leading into the Abbey Church Yard, all ready for the cameras that never rolled.

an apartment in Kingston House as a Pump Room. All of these facilities are recommended by the villainous Sir Montague Revesby to the Dowager Lady Sheringham, in an attempt to inveigle himself into her good books. Dr Wilkinson was an advocate of Russian vapour baths, which Selina Wendover is keen to try. He is also called in by Mrs Grayshott to take a look at her son Oliver on his return from India. Not surprisingly, he recommends a course of hot baths, but reassures Mrs Grayshott that no permanent damage has been done to Oliver's health. As you saw in the sixth walk, Dr Wilkinson also gave lectures at Kingston House, including those on electricity attended by Mary Shelley when she was living nearby and working on *Frankenstein*.

Carry on along York Street, turn right into Stall Street and stop on the corner of Bath Street. At the far end of Bath Street is the Cross Bath, where the Dowager Lady Sheringham goes to bathe. There were also private baths in Stall Street, patronised by Mrs Grayshott, on the corner of York Street, where the gift shop stands today.

To the right of Bath Street, where the pseudo-Georgian block called Arlington House now stands, was the White Hart Inn, whose stables, as you saw in the Jane Austen walk, extended all the way back to the Cross Bath. When Sherry visits George Wrotham, who is staying there, they are interrupted by an 'infernal howling' which George explains is the Harmonic Society singing glees. The *Improved Bath Guide* waxes lyrical over the Harmonic Society, but it was essentially a drinking and dining club, with the members drinking a toast after singing each glee – after five hours, 'howling' would probably have been about right.

Stacey Calverleigh also stays at the White Hart, and, ever optimistic that he will marry money, does not stint himself. When his uncle visits, he ensures that there is a good dinner – giving Heyer a chance to show off her knowledge of Georgian cuisine. When the enticing Mrs Clapham turns up at the inn with her companion Mrs Winkworth, Stacey courts her company and gives her advice on Bath, including one tip lifted straight out of *Persuasion*, that one should never come to Bath without an umbrella. It was, of course, Captain Wentworth who ensured that he came prepared for rain when he visited the city.

Turn right through the colonnade into the Abbey Church Yard. Attending services at the Abbey was part of the social round – which is why Mrs Leavening finds Orange Grove so convenient. In *Bath Tangle* Gerard Monksleigh meets Emily Laleham at the Abbey to arrange their elopement, but finds it full of visitors – just as it is today. A similar meeting at the Abbey takes place between Stacey Calverleigh and Fanny Wendover.

Although it is once again busy, the resourceful Stacey draws Fanny into a dark corner where there is nothing to interest visitors.

Both these assignations are arranged in Meyler's library in the Abbey Church Yard (where Percy and Mary Shelley stayed in 1816-17), which was demolished in the 1890s.[1] Fanny Spenborough divided her patronage between Meyler's library and Duffield's in Milsom Street.

Our tour ends in the Pump Room – the heart of gossip in Georgian Bath. It was built in the 1790s, replacing one dating from 1706. In F*riday's Child*, the Pump Room provides neutral ground for the various characters to meet, particularly as Sherry's mother does not want to see Hero at the Royal Crescent. It is in the Pump Room that Serena first sees Mrs Floore, and is attracted to her hats, one of which sports five ostrich plumes, a bunch of grapes, two bunches of cherries, three large roses and two rosettes. However, it is the snobbery of Mr King, Master of Ceremonies at the Upper Rooms, who apologises that mere vulgar wealth is now able to rub shoulders with my Lady Spenborough, that makes Serena look upon her with an indulgent eye, and so make a good friend.

Another widow who is supposed to have inherited her money through trade is Mrs Clapham, who dupes Stacey Calverleigh into wooing her. Tongues are soon wagging, and once the two are seen together in the Pump Room, the stories quickly get back to Fanny Wendover, through her friend Lavinia.

Even the outrageous Oliver Carleton comes here, crossing swords with Lord Beckenham, who has decided that Annis Wychwood would make a suitable wife. Carleton is also displeased to meet Denis Kilbride, 'who, whenever (for financial reasons) he came to Bath on a visit to his grandmother, dutifully escorted her to the Pump Room, tenderly settled her in a chair, brought her a glass of the hot pump water, took immense pains to discover amongst the company one of her cronies, and, having inexorably led this unfortunate up to her, and seen him (or her) safely ensconced with her, occupied himself for the rest of his stay in the Pump Room in strolling about, greeting chance acquaintances, and flirting light-heartedly with all the prettiest girls present'.

No doubt, like many other impecunious young men, Denis is hoping to be made his grandmother's heir or to find a rich wife – or both. This rather charming vignette sums up the atmosphere of the Pump Room in Regency times, and indeed, of Bath itself. In these five books, Georgette Heyer encapsulates the fading delights of the city in the dying days of the Regency to perfection.

---

1 Photographs of it appear on pages 139 and 148.

11

'GOODBYE TO OLD BATH'
Around Bath with John Betjeman

For our final walk, we turn from writers of fiction who used Bath as a backdrop for their characters to someone who not only celebrated that backdrop in its own right, but also sought to preserve it. Almost 30 years after his death, John Betjeman is still what is termed – somewhat unfortunately – a 'national treasure', but if you are hoping this walk will be a cosy stroll around Bath, with nostalgic anecdotes and quirky aperçus – well, you'll not exactly be disappointed, but you will get something more than you bargained for. There will be jokes, of course – or japes, as Betjeman might have called them – but there will be a good deal else besides. Anger, for a start, mingled with more than a hint of despair. Betjeman was a passionate advocate of what he cared for; unfortunately, he lived to see much of it destroyed. His greatest achievement was not managing to save some of it, but opening other people's eyes to the qualities and beauties of what he loved, and inspiring them to fight for beautiful, threatened things. That is his lasting legacy, and, while he did not make the young executives, corrupt councillors and greedy developers go away, or even think again, he empowered ordinary people to stand up to them.

The first myth we should dispel is that Betjeman was some sort of bumbling Private Godfrey figure. His shambling gait and air of forgetfulness hid a steely ruthlessness. With his family and – as we now know – his string of mistresses, it was Betjeman who always came first. He had an absolute determination to get his own way: his wartime sojourn in Bath was a case in point.

In 1941, he was sent as a cultural attaché to Ireland, where he attended a ceaseless round of functions and parties and relayed any interesting titbits he picked up to his masters in Whitehall. Betjeman seems an unlikely spy, although that is what he was. His bumbling façade was the ideal cover for getting pro-IRA and pro-German acquaintances to drop their guard and feed him potentially useful information. Unfortunately, the IRA eventually saw through his cover and plotted to assassinate him. However, Diarmuid

Left: An early-eighteenth-century doorway in Trim Street. This building, along with many others, was demolished in the late 1960s and replaced by an office block.

Brennan, the IRA Chief of Civilian Intelligence, decided, after reading some of Betjeman's poems about Ireland (as well as his famous poem about Slough), that the assassination should be called off.

He was recalled from Dublin in 1943 and in March 1944 was posted to Bath to work as part of a team editing newsletters for Admiralty staff. Despite having Richard Hughes, author of *A High Wind in Jamaica*, as his boss, and working with an amiable and highly intelligent group of people – including the future Lord Weinstock – he hated it.

He was billeted on a Mrs Helen Holmes, a 65-year-old widow – and talented silversmith – at 16 Macaulay Buildings. His arrival at her house was marked by his wacky sense of humour. Years later she wrote and asked him if he remembered 'the ragged raincoat you wore when you came to see me? And tried to fox me into thinking you a poor old beggar man.'

He worked in the Empire Hotel, which had been requisitioned by the government on the outbreak of war. Surprisingly, given his hatred of bad architecture, he does not seem to have passed any comment on it at the time. His only recorded comment on the building was in 1972, when he described its architect – Major Davis – as a 'monster'. But he had plenty to say about his job and his fears for the future. A few weeks after arriving in Bath, he wrote to Nancy Mitford:

> Darling Nancy,
> I must say I like being here. Extreme Protestant household, lace curtains, regular hours, rain over elms and chestnuts, crumbling Bath stone, wallflowers and lilac and a feeling that one is on the edge of the West Country. My work is so wonderfully boring that I am fascinated (temporarily) by it.

And then he added what, on the face of it, seems a totally uncharacteristic comment:

> One form of state control is as bad as another.

His mood soon darkened, however, and his conviction that he was working for what he termed a 'slave state' deepened into an obsession. In mid-September, he told Geoffrey Taylor that he had never been more miserable in his life and had not written a line of poetry for four months, before declaring that we are in a slave state here and I am beginning to think I would as soon be in prison or dead. Everything one loves threatened by post-war plansters of different types ... No redress, just arrogant destruction by keen young careerists left and right.

One of Betjeman's assistants at the Admiralty was Dawn Macleod. Years later, she recalled that

> in 1944, with the war all but won ... most of us felt cautiously cheerful [but] poor JB so hated being confined to an office that he drooped and wilted day by day, appearing to be on the brink of suicide or at best an early Victorian decline.

> His curious complexion reminded me of some chameleons with whom I once cohabited in the east. It kept changing its hue, not to match the background but apparently influenced by some inner alchemy of thought and emotion ... In his most miserable moods he displayed a countenance of ghastly peasoup green, truly alarming until you got used to it.

She regularly joined Richard Hughes and John Betjeman on lunchtime walks round the city, and described the effect that Bath's buildings had on him:

> His sagging cheeks puffed out, pink and soft. His wet-spaniel eyes developed glamorous sparkle. Without delay he launched upon a sea of inspired documentary, so that we lost our bearings and all track of time ... We must have made an odd assortment of characters even for an ancient city accustomed to freaks, from Bladud to Beau Nash and Beckford. Richard Hughes, in harmony with erect posture and stately, unmodern pace, was invariably well barbered and tailored, while roly-poly John Betjeman looked as if he slept in his clothes – and somebody else's garments grabbed after a shipwreck at that.

She recalled one incident in particular:

> We had compiled some long and boring paper about some plant extension at a shipyard. In it, a reference to 'a bed of retorts' was seized upon by [Betjeman] with infantile glee. Opening the docket out flat, he used the inside of its smooth cover to draw a picture of the Great Bed of Ware, at the Victoria & Albert Museum in London. The illustration, perfect in every detail, showed the entire Retort family tucked up beneath a quilt, heads of all sizes in a row on the bolster. Having put his signature to the report and dropped it into the messenger's bag for Whitehall, the artist leaned back with a happy smile.

> This euphoria did not last. He was utterly downcast next day, when the docket came back with a curt note attached: 'Please instruct your staff to refrain from scribbling on dockets.' It was that cruel word 'scribbling' which caused such pain. *Scribbling*. He read the insult aloud in a hoarse voice. His face, already green, turned eerily blue, the sort of leached colour seen during an eclipse of the sun.

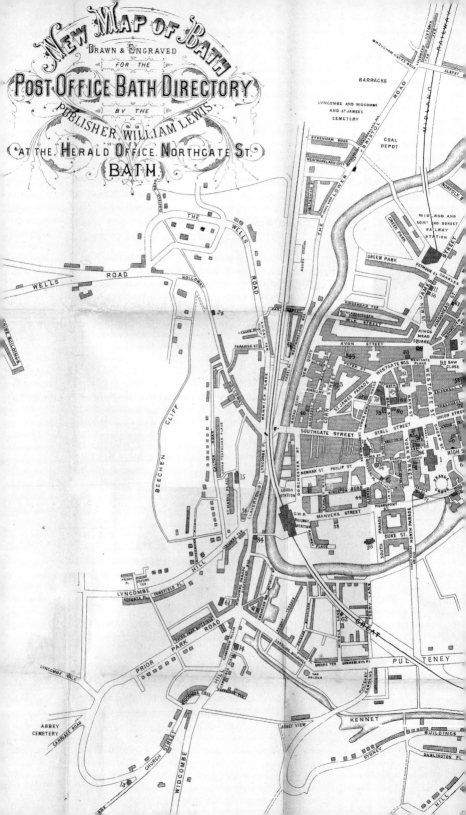

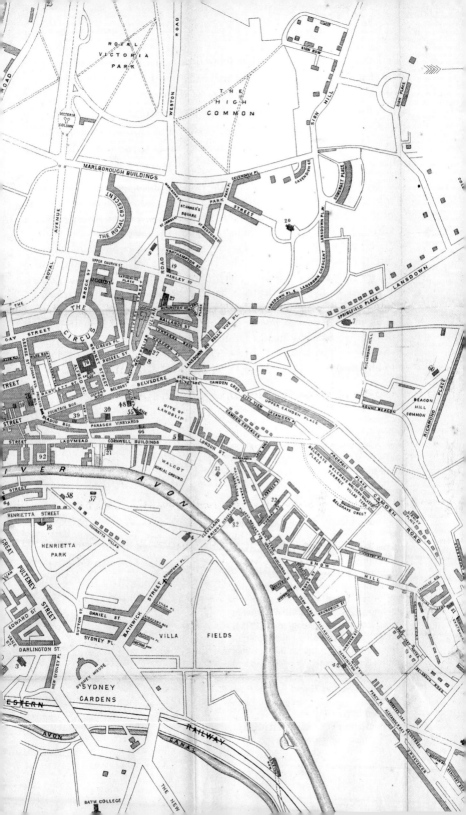

Betjeman spent much of what spare time he had in Bath cycling off on architectural excursions with Bryan Little, another Admiralty slave, who published a book called *The Building of Bath* in 1947. He also kept up some of his newspaper work and wrote a review of a book called *Bath* by RAL Smith, which he described as 'scissors and paste journalism'. In the review, he summed up his view of the city and expressed his fears for the future:

> There are far too many pictures of the Abbey, while many of the loveliest things still to be seen in Bath are sadly neglected. There are no views of the subtle sweep of the Paragon, the seductive S-shape of Lansdown Crescent where it curves to Somerset Place, the pillared gloom of Bath Street, the noble vista down Pulteney Street, intimate blocks in Alfred Street, North Parade, Cavendish Place, the fine extent of Kensington. There are no pictures of the excellent, if modern late Georgian and early Victorian building which make Bath so beautiful and which deserve recognition by the camera – Sydney Place, Daniel Street, Norfolk and Widcombe Crescents, houses on Bathwick Hill, and the numbers of delicate terraces and squares and bridges which will all too probably be swept away by rapacious plansters. A book such as this might have helped to save them.

Right: One of the buildings targeted by post-war plansters was this superb eighteenth-century house in St James Street South. It survived a near miss in April 1942 when a bomb fell 30 metres away, only to be demolished less than 20 years later. The dark alleyway beside Marks & Spencer marks the approximate course of St James Street South.

Previous page: We do not know which maps Betjeman used to explore Bath on his early visits to the city, but, given his antiquarian leanings, he would doubtless have been fascinated by this map from an 1890s postal directory. The area east of Bathwick Street is still shown as 'Villa Fields', while what would later become Hedgemead Park is shown as 'site of landslip' – more on that on page 310. Even better, Bath's 'other' station is still served by the Midland and Somerset & Dorset Railways. Note also that the projected 'Grand Parade' from Pierrepont to Bridge Streets has been sketched in by hand. This extract from the map covers the area described in the accompanying walk.

LITERARY WALKS IN BATH

Then he went on to sketch out his vision of the post-war world:

So many keen young careerists are manoeuvring for good executive positions in post-war planning: terrifying blocks of gleaming hygiene in glass and steel are visualised for the great new insect state of their dreams: civic centres, airports, community kitchens, community this and that, community crèches for the few eccentrics who would sooner have a child than a private aeroplane: so much of this kind of thing is in the air that one turns gratefully to any book, even this, on the largest stone memorial of England's eighteenth century, the City of Bath, a city far less blitzed than its exquisite and even more interesting, though not so obvious neighbour, Bristol.

At the end of November, after a mere eight months in Bath, Betjeman managed to get a transfer to the British Council in Oxford. This was not the first time he had been to Bath, however. He first came in the 1930s, when he described it as arguably 'the most beautiful town in the world – with its crescents, squares, pump room and retired colonels pulled about in Bath-chairs'. In 1939, when he presented a radio programme about Bath with Alderman Alfred Wills and the architect and architectural historian, Mowbray Green, he recalled his first visit to the city:

I shan't forget the first time I saw the Royal Crescent stretching out along the hill and watched from Lansdown Crescent the lights twinkling out in the evening light among the terraces and avenues of this grey stone eighteenth-century spa. Bath might easily have been spoiled, as they are spoiling Cheltenham and Leamington and Brighton and other Georgian spas. Thanks to local effort backed by the outside world, thanks to a far-sighted council and interested private citizens with public spirit such as Mr Mowbray Green and Mr Wills who are here tonight, Bath has remained the handsome planned town it was in the eighteenth century.

He also declared Bath to be a 'model town', showing 'how a town can keep its beauty and still keep up to date if only it has enlightened citizens and, what is more important still, a sympathetic council'. In a poem called 'The Newest Bath Guide', written 34 years later for Adam Fergusson's *The Sack of Bath*, however, he struck a rather different note:

> Goodbye to old Bath. We who loved you are sorry
> They've carted you off by developer's lorry.

On our walk around Betjeman's Bath, we will see how and why he moved from the guarded optimism of 1939 to the desolation of that 1973 poem. Along the way, we will be recalling two short television films he made about Bath in 1962 and 1964. The first was a celebration of the city, set to the music of Handel, the second an architectural survey in which he held a conversation with an imaginary developer who planned to demolish George-ee-an Bath. Fifty years on, both films have been reissued on DVD, giving us an opportunity not only to see what has changed in the interim, but also to review Betjeman's legacy and the future of the architectural heritage he defended so passionately.[1]

Our walk around Betjeman's Bath is a long one, and includes several busy road crossings, a good deal of climbing and numerous flights of steps. As well as seeking out some of those out-of-the-way delights he was so fond of, and the grand architectural set pieces he so admired, we will also see a fair number of those horrors that blighted the city in the post-war years, as well as some more recent ones.

We start outside the entrance to the Empire Hotel, where Betjeman worked for the 'slave state'. As you will see, this is now the entrance to Garfunkel's, an appropriate name for a restaurant with a view of a bridge over troubled water (or Pulteney Weir as it is commonly known). If you look ahead, over Parade Gardens, and to the left of the buildings on North Parade, you will see, in the distance, a row of houses climbing steeply uphill. This is Macaulay Buildings, where Betjeman was billeted in 1944.

If you look over to the Abbey, you will see a small doorway on the right-hand side of the east front. This leads to the tower, and it is through this doorway that Betjeman went, on Thursday evenings in 1944, to carry out firewatching duties on the Abbey roof, even though there was by then little threat of aerial bombardment.[2] One night, he took the daughter of a friend up the tower with him, where, she later recalled, 'he pressed the wrong button and the clock chimed one more stroke than it should have.' This was 'pale Pre-Raphaelite' Mary Shand – 15 years old – whom Betjeman seems to have had a Platonic crush on. 'Her every step on the wet Bath pavement,' he wrote in an unpublished poem, 'bound me more in a sweet enslavement.'

Betjeman's 1962 film featured several shots of old ladies – and a few old men – sitting on the seats around the Orange Grove and enjoying the sun. Bath 50 years ago was, as many people will recall, very much a city of old ladies, as it had been since the mid-nineteenth century. It is extraordinary how it has changed since then. Now, as much as anything else, Bath is a city of students, with over 21,500 studying full-time at its two universities – over a quarter of the city's resident population of 83,992.

Head towards the obelisk in the middle of Orange Grove, bearing to the left of the grass and crossing to the traffic island on the left. Bear right, crossing at the lights and continuing south along Terrace Walk to the Huntsman pub. The fountain you can see on the traffic island stood

---

1 The films can be found on two DVDs: *Betjeman Revisited* and *The Lost Betjemans*, produced by Green Umbrella.

2 You can follow his footsteps by joining one of the Tower Tours which run daily (except on Sundays) throughout the year.

LITERARY WALKS IN BATH

outside the Pump Room in Stall Street in Betjeman's day. It was moved here in 1989. In his 1939 radio broadcast, Betjeman, while praising much of what had been done in Bath in the twentieth century, condemned the demolition of the Literary & Scientific Institution, which once stood here. It was built on the site of the old assembly rooms, which had burnt down over a century earlier, and incorporated a Greek Revival façade by William Wilkins, the architect of the National Gallery.

The Institution on Terrace Walk, demolished in 1933

Turn right by the Huntsman pub into North Parade Passage (originally known as Lilliput Alley). Betjeman's most famous Bath poem, *In a Bath Tea Shop*, which immortalises a brief encounter between a 'very ordinary little woman' and 'a thumping crook', is sometimes taken to refer to an affair he had in 1944 with Alice Jennings, a engineer with the BBC in Bristol, whom he met while making a programme with Geoffrey Grigson. Alice certainly thought so; 'you may be a thumping crook,' she wrote to him after it was published, 'but I'm not an ordinary little woman.' He claimed, however, that he was thinking of another couple they had spotted during one of their afternoon trysts. Although the exact location of the teashop is unknown, it certainly was not Sally Lunn's, which did not open – as a coffee house – until the mid-1960s. Sally Lunn – or Spring Garden – rolls were made here in the eighteenth century, but by the early 1930s the building was derelict and redevelopment seemed inevitable. In 1937, however, it was taken over by an artist called Marie Byng-Johnson who established a studio in it and set about reviving its fortunes. The Sally Lunn legend – suitably embellished – was the focus for the building's regeneration, but it was only after Marie Byng-Johnson left that it was converted to the iconic teashop you see today. A clip which appears at the start of the *Betjeman Revisited* DVD shows him stopping outside it to consult a guide book. Marie Byng-Johnson's prints and paintings can be seen in the window, and it looks much as it does in the photograph on page 83.

Turn left opposite Sally Lunn's along North Parade Buildings, which were originally called Gallaway's Buildings after the man who had them built. You can still see the old name on the wall halfway along on the left. **Turn right halfway along Gallaway's Buildings**, down an alleyway along which, in the 1964 film, a man was seen wheeling a barrowload of sacks, **into Abbey Green.** There were many hidden corners like this when Betjeman first visited Bath, but most are long gone. This one would probably have gone as well, had the developers had their way.

In Abbey Green, turn right up Church Street and head to the left of the Abbey into Abbey Church Yard. In Betjeman's 1962 film, the Abbey, newly cleaned, shines like a golden jewel in the smoke-blackened city, while the Pump Room, by contrast, looks grimy and forbidding. Betjeman did not think much of the services in the Abbey when he was here in 1944. 'Bath Abbey is very low and lazy,' he wrote to Cyril Connolly. 'They had a "religion and life" week in Bath lately – one of those absurd low church and non-conformist get-togethers, where everybody sacrifices a bit of what they believe for the sake of "unity" and the resultant faith amounts to nothing or the Lowest Common Denominator of all those present.'

Walk through the colonnade into Stall Street, turning left and then right along Bath Street. In 1944, Betjeman wrote of 'the pillared gloom of Bath Street', and you can see what he meant from the shots of it in the 1962 film. He would certainly approve of its present appearance, although what he would make of the new Spa, behind to it to the left, is less clear. He would not have approved, however, of the act of civic vandalism inflicted on the building at the end which now forms the entrance to the Spa – the ripping out of a Grade I-listed shopfront and its replacement by plate glass, so that the upper floors look unsupported.[1] In 1996, when work started on the Spa, it was going to cost £13M and open in time for the millennium; it eventually opened in 2006 and cost £45M.

Right: The Georgian shop front at the west end of Bath Street, now replaced by plate glass

Below: 'The pillared gloom of Bath Street' in the mid-twentieth century

---

1 Fortunately the shopfront was saved and can be seen in the Building of Bath Collection.

Turn right by the Cross Bath, walk up to Westgate Street and turn left by the Grapes pub which occupies the left-hand side of one of the most interesting yet neglected buildings in the city, with a superb seventeenth-century plasterwork ceiling – long hidden from public view – on the first floor. It was very nearly demolished in the 1930s for road widening – a similar house a little further along did suffer this fate – but it was saved when it was decided to make this Bath's first one-way street.

Cross the road at the end of Westgate Street and carry straight on into Kingsmead Square. This was built, probably by a Bristol architect called John Strahan, around the same time as Queen Square. The range of buildings on the south side was scheduled for demolition in the 1960s, but after a long campaign was saved and restored in 1975. Today, it is not only an important part of Bath's heritage, contributing inestimably to the character of this corner of the city, but a very attractive piece of real estate. Had it been replaced, you would now be looking at a tatty, nondescript piece of urban blight, ripe for another round of uninspired redevelopment.

Rosewell House, on the west side of the square, with its wonderful carvings, stands on the corner of what was once one of the busiest streets in the city. Kingsmead Street, laid out at the same time as Kingsmead Square, survived for 200 years before being largely flattened by the Luftwaffe in 1942. When Betjeman returned to Bath in the early 1960s, it was being redeveloped, and today you can only **walk a little way along it before a flight of steps leads down to a car park**, with the flats that Betjeman's imaginary developer so much admired on the right. He particularly liked their balconies, where housewives could put 'a kiddy's pram' – for this, he declared, was 'the age of the housewife', where every amenity had to be provided, and these flats showed 'how people ought to be

Kingsmead Street after the raids of April 1942

housed'. The shot of them in the 1964 film was taken from the west end of Kingsmead Street, with the flats looking across waste ground to the ruins of the houses on the south side – a view which today is blocked by more flats.

Betjeman's developer wanted to pull down all of George-ee-an Bath, and as you **turn left through the car park to James Street West, cross the zebra crossing, turn right and walk along to the traffic lights at the end**, he would surely have been pleased at this urban panorama, a post-war planner's vision of paradise. If you look ahead at the crossroads,

Above; Looking north across Kingsmead Street to Monmouth Street after the area had been cleared

Below: The same view today

however, you can see something Betjeman wholeheartedly approved of – Green Park station, opened by the Midland Railway in 1870 as a mini-St Pancras, and one of the finest surviving Victorian stations in the country. A clip at the end of the *Betjeman Revisited* DVD shows him heading towards

the station, where we will follow him **across the road, up the steps and through the old parcels office** (the Green Park Brasserie occupies the old booking hall) to admire its superb single-span roof – and the cars now parked beneath it. Once you could travel from here not just north-west to Bristol and, by catching the Pines Express, north to Birmingham and Manchester, but also south to Evercreech Junction and Bournemouth over the Somerset & Dorset Railway. In one of his most engaging films, made in the summer of 1962, Betjeman took a journey along the Somerset & Dorset from Evercreech Junction to Highbridge, and appealed to Dr Beeching to spare it. His plea was in vain, and the Highbridge branch closed, along with the rest of the Somerset & Dorset and Bath's Green Park station, in 1966.

Carry on through the station, past the supermarket that stands where trains once ran, and, just before you reach the bridge that carried the trains across the river – and now carries cars – turn left down a flight of steps. Turn left alongside the river and, after passing under a road bridge, you will see Green Park Buildings West on your left. Green Park Buildings East, where Jane Austen once lived, stood on the other side of the park and was burnt out by incendiary bombs in April 1942.

Carry on along the riverside path as it drops down to the river. The splendid nineteenth-century industrial buildings on the opposite bank have all been converted to offices and apartments. **Carry on as the path rises to meet the road.** Before crossing at the pedestrian lights, look ahead to the CD-drum-like tower of the new bus station. It stands on the site of Churchill House, built in the 1930s for the electricity board. Its proposed demolition sparked one of the most concerted conservation campaigns ever seen in Bath, with mass rallies, marches and demonstrations – all to no avail. It was demolished in May 2007.

 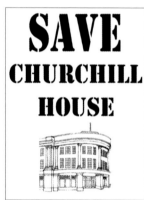

Some clever people with forward-looking ideas – executives and the like – regarded those who wanted to save Churchill House as kneejerk conservationists who want to keep everything just because it is old. Many people thought that of Betjeman as well – the architect Eric Lyons, for example, who, according to Bernard Levin,

> coined the phrase 'Betjemanic depressives' to stigmatise collectively those who would preserve at all costs everything from the past, be it a wrought iron lamp post due for replacement in Chelsea, a Victorian church in Essex complete with its 'blue jowled and bloody' stained glass, or the celebrated Doric portico at Euston station.

But, while the architectural establishment ridiculed Betjeman as a camp joke, millions of TV viewers realised that he was putting into words what they had thought all along. They liked old buildings and saw that much rebuilding was being carried out not because it was necessary but because it would, in Betjeman's words, 'make some unscrupulous town planner or borough engineer or councillor a quick and dishonest buck'.

The Euston arch was Betjeman's most celebrated failure. In the 1950s, when its destruction seemed inconceivable, he wrote that, 'as an essay of the Greek Revival, I consider the arch ... the noblest thing in

London, nobler even than St Pancras church or the British Museum or the Hyde Park screen.' But, despite that, he lived to see it demolished, after a bitter campaign, at the behest of the then prime minister, Harold Macmillan. So intent were the developers on ridding themselves of this relic of a loathsome past, that, when the contractor charged with its demolition wanted to rebuild it elsewhere, he was forbidden to do so. Its destruction was less a matter of expediency than one of machismo.

Similarly, Churchill House had to go not so much because it was in the way, but because the people who wanted it to go had a vision of the future which did not include old buildings, especially old buildings held in affection by a large number of people. The tragic thing is that, by and large, the people committed to clearing old buildings away seem hell bent on replacing them with new ones whose ugliness is exceeded only by their mediocrity. Just to show they have the power to do it, perhaps.

When Betjeman first came to Bath, the area where you are standing was, as it had been for over two centuries, Bath's quayside. The car park across the road stands on the site of streets once lined with terraced houses, tenements, beerhouses and workshops. Among them was Bowler's Works, where mineral water was bottled and where Jonathan Burdett Bowler – brass founder, gas fitter, locksmith, bell hanger and general engineer – established, in Queen Victoria's reign, a business that hardly changed until the day it closed – with the bulldozers poised to move in – in 1969. This extraordinary time capsule would now be no more than a fading memory, had not a group of local people, led by the designer Russell Frears, joined together to save and move it – lock, stock and barrel – to an eighteenth-century tennis court near the Assembly Rooms, where it now forms the nucleus of the Museum of Bath at Work.

Cross the road at the pedestrian lights and head north, away from the river, with the car park on your left. At the end, cross the pedestrian crossing on your left, turn right, walk along to St James's Parade and turn left. As you approach the end of St James's Parade, you will see, on your left, where eighteenth-century houses once stood, the bright new buildings of the City of Bath College. Although they are only a couple of years old, the buildings beyond them were here when Betjeman came in the 1960s, and, as the road curves to the left, you can see ahead of you one that he particularly disliked. His imaginary developer, however, was fulsome in its praise, describing it as

> the vital buttocks of the building. As you can see it expresses its purpose – whatever that may be – sincerely, and this causes it to blend harmoniously and naturally with the George-ee-an.

The George-ee-an building he was referring to was the Hobgoblin pub, to your right – then called the Talbot and owned by Simonds brewery. It stands on the site where John Butler was hanged for his part in the Gordon Riots in 1780. Beyond the buttocks, though, is one of the newest buildings in Bath, a black wedge that forms the new entrance to the college. Whatever you think about the 'buttocks', they were at least built of Bath stone, as decreed by the City of Bath Act of 1925, a requirement which now seems to have been waived – for public buildings at least – in the city.

Left: 'The vital buttocks of the building'

Right: The shell of St James's church in 1956, shortly before it was demolished to build a Woolworth's – now a branch of Marks & Spencer

Cross the zebra crossing to the Hobgoblin and head to the left of it along Lower Borough Walls. As you near the end of the street, you are confronted by modernity in its most dispiriting form. The area in front of you has been redeveloped not once but twice since Betjeman was here. In the 1970s, Southgate Street and the streets to the east, containing an assortment of nineteenth-century and earlier buildings, were cleared to make way for a shopping centre designed by Owen Luder. Thirty years on, Luder's vision of the future was bulldozed to make way for what you see today. The pedestrian thoroughfare leading into it is named after St Lawrence, a third-century martyr who was burnt to death on a gridiron, in recognition of which he is the patron saint of chefs. St Lawrence also gave his name to the medieval bridge at the bottom of Southgate Street, demolished in 1964.

Carry on along New Orchard Street past Marks & Spencer, built where a church dedicated not to St Michael but to St James once stood, before it was bombed and its ruins subsequently cleared away in 1957. Behind it stood streets of early-eighteenth-century houses – such as that shown on page 290 – which survived the bombing but not the developers.

Carry on along Henry Street to Manvers Street, turn right, cross at the pedestrian lights, turn right and walk along to the police station. If

you look back up the street from here you will see South Parade. This view featured in Betjeman's 1964 film, with a lament for the forum John Wood wanted to build here. A photograph from the early twentieth century shows that the area was once covered by orchards and market gardens. By 1964, however, it was a building site with a car park beyond. The police station was built soon afterwards. This too has a literary connection, for it is here that Peter Diamond, Peter Lovesey's fictional detective, is head of CID.

Carry on along Manvers Street to Bayntun's Bookshop, noted for fine bindings and rare books, and also for a clip included on both the Betjeman DVDs, showing him, on his way up from the station, stopping to browse through the books on display outside. In the background, where the monolithic beigeness of Debenhams now blots out the sun, an old Royal Blue coach can be seen parked in the bus station.

Carry on to the railway station, designed by Brunel in 1840 and one of the oldest stations in the country. It was also one of the least changed – until 2012, when, despite a protracted campaign to save it, the ramp to the London-bound platform was demolished so that the arches under the viaduct could be converted to cafés. The only access to the platform is now by a narrow flight of winding wooden stairs or a small lift.

Go through the tunnel to the left of the station and carry on across the footbridge over the river. A dual carriageway now runs along the far bank, but 50 years ago it was lined with houses. Betjeman included a view of them in his 1962 film to give an idea of the Bath John Wood found when he arrived here in the early eighteenth century.

Turn left and walk along the road until you come to a canal lock on your left. This too featured in the 1962 film, with a view up the flight where now a modern bridge stands. At that time the canal was derelict, its rotting gates wedged part way open, with weed on the surface of the water. Betjeman had already saluted 'that splendid man Ted Leather', MP for North Somerset, who had cut the chain which the British Transport

Above, Widcombe from the footbridge; below, the Widcombe flight on the Kennet & Avon Canal – two views transformed almost beyond recognition by the new road punched through Widcombe in the 1970s.

Corporation had placed on the bottom gates to close the canal illegally. Had it not been for the determined efforts of numerous campaigners – including John Betjeman – the canal's dereliction would have become permanent and the road driven through here in the 1970s would probably have obliterated all trace of it. As it was, the old bridge at the top of the flight was demolished and the top two locks replaced by one deep lock to make way for the new road.

Carry on along the canal towpath. After going under the new road bridge, take the path leading up to the right, turn right along the road and follow it round to the pedestrian lights. Cross over, turn left and then right up Prior Park Road. The row of cottages on the right was built by Ralph Allen in the 1730s for his stonemasons, when this road was a quarry tramway. They are among the earliest surviving examples of industrial housing in the country. Beyond them, set back behind gardens and a stream, are Prior Park Buildings, designed by John Pinch in the early nineteenth century. As you pass the bottom of Forefield Rise, you can see, across the road, five pairs of early-nineteenth-century semi-detached villas singled out for especial praise by Betjeman in his 1964 film. Prior Park Buildings was one of the last grand terraces built in Bath, for by this time, as Betjeman pointed out, people were becoming tired of living in terraces or crescents. They wanted a little more privacy – and these semi-detached villas pointed the way forward.

Cross the road and go up Widcombe Rise (to the left of the villas), turn right at the top and follow the road as it swings left uphill. This leads to two little-known gems – Widcombe Terrace on the right, looking out across a view more Tuscan than English, and, on the left, Widcombe Crescent, whose omission from RAL Smith's book on Bath Betjeman was so critical of.

Climb the steps straight ahead, turn left, cross Widcombe Hill and head along the Tyning.[1] Carry on as the road starts to head downhill, before crossing over and turning right down a footpath beside the green. Turn right along the road at the bottom – known as Horseshoe Walk, for reasons that will become obvious when it starts to double back on itself. Eventually, you reach Sydney Buildings, and more early-nineteenth-century buildings. Betjeman thought these splendid, but criticised the replacement of the original glazing bars in No 50, which made the building look 'blind and bombed'. Today, however, the owner of a listed building wishing to

---

1 The Betjeman aficionado may wish, at this point, to make a detour up Widcombe Hill to visit Macaulay Buildings, where he was billeted in 1944. Be warned, though, that, although the view of the city is superb, Macaulay Buildings is over half a mile away and the hill is very steep.

restore its glazing bars is up against English Heritage and the planning department, who have decided that such changes constitute part of the 'continuing history of the building' and are thus sacrosanct.

From here, Betjeman looked back the way you have just come, at the mid-twentieth-century detached houses further along, and declared that they represented 'a falling off' – a view the imaginary developer naturally did not share. Half a century on, it is hard to see why Betjeman so disliked these rather desirable properties in one of the most enviable locations in Bath.

Carry on along Sydney Buildings, turn left down a flight of steps beside No 30, cross the canal and turn right along the towpath. After passing the lock, turn left down a flight of steps and carry on down to Pulteney Road. Turn left under the railway bridge, cross at the lights and carry on along North Parade Road. It was a little way along here that one of the most evocative sequences in Betjeman's 1962 film was shot – of a steam-hauled express, with the sun behind it, heading east across Pulteney Road over a bridge built by Brunel in 1841. Sadly, the bridge, like steam-hauled trains to London, is no more. It was blown up one Sunday morning in 1975 and replaced by the present bridge to make it easier for lorries to drive along Pulteney Road.

Cross North Parade Road and walk down to the Pavilion. When Betjeman visited Bath in November 1954,

> the Avon had overflowed its banks [and] that unworthy little building down in the wooded meadows, which is used for concerts, now that no one can bring themselves to reconstruct the Assembly Rooms, was well under water. A bill outside announced Moiseiwitsch, and I imagined the grand piano floating about over the soaked parquet and bumping into the trivial decoration of this outsize army hut.

General View from Bath Abbey Tower.

The Pavilion – built as an ice-skating rink in 1910 – has not changed very much since Betjeman's day, although flooding is not the problem it once was. It is overshadowed, however, by a far more obtrusive

Princess Margaret at the Pavilion in May 1948 as patron of the first Bath International Music Festival

building – a sports centre opened in 1975. Amazingly, given the praise heaped on other ugly buildings at the time by official bodies, the Royal Fine Art Commission described it as 'heavy and monolithic' and the choice of site 'most unfortunate'. It was built in defiance of covenants governing the site and has now been deemed an illegal building.

Walk past the sports centre and turn right alongside the river bank, which has changed dramatically since it appeared in Betjeman's 1962 film. The river was narrower and the bank on this side extended much farther out, with a broad strip of grass to the left of the path. If you look back at the railway bridge, you will see that the footpath through the archway on the

left is cantilevered out over the river. There was no need for cantilevering in 1962. Even more dramatic are the changes further along. The 1962 film showed men and boys fishing from the old weir that stretched diagonally across the river. Fishing from the new weir – a much more risky proposition – is banned. The new

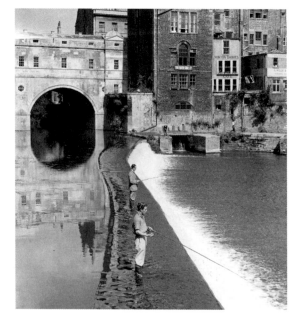

weir may be less picturesque – although it surely makes up for it in sheer drama – but its reprofiling, along with the widening of the river and the demolition of the old bridge at the bottom of Southgate Street, has made the floods that plagued the lower part of the city a thing of the past.

Carry on along the river bank and walk up the steps beside Pulteney Bridge. To your right is 'the noble vista down Pulteney Street' that Betjeman so much admired – although the Laura Place fountain featured in the 1962 film has unfortunately been replaced by one rather less picturesque – apparently because, whenever the wind got up, the old one sprayed water over the ladies of Bathwick as they passed by.

Turn left across Pulteney Bridge, carry on up Bridge Street and turn left along the High Street to the Guildhall. The Guildhall Banqueting Room, which featured in Betjeman's 1962 film, is still as splendid, although the carpet that covered much of the floor has gone.

Cross at the pedestrian lights and walk through the Corridor, which in 1962 had a uniformed commissionaire, who appears in the film. **Turn right along Union Passage, go up the steps to Upper Borough Walls and turn left.** Old Bond Street, which you pass on the right, featured in the 1962 film, with a lady looking into the window of what was then Mallory's antique shop.

After passing the last surviving section of the old city walls, turn right along Trim Bridge. No 2, on the corner of Trim Street – which was William Smith's showroom when Jane Austen lived (unwillingly) along here, was occupied by RJ Bossi, clockmaker, when Betjeman made his 1962 film. If you look to the left, you will see, on the north side of the street, more civic vandalism – a bland and depressing office block, to make way for which a row of early Georgian buildings – including the one on page 284 – was swept needlessly away.

Go under the archway and walk along Queen Street to the Raven pub. At the start of his 1964 film, Betjeman was seen standing beside a portrait of John Wood 'in a public house on the corner of Queen Street'.

Known as Hatchett's in 1964, today it has been renamed the Raven; the picture is now at Berkley House near Frome.

Carry on up John Street, turn left into Old King Street and walk along to the corner of Queen Square. Ahead of you is the north side of the square, which, Betjeman declared in his 1964 film, 'looks like a huge country house but when you come to look closely you see a whole row of front doors along the ground-floor storey. Queen Square, Bath must be the first terrace in the world that looked like a single house.'

Don't cross over, but turn right up Gay Street and right into George Street. After crossing the top of Milsom Street, cross at the pedestrian lights, carry on up Bartlett Street and turn left along Alfred Street to the front of the Assembly Rooms. When Betjeman made his 1939 radio broadcast, the Assembly Rooms had just been reopened after a painstaking restoration financed by Ernest Cook, heir to the Thomas Cook travel company. Three years later, the rooms were gutted in the Bath Blitz, and, in the immediate post-war years, their future was far from certain, with many calling for them to be demolished and replaced by flats or a concert hall. It was eventually decided to restore them and they reopened in 1963. The film Betjeman made the following year featured an interview with Oliver Messel, a leading theatre designer, who had been involved in the restoration. It also included a tour of the building and a visit to the Museum of Costume which had been established in the basement. Now renamed the Fashion Museum, it is still there, and it is instructive, comparing today's displays with those in the film, to see how far gallery design has come in the last half century.

Walk to Bennet Street, turn left and walk along to the Circus, designed, according to Betjeman in his 1964 film, so that 'the invalids who came to Bath would be able to watch performing animals'. One trusts that he had his tongue firmly in his cheek, but with Betjeman it is not always easy to tell. The Circus also featured in his 1962 film, at a time when cleaning the city's soot-blackened stone was only just getting under way. Some of the buildings in the Circus had been cleaned, others had not, and the contrast between them was startling. You will notice that all the windows in the Circus have their glazing bars – one of the few places in Bath where this unanimity has been achieved, and it looks splendid. In 1962, though, many of the windows still had plate glass in them.

Cross the Circus and head along Brock Street to the Royal Crescent, built, as Betjeman said, 'high up on a sunny slope above the stuffy hollow of the city'. It isn't quite as John the Wood the Younger built it, for the first-floor windows have been lengthened, disrupting its proportions. The windows of No 1, however, owned by the Bath Preservation Trust and now housing a museum, which were still lengthened like the rest when Betjeman came in 1964, have since been restored to their original dimensions. You will notice also that, unlike the Circus, several of the houses still have plate glass in their windows. Betjeman's imaginary developer was particularly critical of the Royal Crescent, comparing it unfavourably with the new flats at Snow Hill – which prompted Betjeman to describe him as 'stupid and also malevolent'.

Walk to the end of the Royal Crescent, cross the road and turn left down Marlborough Buildings. Just past the last house turn right up a narrow lane. At the end, turn right and walk up the road, with the back of Marlborough Buildings on your right and the park on your left. Go through the gateway at the top, cross the zebra crossing and take the path heading diagonally to the right across High Common. When you reach Cavendish Road, cross over and walk uphill past Cavendish Place towards the high crescents that Betjeman so much admired. First though comes Cavendish Lodge, which Betjeman did not live to see, by one of Prince Charles's favourite architects, William Bertram – executive apartments in Bath stone, with *faux* dry-stone walling and Quality Street bows. Above

it is Cavendish Crescent, designed, like Cavendish Place, by John Pinch, who many hold to be an even greater architect than the Woods, father and son. It was the last of the great crescents to be built – in Bath that is, for, as Betjeman pointed out, this was a style that was – and still is – imitated all over the world.

At the crossroads above Cavendish Crescent, head up the steps to the right of Somerset House. At the top is Somerset Place, a crescent in all but name, designed by John Eveleigh, never

Somerset Place in the 1950s, before the three houses destroyed by bombing at the west end were rebuilt

completed, partly destroyed by bombing, rebuilt, converted to student accommodation, and now, after several years standing empty, being converted to luxury homes.

Walk along Somerset Place and carry on up Lansdown Place West to Lansdown Crescent. 'These crescents, high above Bath,' said Betjeman in his 1964 film, 'were among the last to be built. I like them best of all. They depend on proportion [and] ironwork instead of carved stone.' Betjeman, like many others, ascribed Lansdown Crescent to John Palmer, although there is no evidence to support this; what evidence there is seems to suggest it was the work of a gentleman architect called John Lowder.

Walk along the crescent and carry on down Lansdown Place East. When you reach Lansdown Road, cross and turn right downhill. Turn left by the Lansdown Grove Hotel and follow the road uphill. At the T junction, with Heathfield ahead, turn right downhill, follow the road as it curves round to the left and go down a flight of steps on the right. Turn right and right again at the bottom into Camden Crescent and cross to the left-hand side of the road. Camden Crescent was built by John Eveleigh for the Earl of Camden, whose crest – an elephant's head – can be seen above its doorways. It is not elephants but pigs that have been brought in to clear the waste land below the crescent – a reminder that the curative powers of Bath's hot springs were discovered by Bladud's pigs. When Betjeman came here in 1964, however, he was more taken by the view westward to the green roofs of Snow Hill, then only a few years old, which prompted his imaginary developer to exclaim, 'that's how people ought to be housed'.

Carry on along Camden Crescent and, after making your way gingerly alongside a castellated wall – a bit of late-nineteenth-century whimsy – **double back on yourself down Upper Hedgemead Road and turn right down steps towards Gloster Villas. Carry on past the end of a cul-de-sac and turn right through a gateway into Hedgemead Park**, laid out in the late nineteenth century after the rows of terraced houses that once covered this hillside slid down it in a series of landslips. A photograph of them being demolished can be found on page 119. **Turn left and follow the path round to the right past a Victorian fountain topped by an eagle.** Carry on, with St Swithin's church on your left and a view of what Betjeman described as 'the subtle sweep of the Paragon' ahead. Up to your right, as you carry on, you will see a late Victorian medieval turret. To the left, across the road, is a building that Betjeman described in his 1939 radio broadcast as 'one of the most brilliant pieces of architecture in the town' – Walcot

Above: 'The subtle sweep of the Paragon' from Hedgemead Park – marked as 'site of landslip' on the map on pages 288-9

Below: Walcot Schools – 'one of the most brilliant pieces of architecture in the town' according to Betjeman – with the Star Inn on the right

Bottom: The Star Inn, hardly changed since the mid-nineteenth century, but only saved because of a spirited campaign in 1991

Schools, designed by James Wilson in 1840. This was long before Victorian architecture was fashionable, and it says a lot about the keenness of Betjeman's idiosyncratic vision that, in a city so full of iconic Georgian architecture, he was able to see the merits of this building, which most people still overlook today.

Below it, with its back door – if you are lucky – invitingly open, is the Star Inn, built in the 1760s but refitted by Gaskell & Chambers, bar-fitters and beer-engine manufacturers, at around the time Walcot Schools was being built next door, and hardly changed since. When Betjeman was filming in Bath in 1964 there were plenty of pubs like this still around, not just here but all over the country. After half a century of wholesale refurbishment, of gutting and re-gutting to chime with fleeting fads, there are only a

Left: The steps from the Paragon down to Walcot Street

Below: The drinking fountain and horse trough in Walcot Street as it looked in the 1960s. It was restored (although not connected to a water supply) in 2006.

Bottom: The tramshed – now converted to a bar with offices and apartments above

Right: The Hilton Hotel

handful left. Although the Star's qualities are now appreciated and its future secure, it too would have been transformed out of all recognition in 1991 if the landlord and regulars had not put up a spirited fight to save it.

Turn left, walk down to the gate out of the park, cross at the pedestrian crossing (after an optional diversion to the Star should you feel so inclined) **and turn right. Walk along to No 1 at the far end of the Paragon and take the steps leading down through the building to its right. At the bottom, cross Walcot Street and look back across the road.** Betjeman's 1964 film included a shot of the house to the right of the steps – where Jane Austen's aunt and uncle once lived – before panning down to the drinking fountain and horse trough in the street below, surrounded by hoardings advertising beer and cigarettes. The view today, with the fountain restored and the hoardings gone, is a definite improvement.

The same cannot be said, unfortunately, for **the south end of Walcot Street, which we walk along on our way back to the city centre.** Past Beehive Yard, from where electric trams rattled out to do battle with the hills of Bath, and the long-derelict Corn Exchange, now lies a car park where once were buildings, including the Pelican Inn. Beyond it is the Hilton Hotel, originally the Beaufort. The press release issued to mark its opening in 1972, which could have been penned by Betjeman's imaginary developer, boasted that the architect had

> caught the dignity, the style appropriate to Bath's rich tapestry of history, while at the same time infusing the clean lines of modern architectural practice. It is a combination that ... illustrates the company's policy of observing and respecting the need for harmony with the local background.

That may have fooled people into thinking they should like it at the time, but the spin soon wore thin. In 2003, the *Pevsner Architectural Guide to Bath* called it 'the most reviled building in Bath', a judgement Betjeman would certainly have agreed with.

Despite everything Betjeman achieved, for much of the time he was struggling, Canute-like, against the tide. His greatest achievement was giving people the confidence to trust their own feelings about buildings instead of being told by councillors, developers and 'experts' what they should like and what they shouldn't. But, as campaigners and preservationists have become more articulate and organised, so those ranged against them have grown ever smarter, ever more secretive, ever more skilled in the politics of spin.

If Betjeman were alive today, he would be carrying on his battle against those intent on destroying our heritage, but it is hard to resist feeling that he would find the battle harder, and the odds even more uneven, than in the 1960s.

We end with a poem inspired by Betjeman's 'Newest Bath Guide' and written in 2007 to mark the destruction of Churchill House.

The Very Latest Bath Guide

> *Official designs are aggressively neuter,*
> *The Puritan work of an eyeless computer.*
> *Goodbye to Old Bath! We who loved you are sorry.*
> *They're carting you off by developer's lorry.*
> John Betjeman, 1973

When Betjeman inscribed those powerful verses
In Fergusson's diatribe, which called down his curses
On heedless developers and needless destruction,
Their effect was far greater than solemn instruction.
And to everyone's pleasure, at last came the day
When the philistine tide had quite ebbed away.
A time for rejoicing – that's what we all thought.
The battle was won – the good fight was fought.

But remember John Betjeman's 'evil voice' in his ear
Of a London developer? Well, he's back – and he's here
With cheap Georgian pastiche and a giant dustbin,
Convenient to put flouted planning rules in.
Economics, not elegance – aluminium, not stone:
Bath's most famous attributes are left well alone.
  'I'm afraid they're old-fashioned – don't sit with our plan.'
  'Never mind,' says the council, 'Just do what you can.'

'Well, there is one building we were going to keep,
But let's knock it down while Bathonians sleep –
As for all of that ashlar, we're afraid that it must
Be smashed into pieces and ground into dust.
This tower, you'll find, brings modernity here.'
'Jolly good,' say the councillors 'What a spiffing idea!'
  And one of them cries 'Let's rebuild the whole town!
  Bring on the bulldozers! Knock old buildings down!'

Oh Betjeman, Betjeman, what would you say,
If you could but see our poor city today?

Kirsten Elliott 2007

DISTANCES & ACCESSIBILITY

1   The Lost Inns of Bath: 1.2 km (0.8 miles)
    One flight of steps with step-free alternative

2   The Bath Stage: 1.5 km (0.9 miles)
    Step-free

3   Tobias Smollett in Bath: 1.3 km (0.8 miles)
    Step-free

4   An Introduction to Philip Thicknesse: 2.1 km (1.3 miles); with
    optional 1.0 km (0.6 mile) extension
    Step-free

5   Fanny Burney in Bath: 5 km (3.1 miles)
    Two flights of steps with step-free alternatives

6   Rebels and Romantics: 1.5 km (0.9 miles)
    Step-free

7   'The Rhythm of Tom Paine's Bones': 1.6 km (1 mile)
    Step-free

8   Jane Austen's Bath: 9.0 km (5.6 miles); with optional extensions to:
    Beechen Cliff (4.8km/3 miles);
    Charlcombe (7 km/4.4 miles);
    Weston (7km/4.4 miles)
    *Main walk: Two flights of steps with step-free alternatives;
    the optional excursions include steps, rough paths and some stiles*

9   In the Footsteps of Charles Dickens: 3.0 km (1.9 miles)
    Step-free

10 Bath Through the Eyes of Georgette Heyer: 5.5 km (3.4 miles)
    Two flights of steps with step-free alternatives

11 Around Bath with John Betjeman: 10.5 km (6.5 miles)
    Several flights of steps

ACKNOWLEDGEMENTS & PICTURE CREDITS

Thanks must go first to James Runcie, Artistic Director of the Bath Literature Festival, and to the previous artistic directors, Nicola Bennett and Sarah LeFanu, who commissioned the guided walks on which most of the walks in this book are based. Thanks also to Zoë Steadman-Milne, Literature Festival Producer, for her support.

Thanks also to Mrs EJ Tollyfield for extracts from the transcript of John Betjeman's 1939 radio broadcast on Bath; to Martin Salter for donning his Regency costume for the Georgette Heyer walk and giving details of his research; to Jennifer Kloester for confirming that Paterson's Roads *was in Georgette Heyer's library; and to Peter Lovesey for writing the foreword.*

Thanks to Colin Johnston of Bath Record Office for permsision to reproduce the maps on pages xii, 10, 36, 81, 94, 98, 114, 150, 178 & 202. The maps on pages 17, 176-7, 220, 262-3 & 288-9 are from the Akeman Press Archive.

Thanks to the following for permission to reproduce photographs: Stuart Burroughs of the Museum of Bath at Work (pages 233 & 295); Paul De'Ath (pages 34 & 119); Colin Johnston of Bath Record Office (page 312 middle); Jim Warren of the Bath Blitz Memorial Project (page 181 (right); Bath Central Library (pages 5, 225 & 226). The photographs on pages 147, 301, 306 (bottom) & 309 are by Bruce Crofts.

The following illustrations and photographs are from the Akeman Press Archive: cover, 2, 3 (bottom), 4, 6, 7, 28, 40, 52, 56, 60, 61, 62, 64, 65, 66, 83, 85, 88, 89, 91, 92, 93, 102, 103, 105, 108, 111 (top), 112, 114 (top), 115, 118, 125, 139, 146, 148 (both), 154, 155, 158, 163, 164, 166 (top), 168 (right), 172, 178 (top), 181 (left), 182, 184, 186, 188, 192, 194, 195 (both), 198, 201, 202, 207, 211, 216, 217, 222 (both), 228, 229, 235, 239, 242, 244, 245 (bottom), 251, 254, 259, 264, 267, 268, 270-1, 272 (bottom), 274, 279, 281 (bottom), 284, 286, 290, 293, 294 (bottom), 296 (all), 298 (bottom), 299, 300, 302, 303 (bottom), 305, 306 (top), 307, 311 (all), 312 (top & bottom), 313, 314 (both), 315.

FURTHER READING

The starting point for any study of literature in Georgian Bath is *Life & Letters at Bath in the Eighteenth Century* by A Barbeau, first published in 1904 and republished in 2009 by The History Press. For an overview of the period, see *The Pleasures of the Imagination: English Culture in the Eighteenth Century* by John Brewer (London, 1997). A study of how Bath's development reflected changing aesthetic ideas can be found in *Genius of Place: The City and its Landscape* by Christopher Pound (Bath, 1986). An idea of the range of books published in Georgian Bath, can be found in *Georgian Imprints: Printing & Publishing at Bath, 1729-1815* by Trevor Fawcett (Bath, 2008).

The best introduction to the city and its history is *Bath* by Kirsten Elliott and Neil Menneer, published by Frances Lincoln in 2004 and described by Matthew Zuckerman in the *Bath Chronicle* as 'the definitive guide to our favourite city'. The standard work on the city's architecture is the *Pevsner Architectural Guide to Bath* by Michael Forsyth (Yale University Press, 2003). Social and economic histories of the city include: *Bath: A Social History, 1680-1850 or A Valley of Pleasure, yet a Sink of Iniquity* by RS Neale (London, 1981) and *A History of Bath: Image and Reality* by Graham Davis and Penny Bonsall (Lancaster, 2006).

For more on Bath's lost inns, see *The Lost Pubs of Bath* by Andrew Swift & Kirsten Elliott (Bath, 2005).

Books on the Georgian theatre in Bath include: *The Bath Stage: A History of Dramatic Representations in Bath* by Belville S Penley (London & Bath, 1892); *The Theatre Royal at Bath* by William Lowndes (Bristol, 1982); *Theatre Royal, Bath: The Orchard Street Calendar, 1750-1805*, edited by Arnold Hare (Bath, 1977); and *Bath's Old Orchard Street Theatre* by Malcolm Toogood (Frome, 2010). For an in-depth discussion of the idea of a polite society, see Mark Girouard's *The English Town* (London, 1990).

The most recent study of Smollett's life and work is *Tobias Smollett* by Jeremy Lewis (London, 2003).

There is no modern study of Philip Thicknesse; Philip Gosse's *Dr Viper: The Querulous Life of Philip Thicknesse* (London, 1952) remains the standard work. Ann Ford Thicknesse's semi-autobiographical novel, *The School for Fashion*, published in 1800, is also well worth trying to track down.

For more on Fanny Burney in Bath, see *A City of Palaces: Bath Through the Eyes of Fanny Burney* by Maggie Lane (Bath, 1999). Maggie Lane is also the author of *A Charming Place: Bath in the Life and Times of Jane Austen* (Bath, 1988). For more on the background to Georgette Heyer's Bath novels, see *Georgette Heyer's Regency World* by Jennifer Kloester (London, 2005). The story of Sydney Gardens, which feature in the Fanny Burney, Jane Austen and Georgette Heyer walks, can be found in *The Last Promenade: Sydney Gardens, Bath* by Brenda Snaddon, 2000.

More on the background to Pitt's 'Reign of Terror' in Bath can be found in 'Radicalism, Loyalism and the "Reign of Terror" in Bath, 1792-1804' by Steve Poole, in *Bath History*, III (1990), pp114-37.

The Sack of Bath by Adam Fergusson, in which John Betjeman's 'Very Latest Bath Guide' appeared, was first published in 1973. It was republished, with a new preface by Adam Fergusson, by Persephone Books in 2011. More on Betjeman's wartime sojourn in Bath can be found in Volume 1 of John Betjeman's *Letters*, edited by Candida Lycett-Green (London, 1994), Bevis Hillier's *John Betjeman: New Fame, New Love* (London, 2002), and AN Wilson's *Betjeman* (London, 2006).

BOOKSHOPS

Bath is well supplied with excellent bookshops. In the city centre, **Mr B's Emporium of Reading Delights** in John Street was voted Independent Bookshop of the year in 2008 and 2011; **Topping & Company**, with one of the largest stocks in the country, can be found on the Paragon; **Good Buy Books**, on North Parade, has a good range of local books. There is also a branch of **Waterstones** in Milsom Street.

Out of the centre, **The Oldfield Park Bookshop** on Moorland Road and **The Titfield Thunderbolt** in Upper Lambridge Street in Larkhall, both specialise in local books; the Titfield Thunderbolt is also one of the top transport bookshops in the country.

There are two excellent second-hand bookshops: **Bath Old Books** in Margaret's Buildings, off Brock Street, and **George Bayntun**, near the railway station in Manvers Street.

MUSEUMS & GALLERIES

The **Victoria Art Gallery** in Bridge Street has a comprehensive collection of prints, paintings and engravings of Bath from the seventeenth century onwards. These give a unique insight into the way in which the walled city developed into an internationally-famous spa, before decline set in in the nineteenth century. Many of these are kept in cabinets in the smaller room on the ground floor and can normally be viewed during gallery opening hours (1000-1700 Tuesday-Saturday, 1330-1700 Sunday, closed Monday).

Tours of the Masonic Hall in Old Orchard Street – originally the **Old Orchard Street Theatre** and one of the most fascinating buildings in the city – currently run at 1100 and 1430 on Tuesdays, Wednesdays and Thursdays and 1430 on Saturdays.

The **Roman Baths Museum** is one of Britain's major tourist attractions, and, while much of it has little direct relevance to the writers featured here, it does give you the opportunity to get close to the King's Bath, which figured so largely in their experiences of the city. Open daily.

The **Fashion Museum** and **Fashion Bookshop** in the Assembly Rooms are open daily from 1030 to 1800 (1700 in winter). The **Assembly Rooms** themselves are open daily from 1030 unless an event is being held.

The **Museum of Bath at Work**, just north of the Assembly Rooms on Julian Road, tells the often-overlooked story of the 'other Bath' – the one that the overwhelming majority of the city's residents were involved in. Fascinating, unmissable and probably like no museum you've ever visited before. Current opening hours are 1030-1700 daily from April to October; weekends only from November to April but closed in December.

The **Spa Visitor Centre** in Hot Bath Street tells the story of bathing in Bath from earliest times. Open daily from April to October, 1000-1700 Monday-Saturday, 1100-1600 Sunday.

The **Holburne Museum** in Great Pulteney Street has a collection of eighteenth-century portraits, including several Gainsboroughs, and other objects relating to Georgian Bath. Open daily.

The **Building of Bath Collection** in the former Countess of Huntingdon's Chapel on the Paragon tells the fascinating story of how Georgian Bath was built. Normal opening hours are 1030-1700 Saturday to Monday.*

No.1 Royal Crescent is a magnificently restored Georgian town house that reflects the sort of lifestyle enjoyed by Philip Thicknesse, who lived a few doors along. Normal opening hours are 1030-1700 Tuesday to Sunday (closed Mondays except for Bank Holidays).*

The **Herschel Museum of Astronomy** occupies the house in New King Street where William Herschel was living when he discovered Uranus in 1781. Restored in late eighteenth-century style, it gives an idea of the smaller type of townhouse Jane Austen and Fanny Burney visited when they went house-hunting. Normal opening hours are: weekdays (except Wednesdays) from 1300-1700; weekends and bank holidays 1100-1700.*

Finally, as acolytyes of Bath's tutelary deity will not need reminding, there is the **Jane Austen Centre** on Gay Street, where visitors can, in the words of its website, 'escape into the world of Jane Austen' .

All opening hours are subject to change. There is a charge for entry to all museums and galleries except the Victoria Art Gallery, the Spa Visitor Centre and the Holburne Museum.

---

* These three museums are run by the Bath Preservation Trust and are generally closed during the midwinter months.

OTHER TITLES FROM AKEMAN PRESS

Awash with Ale: 2000 Years of Imbibing in Bath
Andrew Swift & Kirsten Elliott   £12.99

A social history of Bath – seen through the bottom of a glass darkly.

'A true delight ... Local historians up and down the country should read *Awash with Ale* as an object lesson in how to present their subject. The rest of us should read it for pure pleasure.'
Ted Bruning, *What's Brewing*

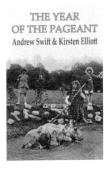

The Year of the Pageant
Andrew Swift & Kirsten Elliott   £15

1909 – the year the modern world was born, and the year in which Bath staged an epic extravaganza to mark its transition from faded health resort to heritage visitor destination. With chapters on miners' strikes, fashion, feminism, suffragettes, sport, shopping, transport, pit disasters, street life, the Abode of Love at Spaxton and much more, *The Year of the Pageant* evokes the sights and sounds of a fascinating bygone age.

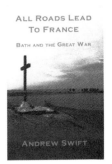

All Roads Lead to France: Bath and the Great War
Andrew Swift   £30 (hardback)

Between 1914 and 1918 thousands of men from Bath answered their country's call. Over 1800 never returned. This is their story, and the story of how four years of total war changed Bath, and the world, for ever.

'Highly recommended.'
Michelle Young, *Western Front Association*

'A tragic and compellingly beautiful tapestry.'
Hylda Holden, *The Regional Historian*

OTHER TITLES FROM AKEMAN PRESS

The Myth-Maker: John Wood, 1704-1754
Kirsten Elliott £10

A bicentennial tribute to Bath's most famous – and most enigmatic – architect. Druid, alchemist and mythmaker extraordinaire, Wood's ambition was nothing less than the building of a latter-day Stonehenge, with temples to sun and moon, on the hills of Bath.

'A pleasing pot pourri of a book with signposts, cul de sacs and a fascination for the myths that drive men mad'.
Ancient Monuments Society

The Ringing Grooves of Change:
Brunel & the Coming of the Railway to Bath
Andrew Swift £12

Brunel changed the face of Bath and brought the coaching trade – the bedrock of its prosperity – to an abrupt end. This is the story of Bath's invasion by an army of navvies, while armed Chartists paraded in the streets and local elections descended into drunkenness and anarchy.

'A fitting tribute to Brunel and the GWR.'
Regency World

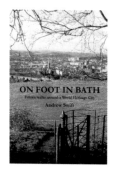

On Foot in Bath:
Fifteen Walks around a World Heritage City
Andrew Swift
(To be published Summer 2012)

For a list of other titles and details of how to order go to www..akemanpress.com

PERSONALISED WALKING TOURS OF BATH

Bath is one of the world's great cities. and has the advantage that most of it can be visited easily on foot. Yet its maze of streets, laid out over centuries, seems purposely designed to mislead the unwary. So while the tourist honeypots swarm with daytrippers, little-known gems lie hidden away in unfrequented back streets.

Bath Walks, founded in 1992, offers private guided tours of the city for small groups and independent travellers. As well as having an in-depth knowledge of the city's history and traditions, our guides can advise on restaurants, leisure and entertainment facilities, take you to traditional pubs and show you a side of this fascinating city that few visitors see.

Walks are tailor-made to your requirements, starting when and where you decide, and taking in the sort of sights that you want to see. As well as general introductory tours of the city, themed tours are also available.

Although it may be possible to book walks at short notice, it is advisable to book as far in advance as possible, so that suitable arrangements can be made.

For more details and to contact us, visit
www.bathwalks.com